THE CULTIVATED CONIFERS
IN NORTH AMERICA

ALLANHELD, OSMUN & CO. PUBLISHERS, INC.
19 Brunswick Road, Montclair, New Jersey 07042

Originally published in 1933 by The Macmillan Co., New York
Published in the United States of America in 1978
by Allanheld, Osmun & Co. and by Universe Books
381 Park Avenue South, New York, N.Y. 10016
Distribution: Universe Books

Library of Congress Catalogue Card Number: 78-51430
International Standard Book Number: 0-87663-831-0

Printed in the United States of America

BOOK I

THE KINDS OF CONIFERS

The photographs from which these plates are made come from many places and sources. The United States Forest Service supplies I, II, III, XI, XIII, XVI, XVII right, XXII, XL below, XLII, XLIV, XLV; James A. G. Davey furnished XXX, XXXII, XXXIV right, XXXV; D. Hill Nursery Company, XXXVI; Rochester Parks, IX top, XXI bottom, XLIII bottom; remainder are by the author.

THE CULTIVATED CONIFERS
IN NORTH AMERICA

CHAPTER I

PREVIEW OF THE SYSTEMATIC TREATMENT

THREE general efforts are noticeable in the planting of conifers aside from their extensive utilization in forestry. In the early days in this country the conifers or "evergreens" were set commonly for shelter-belts and windbreaks; on large areas or estates of character, many kinds were grown as specimen trees, given plenty of room and as far as possible the best conditions for the development of each particular species, and the planter took great pride in admiring them; in recent years the dwarf evergreens have come into prominence for the decoration of small places, so much so that the desire for them has become a vogue.

There is a living interest in the many coniferous evergreens, and now a new book is wanted to describe the kinds and to advise on the growing of them. Never was there a time when so many articles about them appear in the press, in books, and in the literature of nurserymen. They are propagated extensively. More persons in this country plant them now than ever before. The list of available species, from many parts of the world, has greatly increased since the first American book on the conifers, "The Book of Evergreens," by Josiah Hoopes, was published sixty-five years ago, and the varieties or forms are probably more extensive still. On all the subjects of propagation, care, protection, and utilization in the landscape, new ideas have come to the fore. Nor does there seem to be any formal bounds to the subject. We record the knowledge and experience of our day, but the interest in the conifers expands and changes: thus is the subject ever new and worth while.

tively unmixed, the conifers are steadfast attractive examples of strong original lines in nature.

On the other hand, many of the species are extensively variable within themselves when propagated under the conditions of cultivation. This means that forms of conifers may be chosen for particular uses and discriminating tastes at the same time that the integrity of natural relationships is maintained. More than 600 varieties are entered in this book, about twice as many as the number of species. Often the horticultural variety is more useful than the straight species itself, and variations that may appear unimportant to the general observer and be indistinguishable by the usual botanical tests may make all the difference between failure and success in a particular planting, perhaps in extra hardiness, in holding color late in the season, in a pleasing shade of green, or an interesting shape. Species and varieties together, the inventory is approximately 1,000 kinds at command of propagator and planter.

It is understood that this book approaches the conifers from the horticultural point of view, as expressed in their ornamental qualities and the appeal to human interest and their value in the development of grounds and estates. The other uses of the conifers are mostly well recognized, particularly the great supplies of timber provided by many of the species. Numbers of the conifers are invaluable forest trees, specially pines, firs, and spruces. The conifers are extensive sources of pitch, resins, and turpentine, and some of them yield balsams or oils employed in medicine and the arts. It may not be so well known, however, that a good number of the species, in various parts of the world, yield edible products in seeds and fruit-like parts. Nut pines are known in many countries, the seeds being large and edible. *Pinus Sabiniana* supplies important food for the Digger Indians of California, as its vernacular name, the Digger pine, testifies. All the pinyon pines, *P. cembroides*, *P. monophylla*, *P. edulis*, and *P. quadrifolia*, yield substantial food-supplies to the Indians of their regions. Other American species bear edible seeds. The seeds or nuts of *Pinus Pinea* and *P. Cembra* are much eaten in parts of Europe. Edible seeds are produced by *P. koraiensis* in eastern Asia, by *P. Gerardiana* and *P. Roxburghii* in the Himalayas. Certain araucarias, sometimes called pines in their native countries, furnish edible seeds, as *Araucaria araucana* in Chile, *A. angustifolia* in Brazil, *A. Bidwillii* in Australia. Berries of several species of juniper are recorded as edible; *Juniperus occidentalis* fruit is said to be largely consumed by Indians in Arizona and New Mexico, and *J. drupacea* of southeastern Europe and adjacent Asia produces a large sweet fruit much esteemed in its region. The kernels of the drupes of *Torreya nucifera* are a favorite article of food in Japan. It is written that yew-berries are eaten by natives in parts of the Himalayas.

Conifers, and their terminology

The conifers comprise the pines, firs, spruces, hemlock spruces, cypresses, arbor-vitæ, cedars, larches, junipers, retinosporas, yews, araucarias, and many others like them but not generally known by vernacular names. An enumeration like this is the best definition of the group for the general planter, because not all the conifers bear cones and only a special student can undertake an exact discussion of the features common to the many kinds.

This means that cone-bearing is not the most important characteristic of these plants. The junipers do not bear typical cones but more or less soft berry-like bodies, and the yews yield a pulpy organ in which the seed is set. Yet the cone is such a conspicuous feature in the greater number of species that the class or group together has been called the Coniferæ or cone-bearers.

The vegetable community divides itself into two vast groups, the spore-plants (ferns and lower plants) and the seed-plants, the seed differing from the spore in containing an embryo or undeveloped plantlet. The seed-plants or spermatophytes are again of two great divisions, the conifer-like plants without

families is accepted in the present book as a popular presentation.*

Nearly 400 species of conifers are now recognized; they are in 43 or 44 genera of which 31 are of the Pinaceæ or true cone-bearers. Less than half the genera are native in North America. The species are largely of the north temperate zone, and some of them abound in frigid regions and on high mountains. A few genera are distinctly tropical or semi-tropical, and even the pines extend extensively into lower latitudes but they are mostly on the higher levels or mountains in tropical regions. As a group of cultivated plants the conifers are known for the most part as cool-climate subjects.

Forms subordinate to the species

The varieties of conifers, particularly of horticultural origin, are very many and the number is constantly increasing by new originations from variation of seedlings in the nursery row; seedlings with noticeable or desirable new features in stature, habit of growth, color of foliage, ability to withstand untoward conditions, are propagated by means of cuttings or grafts and are named as novelties. It is important to clarity of record that horticulturists distinguish sharply between species and varieties and that they do not employ the terms interchangeably. A species is not a variety, and a variety is not a species. The common habit in speaking and writing of the kinds of plants as "varieties" is much to be regretted. It obscures relationships.

*Even the horticultural reader must not be left with the impression that the classification of the conifers into two families meets all the requirements of contemporaneous technical botanical study. The group or natural class has been variously divided. Pilger in his recent close study of the Gymnospermæ (Engler-Prantl, Die Natürlichen Pflanzenfamilien, Zweite Auflage, Band 13, 1926) accepts separation of the Class Coniferæ into seven families: Taxaceæ, comprising Taxus, Torreya, and Austrotaxus; Podocarpaceæ, with Pherosphæra, Microcachrys, Saxegothæa, Dacrydium, Acmopyle, Podocarpus, Phyllocladus; Araucariaceæ, including Araucaria and Agathis; Cephalotaxaceæ, containing the genera Cephalotaxus and Amentotaxus; Pinaceæ, covering Abies, Keteleeria, Pseudotsuga, Tsuga, Picea, Pseudolarix, Larix, Cedrus, Pinus; Taxodiaceæ, holding Sciadopitys, Sequoia, Taxodium, Glyptostrobus, Cryptomeria, Athrotaxis, Taiwania, Cunninghamia; Cupressaceæ, with Actinostrobus, Callitris, Tetraclinis, Callitropsis, Widdringtonia, Fitzroya, Diselma, Thujopsis, Thuja, Libocedrus, Fokienia, Cupressus, Chamæcyparis, Arceuthos, Juniperus, Macrobiota.

Clear thinking, of course, expresses itself in the use of discriminating language.

Many of the varieties of conifers, as of other plants, are only stature-forms and are not permanent. In any extensive wild domain where hemlocks or arbor-vitæ or other big conifers are seeding freely, one sometimes finds marked differences in size, shape, and growth of seedlings of the same age; but if one were able to observe these plants until they become mature forest trees, one would note that most or all of these juvenile characteristics have disappeared and the trees resemble each other so closely as not to be worth separating by names. Very likely many of the dwarf and slow-growing forms may be smothered by the more vigorous larger offspring and therefore not appear in the final result. It is significant that many conifers known in cultivation in numerous varieties have no varietal names applied to them as they occur in nature; examples are Lawson cypress, hinoki and suwara cypress, American arbor-vitæ, hemlock, red-cedar.

The horticulturist, however, saves the peculiar juveniles he finds in nature or in the nursery row or as bud-sports, names and propagates them; but with age (if the plants are allowed to remain on his grounds until maturity) the juvenile characters tend to vanish and he may no longer have compact Compactas or fastigiate Fastigiatas or globose Globosas or pigmy Pygmæas. Yet in many cases the juvenile characteristics hold more or less indefinitely if care is exercised in the choice of cions or cuttings and if proper attention is given in selection and cultivation; some of the dwarf forms may retain the low stature and bear cones. It will be interesting for someone to observe some of our present-day popular dwarfs when the plants are fifty or one hundred years old or more.

Practically the same form may originate over and over again somewhere or sometime in the nursery row; so may there be compactas and densas and pyramidales of different date and genesis, although the originator may not call them by these

able, to carry the author citations with the name of the plant. This devious history is indicated in a bibliographical way following the description of the white spruce on a subsequent page.

In the systematic treatment in Book I similar synonymy is inserted for such varieties of species (as well as of species themselves) as have been accorded specific rank in the past, or represent geographic forms, or occur in nature and have been transferred to gardens. These are "natural" rather than horticultural varieties or cultivars. Example may be seen in the treatment of *Juniperus chinensis*, in which vars. *japonica* and *Sargentii* are given their regular synonymy with authority for the name and places of publication, whereas the cultivars *pendula, globosa,* and others are not so fully treated as to bibliography. That is, effort is made to distinguish between main or natural varieties and those of horticultural origin; but this distinction does not imply any relative importance in the plants for purposes of cultivation. All cultivars known to be grown at present in North America are given brief description for identification, as far as possible under the existing state of information about them.

There are two main reasons why the cultivars are given a less full treatment as to synonymy and record: first, because it is desired to distinguish quickly between natural species and the forms originating under the stimulus of nursery practice, as an educational effort; second, the horticultural forms or varieties are of many grades of difference and usually have not been described with such care and precision as to make the accounts of them comparable or to give them equal rank among themselves in a systematic document or to enable one to arrange synonymy with accuracy.

Mostly, the horticultural varieties are propagated asexually, all the stock in cultivation being parts, once or more removed, of one original plant; they are genetically different, therefore, from continuing series in nature that must take their chances by normal seed propagation. In the course of extensive seed propagation of conifers, practically the same form may originate again and again and be brought into cultivation under new names; as no two plants are exact duplicates, however, differences will exist but perhaps so slight as to baffle description.

In nomenclature, the abbreviated term Var. (variety) may stand for different ranks when employed for natural (or native) variations and for horticultural variations. Certain students of the subject would prefer to use Forma rather than Var. for the latter, as of less botanical distinctness, but the term variety is so long established in horticultural literature and in trade practice that it cannot be dislodged. It runs through all the books. The present author prefers the word (of his own) Cultivar, but it is hardly to be expected that it will ever be adopted in nomenclatorial practice. Plant-growers are not accustomed to make close distinctions of this kind.

In practice, the treatment in this book as to citation rests mostly on the question whether the given variety or form has a recognized botanical or bibliographic history. At present, nomenclature of varieties can be only approximate. When a varietal name, in this book, has no citation it is understood that the particular combination is on the authority of the author of the volume. Certain cultivated kinds recently named under the designation Forma by Arthur D. Slavin (as in the report of the Conifer Conference in England) are in this volume ascribed to him as Vars. with his sanction.

The word variety, when employed in a nomenclatorial sense, has been used in so many different ways that it is difficult to give it precise meaning; long usage cannot be easily overcome. Perhaps it would be better if the systematists themselves were to adopt another term to designate the particular or narrow status to which many of them wish to restrict it in botanical practice.

Sometimes the varietal status is not indicated by the abbreviation "var." after the species, but the names are placed con-

Let us suppose that a grower obtains a plant labeled *Thuja aurea*. This would be an error. There is no such species among the half dozen thujas of the world. The plant labeled *aurea* might be a variety of *Thuja occidentalis*, of *T. orientalis*, of *T. plicata*, or of other species. To suppress the specific name (or species-name) is to confuse the subject, so that the grower does not know what kind of an arbor-vitæ he has. No one has any warrant to make such short-cuts, although no one can prevent a person from so doing. It may be said that the name *aurea* designates a golden plant (aureus: Latin, *golden*) and is "good enough"; but no name is good enough unless it is accurate.

Or assume again, that the grower acquires a pine under the name *Pinus nepalensis* but that it turns out, at coning-time, to be *P. Armandi*. He becomes confused in the names and may not know how to apply them in other cases. This, however, is not primarily a question of nomenclature but of misidentification, although names become involved in the result. Examples of plants selling under wrong name are numerous, and they are beyond the reach of regulations.

These three examples might be multiplied indefinitely, but they are sufficient to show that rules and standard lists cannot eliminate all the disharmonies in practice although, of course, such codes and agreements are much to be desired. Many kinds of plants are mixed up in the trade as to names, but the names cannot be straightened out until identification has been made. One must know the plant before one can apply names with accuracy.

These simple cases suggest a few of the problems in nomenclature. Such problems, for the most part, are not difficult to understand, yet growers seldom approach these questions with a desire to get at the real reasons for them. Busy persons engaged in other pursuits want an off-hand name for a plant as they do for a packet of merchandise or an object of art, and have little time to try to understand the situation in relation to living objects in nature and the tangled histories associated with them.

One who raises plants attentively should be as keen to keep abreast the main progress in nomenclature as in new methods of cultivation or of fertilizing or of control of pests. Nomenclature of plants and animals is a living language, subject always to change to express the requirements of new knowledge, although in most cases (aside from horticultural varieties) the names have now arrived at essential or sufficient stability. If one understands the reasons for changes in nomenclature and for the differing opinions, the subject loses its terrors and becomes interesting. To make active contact with this subject is one of the satisfactions in horticulture, and leads to a general attitude of accuracy.

Basis of the work

The systematic treatment of the conifers in this volume is based on the excellent work of Alfred Rehder, of the Arnold Arboretum, in "The Cultivated Evergreens," first issued in 1923, much of which has been incorporated without essential change. Since that time new varieties have come into prominence and certain changes in nomenclature have arisen. The descriptions have been drawn or verified as far as possible from observations of growing plants, and from specimens preserved in the author's herbarium and elsewhere. Much material has accumulated from nurseries and test-grounds in this country and abroad, representing species and varieties currently in cultivation. The outstanding living museum of conifers in the public parks of Rochester, New York, has been much consulted; as also the growing collections at the Arnold Arboretum, the New York Botanical Garden, and in many private grounds and nurseries, to all of which the author acknowledges his indebtedness. Ever in the background have been the fields, hills, and mountains of the vast country, where the conifers add their note of color, strength, and grandeur to the landscapes of the earth.

c. Leaves awl-like or scale-like, covering the slender branchlets. . .2. DACRYDIUM, 26
cc. Leaves reduced to minute scarcely noticeable scales, the foliage
    represented by flattened leaf-like branches................3. PHYLLOCLADUS, 27
AA. Seed-bearing body a small aggregate terminal structure with connate
    joined spine-pointed seeds: leaves linear to linear-lanceolate......4. SAXEGOTHÆA, 27
AAA. Seed-bearing part a drupe-like or plum-like body but sometimes the
    exterior scarcely fleshy: leaves mostly prominent, long-linear to
    ovate.
    B. Drupe or nut sitting on an enlarged receptacle or a fleshy often
       colored stalk often thicker than itself......................5. PODOCARPUS, 28
    BB. Drupe or nut on a prominent slender pedicel, maturing the first
       season..6. CEPHALOTAXUS, 33
    BBB. Drupe or nut sessile or practically so, maturing the second season.7. TORREYA, 34

The other genera of the Taxaceæ are: **Acmopyle** (Pilger, Das Pflanzenreich, iv, pt. 5, p. 117) represented by one species, *A. Pancheri*, in New Caledonia, Pacific Islands, a tree somewhat like Podocarpus; **Amentotaxus** (Pilger in Engler Jahrb. lix, 41, 1917), *A. argotænia*, China and Formosa, an evergreen shrub first described as a Podocarpus and then placed in Cephalotaxus; **Austrotaxus** (Compton in Journ. Linn. Soc., Bot. xlv, 427, 1922), of New Caledonia, *A. spicata*, a large tree resembling Podocarpus in foliage and habit of growth; **Microcachrys** (Hooker f. in Journ. Bot. iv, 149, 1845), *M. tetragona*, mountains of Tasmania, an evergreen shrub with whip-like 4-angled branchlets, once included in Dacrydium; **Pherosphæra** (Archer ex Hooker in Journ. Bot. ii, 52, 1850), evergreen shrubs, allied to Dacrydium, *P. Hookeriana*, Archer, in Tasmania and *P. Fitzgeraldii*, F. Mueller, in New South Wales. Some of these taxads have been introduced into England but apparently not into North America, although private collectors of novelties in the milder parts of the country may have them or have tried them.

1. **TAXUS.** YEW. Evergreen mostly diœcious trees and shrubs with long-linear alternate mostly 2-ranked flat leaves green underneath, little scaly winter-buds, small usually axillary flowers in early spring from buds of previous autumn, the staminate in little heads of 4–8 stamens, pistillate of a single ovule ripening into a hard little nutlet sitting in a fleshy ring or cup that is normally scarlet but in some varieties yellow. Widely distributed in the northern hemisphere and one crossing the equator; species considered by Pilger and others to be one, with subspecies or varieties in different parts of world, but for our purposes at least regarded as perhaps seven or eight species that may be separately named. It is impossible to make a key to the species that will cover the exceptions met in the horticultural varieties. The scales of the winter-buds are usually good marks of identification of species; these scales may be seen throughout the summer persisting at the base of the season's growth. Taxus (táx-us) is the classical name of yew.—*Taxus*, Linnæus, Species Plantarum, 1040 (1753).

The European yew is closely associated with folk-lore and history, and

II. Native conifer landscape, Selway National Forest, Idaho, composed mostly of *Thuja plicata*, *Pseudotsuga*, and *Pinus monticola*.

III. Limber pine, *Pinus flexilis*, at timber-line; Pike National Forest, Colorado.

IV. The attractive staminate bloom of white pine, *Pinus Strobus*, about natural size; New York.

V. Yews. Hicks yew, *Taxus media* var. *Hicksii* at left; Hicks' Nurseries on Long Island. *Taxus canadensis;* native in woods of New York.

VI. Podocarp and Torreya. *Podocarpus macrophylla* var. *Maki* and *Torreya taxifolia*, both natural size; Florida. One fruit of the Torreya is cut to show the nut.

VII. Spring condition of Austrian pine, *Pinus nigra*. Left, staminate catkins; right, young cones and new shoots, about two-thirds natural size. New York.

VIII. Japanese Black pine, *Pinus Thunbergii*, natural size but not mature; Connecticut.

IX. Dwarf pines. *Pinus nigra* var. *Hornibrookiana* above; *Pinus Mugo* var. *compacta* beneath. New York.

X. Japanese Red pine, *Pinus densiflora*, above, immature cones (in July), natural size; Connecticut. Table Mountain pine. *Pinus pungens*, beneath, natural size; Connecticut.

XI. Native stand of Longleaf pine, *Pinus palustris*; Choctawhatchee National Forest, Florida.

XII. Torrey pine, *Pinus Torreyana*; Torrey Pines, San Diego.

XIII. Pinyon pine, *Pinus edulis;* near San Isabel National Forest, Colorado.

XIV. Two good pines. Korean pine, *Pinus koraiensis*, at left, natural size but not mature; Connecticut. Limber pine, *Pinus flexilis*, at right, three-fourths natural size; Massachusetts.

XV. Foliage of Chinese White pine, *Pinus Armandi*, about one-half natural size; New York.

XVI. Bole and bark of Western White pine, *Pinus monticola;* Coeur d'Alene National Forest, Idaho.

XVII. White pine, *Pinus Strobus.* Cones not fully mature, in midsummer condition, about three-fourths natural size; Connecticut. Open-field tree in Huron National Forest, Michigan.

has been long in cultivation in many forms. It is hardy on the Atlantic side as far north as the milder parts of New York, and some forms even farther, as in Massachusetts. The Japanese yew, now much grown, thrives farther north. All the yews are interesting and attractive where they can be well grown. They are slow-growing durable subjects; usually thrive in partially shady places where not too dry. Propagation is by seeds, which should germinate the second year; also by cuttings and sometimes by layers.

Although it may be held, as we have learned, that there is only one species of yew, *Taxus baccata*, and that the others are geographical varieties of it, that treatment need not be adopted for horticultural purposes; but it nevertheless indicates how much alike they all are, how difficult it is to distinguish them positively, and also how uncertain to determine hybridity amongst them particularly as the cytology is not distinctive.

KEY to the species of Taxus:

A. Plant making a distinct trunk, a tree in nature: diœcious.
  B. Leaves on typical or native forms prevailingly acuminate, gradually tapering to point, to 1 inch or more long, commonly appearing 2-ranked or flat on horizontal branches, midrib prominent above: scales of winter-buds persistent, blunt and not keeled: nutlet sometimes 3–4-angled....1. *T. baccata*
  BB. Leaves abruptly or suddenly very short-pointed.
    C. Position of leaves distinctly and flatly 2-ranked (see also No. 5).
      D. Length of leaves usually 1 inch or more: midrib only slightly raised on upper surface: scales of winter-buds deciduous, obtuse and not keeled...2. *T. chinensis*
      DD. Length of leaves ¾ inch or less: midrib moderately prominent: scales of winter-buds persistent, acute and keeled.....................3. *T. brevifolia*
    CC. Position of leaves on horizontal or spreading twig ascending, making a V-shaped appearance (exception in No. 5): midrib prominent.
      D. Branchlets brown the second season: scales of winter-buds persistent, acute and keeled...4. *T. cuspidata*
      DD. Branchlets olive-green: scales of winter-buds obtuse...............5. *T. media*
AA. Plant a low straggling spreading ground-bush without trunk: monœcious...6. *T. canadensis*

1. Taxus baccata. ENGLISH or EUROPEAN YEW. Fig. 1. Durable slow-growing tree of wide distribution in the Old World, usually attaining a height of 25–40 feet but sometimes to 60 feet, and a great girth with age, with exfoliating bark and furrowed trunk, wide-spreading branches making a broad and mostly low head or crown, the branchlets more or less pendent and most retaining the green color the second year: leaves spirally attached but taking nearly opposite positions on the twig, ½–1 inch or more long but shorter in some varieties, midrib prominent, very dark glossy green above and paler underneath, 1/16 inch to 1 line broad: staminate flowers in an axillary globose little cluster; pistillate flower axillary toward end of shoots, the seed ripening into a somewhat compressed or angled ellipsoid nutlet ¼ inch long sitting in a fleshy normally bright red cup or disk higher than itself. Widely spread from England to north Africa and western Asia; the closely allied *T. Wallichiana*, by some authors considered a variety or subspecies, ranges from India to the East Indies and Philippines.—*Taxus baccata*, Linnæus, Species Plantarum, 1040 (1753).

There are many cultivars or horticultural kinds bearing varietal names, particularly well known abroad. Names occurring in North American horticulture are as follows:

Var. **adpressa,** sometimes incorrectly called *T. brevifolia.* Much - spreading shrub or small tree of irregular dense habit and very short abruptly pointed leaves (only ½ inch or less long): disk shorter than the nutlet. A very distinct looking plant, quite unlike usual forms of *T. baccata* but a seedling from it in Great Britain about 1838; sometimes erroneously said to be Japanese.— *Taxus baccata* var. *adpressa,* Carrière; *T. tardiva,* Knight.

Var. **adpressa aurea.** A form of the above with golden young foliage.—*Taxus baccata* var. *adpressa aurea,* Masters.

Var. **adpressa erecta.** A columnar plant with foliage of *adpressa* itself.— *Taxus baccata* var. *adpressa erecta,* Nicholson.

Var. **adpressa stricta.** Columnar bush with upright or ascending branches. —*Taxus baccata* var. *adpressa stricta,* Carrière.

1. Taxus baccata, showing the flat leaf-spray on typical horizontal twigs. Somewhat enlarged.

Var. **aurea.** Leaves golden-yellow, particularly bright on tips and margins: compact.—*Taxus baccata* var. *aurea,* Carrière; *T. baccata* var. *elvastonensis aurea,* Beissner.

Var. **Barroni.** Young shoots orange, changing to copper tint with age.—*Taxus baccata* var. *Barroni,* Barron.

Var. **cheshuntensis.** Somewhat like the Irish yew but makes a broader plant.— *Taxus baccata* var. *cheshuntensis,* Gordon.

Var. **compacta.** Compact, with dark green shining leaves.—*Taxus baccata* var. *compacta,* Beissner.

Var. **Dovastoni.** DOVASTON or WESTFELTON YEW. Tree with erect trunk, branches horizontal with pendulous spray: leaves short and abruptly pointed. Raised about 1777 by John Dovaston of Westfelton, England.—*Taxus baccata* var. *Dovastoni,* Lawson.

Var. **Dovastoni aureo-variegata.** Young foliage yellow-variegated.—*Taxus baccata* var. *Dovastoni aureo-variegata,* Beissner.

Var. **elegantissima.** Young foliage striped pale yellow, older leaves with whitish margins: vigorous but compact.—*Taxus baccata* var. *elegantissima,* Beissner; *T. baccata* var. *aurea elegantissima,* Hort.

Var. **epacridioides.** Dwarf, erect: leaves seldom exceeding ½ inch long and bronzing in winter.—*Taxus baccata* var. *epacridioides,* Beissner.

Var. **erecta.** Erect and formal but less compact than the Irish yew.—*Taxus baccata* var. *erecta,* Loudon; *T. baccata* var. *stricta,* Hort.; *T. Crowderi,* Hort.

Var. **erecta aurea** is listed.

Var. **ericoides.** Low and spreading: leaves narrow and crowded, ½ inch or less long, bronzing or purpling in winter.—*Taxus baccata* var. *ericoides*, Carrière; *T. empetrifolia*, Gordon; *T. microphylla*, Hort.; *T. Michelii*, Hort.

Var. **expansa.** Erect: leaves to 1½ inches long, color of upper and under surfaces contrasting.—*Taxus baccata* var. *expansa*, Carrière; *T. baccata* var. *procumbens*, Kent.

Var. **fastigiata.** IRISH YEW. Narrow-growing stiff pistillate tree making a striking columnar subject, branches and twigs erect and with radiating bluntish leaves. Found in Ireland about 1780.—*Taxus baccata* var. *fastigiata*, Loudon; *T. hibernica*, Hort.

Var. **fastigiata aurea.** A golden form of the above.—*Taxus baccata* var. *fastigiata aurea*, Standish.

Var. **fastigiata variegata.** Leaves variegated yellowish-white.—*Taxus baccata* var. *fastigiata variegata*, Carrière.

Var. **glauca.** Leaves, specially when young, glaucous or bluish-green underneath: a strong plant with branches ascending.—*Taxus baccata* var. *glauca*, Carrière.

Var. **gracilis pendula.** Branchlets elongated and slender, drooping.—*Taxus baccata* var. *gracilis pendula*, Lancke.

Var. **horizontalis.** Much like var. *Dovastoni* but branchlets not weeping, tree without leader; there is a variegated form.—*Taxus baccata* var. *horizontalis*, Knight.

Var. **imperialis.** Erect and compact but less stiff than Irish yew.—*Taxus baccata* var. *imperialis*, Hort.

Var. **Jacksonii.** Branches spreading and pendulous at tip, branchlets many, short and curved: leaves rather broad, crowded, curved.—*Taxus baccata* var. *Jacksonii*, Gordon.

Var. **lutea.** Berry or disk yellow: an old kind.—*Taxus baccata* var. *lutea*, Endlicher; *T. baccata* var. *fructu-luteo*, Hort.

Var. **nana.** Very dwarf, usually less than 3 feet high, very widely spreading, bearing small dark green leaves.—*Taxus baccata* var. *nana*, Knight.

Var. **pyramidalis.** Branches erect and crowded, sparingly leafy on branchlets.—*Taxus baccata* var. *pyramidalis*, Carrière.

Var. **recurvata.** Branches horizontal with recurved leaves.—*Taxus baccata* var. *recurvata*, Carrière.

Var. **repandens.** SPREADING YEW. A low form with long much-spreading branches, narrow long somewhat curved leaves.—*Taxus baccata* var. *repandens*, Parsons.

Var. **semperaurea.** Golden-leaved throughout the first or second year.—*Taxus baccata* var. *semperaurea*, Dallimore; *T. baccata* var. *erecta semperaurea*, Beissner.

Var. **variegata.** Foliage variegated white or whitish.—*Taxus baccata* var. *variegata*, West; *T. baccata* var. *argentea*, Loudon.

Var. **Washingtoni.** Leaves golden-yellow, particularly underneath: wide-spreading habit.—*Taxus baccata* var. *Washingtoni*, Beissner.

Other kinds listed in North America are vars. *Livingstonii, major, polycarpa.*

2. **T. chinensis.** CHINESE YEW. Tree to 50 feet, with mature branchlets yellowish-green: leaves to 1¾ inches long, abruptly pointed, 2-ranked, usually falcate or curved, midrib only slightly raised, shining above and grayish underneath: nutlet broad-ovoid and slightly 2-angled: winter-buds smaller than in *T. baccata*, scales deciduous.

Central China; hardy in protected places as far north as Massachusetts; little planted as yet but promising.—*Taxus chinensis*, Rehder in Journ. Arnold Arb. i, 51 (1919); *T. baccata* subsp. *cuspidata* var. *chinensis*, Pilger in Engler, Das Pflanzenreich, iv, pt. 5, 112 (1903); *T. baccata* var. *sinensis*, Henry in Elwes & Henry, Trees of Great Britain and Ireland, i, 100 (1906); *T. cuspidata* var. *chinensis*, Rehder & Wilson in Sargent, Plantæ Wilsonianæ, ii, 8 (1916).

3. **T. brevifolia.** PACIFIC, WESTERN, or OREGON YEW. Tree sometimes to 80 feet and sometimes 4 feet diameter; branches horizontal, somewhat drooping, the crown broadly conical: leaves 2-ranked, ¾ inch or less long, abruptly short-pointed, midrib somewhat prominent: nutlet ovoid, 2–4-angled. British Columbia to California and Montana. Not successful in the northeastern country, needing probably to be grown from seed selected for hardiness. The name *brevifolia* has been inaccurately applied to *T. baccata* var. *adpressa*, which is also a short-leaf yew; also to a form of *T. cuspidata*.— *Taxus brevifolia*, Nuttall, North American Sylva, iii, 86 (1849); *T. Bourcieri*, Carrière in Rev. Hort. iv, 228 (1854); *T. Lindleyana*, Lawson ex Carrière, Traité Général des Conifères, 523 (1855); *T. baccata* var. *brevifolia*, Koehne, Deutsche Dendrologie, 6 (1893); *T. baccata* subsp. *brevifolia*, Pilger in Engler, Das Pflanzenreich, iv, pt. 5, 113 (1903).

4. **T. cuspidata.** JAPANESE YEW. Fig. 2. Tree to 50 feet with widely spreading or ascending branches, becoming 2 feet diameter, but with us known mostly as a low or bushy plant; branches commonly brown the second year: leaves about 1 inch long, abruptly cusp-pointed, often falcate or curved, contracted to short stalk, midrib

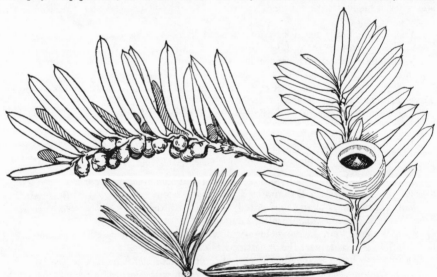

2. Taxus cuspidata, showing characteristic trough-shaped disposition of leaves on horizontal young twigs, and separate leaf (enlarged) with prominent midrib and short point; also fruit. Lower left-hand spray, natural size.

prominent on upper surface and particularly underneath, standing partially upright so that they appear irregularly V-shaped or trough-like when twig is seen endwise: nutlet ovoid, about ¼ inch long, compressed and lightly angled, in a scarlet disk that is partly closed over it. Japan, Korea, Manchuria; hardy to Ontario and New England, and now much planted, being attractive and adapted to many uses; in cultivation usually bush-like but with a single trunk or stock. Although introduced about seventy years ago it is only in the past quarter century that *T. cuspidata* has become generally popular. The bushy form raised from cuttings yields seed that produces the tree form. —*Taxus cuspidata*, Siebold & Zuccarini, Floræ Japonicæ Familiæ Naturales, ii, 108 (1846); *T. baccata* var. *cuspidata*, Carrière, Traité Général des Conifères, ed. 2, 733 (1867); *T. baccata* subsp. *cuspidata*, Pilger in Engler, Das Pflanzenreich, iv, pt. 5, 112 (1903); *T. Sieboldii*, Hort.; *T. cuspidata* var. *capitata*, Hort.

Var. **aurescens.** Low, the young branchlets deep yellow changing to green.— *Taxus cuspidata* var. *aurescens*, Rehder; *T. tardiva aurea*, Hort.

Var. **densa.** Low form with short leaves and ascending branches, sometimes almost hemispherical in shape.—*Taxus cuspidata* var. *densa*, Rehder.

Var. **minima.** Very dwarf, less than 1 foot high, with shining dark green leaves.— *Taxus cuspidata* var. *minima*, Slavin; *T. cuspidata* forma *minima*, Slavin.

Var. **nana.** DWARF JAPANESE YEW. Slow-growing compact plant suitable for small rock-garden when young, the spreading branches closely covered with short branchlets or twigs: leaves short.—*Taxus cuspidata* var. *nana*, Rehder; *T. cuspidata* var. *compacta*, Bean; *T. cuspidata* var. *brevifolia*, Hort.

Var. **Thayeræ.** A flattened wide-spreading bush with horizontal or slightly ascending plumose branches well clothed with leaves arranged in one plane, foliage rather lighter green than that of *T. cuspidata*, as described by the late E. H. Wilson and named for Mrs. Bayard Thayer of Lancaster, Massachusetts (Horticulture, Sept. 15, 1930).

Vars. *fastigiata*, *erecta*, and *intermedia* are mentioned.

T. Hunnewelliana. Described by Rehder as a hybrid between *T. cuspidata* and *T. canadensis*, of slenderer habit than the former with narrower leaves, lighter green with reddish tint in winter, bears the name of the Hunnewell estate at Wellesley, Massachusetts.—*Taxus Hunnewelliana*, Rehder in Journ. Arnold Arb., vi, 201 (1925).

5. **T. media.** MIDDLE YEW. A set of hardy cultivated yews described by Rehder as hybrids of *T. baccata* and *T. cuspidata:* "from *T. baccata* the hybrid may be distinguished by the darker olive-green often slightly reddish color of the branchlets, not light or yellowish-green as in that species, by the keeled scales of the winter-buds, by the stouter and broader more abruptly acuminate leaves with a more prominent midrib above, and by the abrupt enlargement of the leaf-cushion into the petiole. From *T. cuspidata* it differs chiefly in the olive-green color of the branchlets, not brown the second season as in that species, at least on the more vigorous branchlets, in the obtuse winter-buds with obtuse scales, in the leaves spreading distinctly in two ranks and rather lustrous above." First raised by T. D. Hatfield, Wellesley, Massachusetts, about thirty years ago.—*Taxus media*, Rehder in Journ. Arnold Arb. iv, 107 (1923).

Var. **Hatfieldii.** Compact, of conical outline, branches ascending, leaves widespreading. Named for the late T. D. Hatfield of Wellesley, Massachusetts.—*Taxus media* var. *Hatfieldii*, Rehder.

Var. **Hicksii.** Plate V. Columnar bush, also with wide-spreading leaves; raised at the Hicks Nurseries, Westbury, Long Island, New York.—*Taxus media* var. *Hicksii*, Rehder.

6. **T. canadensis.** Plate V. Fig. 3. CANADA or AMERICAN YEW. GROUND-HEMLOCK. Diffuse low straggling usually monœcious bush with many ascending

branches to 4 or 6 feet, main stems prostrate and rooting. forming large colonies or patches: leaves mostly less than 1 inch long and 1 line broad, abruptly pointed, midrib prominent on both surfaces, mostly flatly 2-ranked: n u t l e t usually broader than high, in a

3. Taxus canadensis. One-half natural size.

light red disk or cup with somewhat constricted orifice. In shady woods and on cool banks, Newfoundland to Manitoba and Iowa and in the mountains to Virginia; suitable for ground-cover in appropriate places.—*Taxus canadensis*, Marshall, Arbustrum Americanum, 151 (1785); *T. baccata* var. *minor*, Michaux, Flora Boreali-Americana, ii, 245 (1803); *T. baccata* var. *procumbens*, Loudon, Arboretum et Fruticetum Britannicum, iv, 2067 (1838); *T. minor*, Britton in Mem. Torr. Bot. Club, v, 19 (1893); *T. baccata* subsp. *canadensis*, Pilger in Engler, Das Pflanzenreich, iv, pt. 5, 113 (1903).

Var. **aurea.** Slightly variegated with yellow.—*Taxus canadensis* var. *aurea*, Hort.

Var. **stricta.** A dwarf stiffish form.—*Taxus canadensis* var. *stricta*, Hort.

A third species of yew, *T. floridana*, is native in the United States, on the eastern side of the Apalachicola River in northwestern Florida, but not known as a cultivated subject. It is a bushy small tree with falcate leaves about 1 inch long, nutlet minutely wrinkled and narrowed to tip in a bright red fleshy disk.—*Taxus floridana*, Nuttall, North American Sylva, iii, 92 (1849).

2. DACRYDIUM. Diœcious or sometimes monœcious evergreen trees and shrubs of the southern hemisphere often with leaves of different kinds on young and old trees, those of mature plants small closely imbricate scales, those of juvenile plants or lower branches of large trees awl-like or linear and spreading: staminate flowers nearly or quite terminal on branchlets; pistillate also at or near the ends under bracts that resemble the foliage leaves: seed nut-like, ovoid, in a scale-like or membranous more or less thickened cup. Species about sixteen; two of them (perhaps more) are somewhat grown in California. They inhabit New Zealand, Australia and Tasmania, Borneo, Pacific Islands, Chile. Dacrýd-ium: from Greek for *tear*, alluding to resinous exudations.—*Dacrydium*, Solander ex Forster f., De Plantis Esculentis, 80 (1786).

Leaves dimorphous, of young trees to ¼ inch long and of old trees to
⅛ inch long: seed or nutlet single...............................1. *D. cupressinum*
Leaves all very small (½ line), closely imbricated all round the twig:
nutlets 4–8...2. *D. Franklinii*

1. **Dacrydium cupressinum.** Rimu. Tree sometimes to 100 feet, with long pale green drooping branches, trunk sometimes 5 feet diameter: leaves of young trees more or less awl-shaped, to ¼ inch long, gradually merging to the keeled linear smaller scale-leaves of older parts: nutlet ovoid, about ⅛ inch long, in a cup-like disk that may become fleshy. Forest tree in New Zealand.—*Dacrydium cupressinum*, Solander ex Forster f., De Plantis Esculentis, 80 (1786).

2. **D. Franklinii.** Huon-Pine. Tree to 100 feet, young branchlets pendulous but main ones spreading or erect: leaves numerous tightly placed scales that measure 24 to the inch, covering the branchlets: nutlets broadly ovoid and compressed. Tasmania. Named for Sir John Franklin, once Governor of Tasmania.—*Dacrydium Franklinii*, Hooker f. in Hook. Lond. Journ. Bot. iv, 152 (1845).

3. **PHYLLOCLADUS.** A half-dozen diœcious or monœcious evergreen trees and shrubs of the southern hemisphere and Philippines with branches flattened into leaf-like structures or cladodes and the true leaves reduced to small linear deciduous scales: staminate flowers in catkin-like spikes at ends of branchlets; pistillate flowers sessile on cladodes or on peduncles arising from them: seed ovoid or oblong and flattened sidewise, each in a cup-shaped disk, two or more together. Two species are planted in California. Phyllóc-ladus: *leaf-branch.*—*Phyllocladus*, L. C. & A. Richard, De Coniferis, 129 (1826.)

Cladodes or leaf-like branches pinnate . . . . .1. *P. trichomanoides*
Cladodes entire. . . . . .2. *P. rhomboidalis*

1. **Phyllocladus trichomanoides.** Tree to 70 feet and 3 feet diameter, with whorled slender spreading branches: cladodes distichous, to 3 inches long, pinnate with the parts lobed, seedling leaves linear and soon falling. Forests, New Zealand.—*Phylloc-ladus trichomanoides*, D. Don ex A. Cunningham in Ann. Nat. Hist. i, 211 (1838).

2. **P. rhomboidalis.** As seen in gardens, a small tree or bush, but in its native place a tree up to 60 feet, or shrub on mountain tops; persistent branches more or less reticulate, cladodia cuneate or rhomboidal: leaves very small, subulate: male catkins 2 or 3 together; female catkins globular, with 1, 2, or 3 fertile scales surmounted by 1 or 2 barren ones. Tasmania.—*Phyllocladus rhomboidalis*, L. C. & A. Richard, De Coniferis, 23 (1826); *P. asplenifolius*, Hooker f. in Hook. Lond. Journ. Bot. iv, 151 (1845).

4. **SAXEGOTHÆA.** Prince Albert Yew. One evergreen monœcious tree in Chile, somewhat planted in California, with taxus-like alternate leaves: staminate flowers single in axils aggregated in spikes; pistillate flowers also in short spikes terminating brief branches: fruit a subglobose compound structure formed of more or less united sharp-tipped seeds or nutlets, the cone ½–¾ inch across. Name in honor of Prince Albert of Saxe-Coburg-Gotha, consort of Queen Victoria (saxegothè-a).

Saxegothæa conspicua. Fig. 4 (adapted from Flore des Serres, vii, p. 84). Tree to 40 or more feet with dense head and drooping branches in whorls: leaves linear or linear-lanceolate, ⅓–1 inch long, ⅛ inch more or less broad, abruptly sharp-pointed, midrib prominent on both surfaces.—*Saxegothæa conspicua*, Lindley in Journ. Hort. Soc. vi, 258 (1851).

5. **PODOCARPUS.** Podocarp. Evergreen monœcious or diœcious trees or shrubs with mostly elongated and rarely narrow-ovate leaves that bear little general resemblance to Coniferæ: foliage very various, the leaves seldom scale-like but prevailingly flat, linear to 1 inch broad, firm, mostly alternate, but sometimes opposite and arrangement perhaps 2-ranked: staminate flowers in catkin-like spikes; pistillate flowers solitary with an inclosing scale and bracts beneath, the under parts becoming at maturity a thickened receptacle or a much swollen colored peduncle-like body on which the drupe-like or nut-like seed is borne. About sixty species in warm

4. Saxegothæa conspicua. 1, staminate spike (× 5); 2, staminate flower, enlarged; 3, ovule; 4, pistillate spike (× 2); 5, seed. Foliage spray about natural size; other parts enlarged.

parts of world, as West Indies and South America, New Zealand, Australia, Asia, Africa; somewhat planted in the southernmost eastern states and in California. Podocár-pus: *foot-fruit,* because of the fleshy fruit-stalk of species first described.—*Podocarpus*, L'Héritier ex Persoon, Synopsis Plantarum, ii, 580 (1807).

The podocarps are not hardy in the northern states but are sometimes seen as tub specimens under glass, in the juvenile state. They are not common, as a class, in cultivation in the United States. In Florida and along the Gulf Coast some of the species are useful, particularly *P. macrophylla* and *P. Nagi*. *P. alpina* will probably stand much farther north. Most of the species entered here are planted in California. Other species appear in European collections. In their native countries, some of the kinds are important timber trees. They are propagated by seeds and by cuttings of nearly ripened wood.

KEY to the species of Podocarpus:

A. Leaves on mature trees or parts scale-like and closely appressed to the branchlets on all sides.. 1. *P. dacrydioides*
AA. Leaves broad and relatively short, ovate or nearly so, to ¾ inch or more wide... 2. *P. Nagi*
AAA. Leaves narrow, linear to narrow-lanceolate, mostly less than ½ inch broad.
  B. Foliage yew-like, the leaves of old or mature plants very narrow and usually not exceeding ½ or ¾ inch long but sometimes reaching 1 inch or so.
    C. Apex of leaves rounded although perhaps mucronate (with a little point in center).
      D. Staminate flowers in spikes: trees.
        E. Arrangement of leaves distichous or 2-ranked.............. 3. *P. spicata*
        EE. Arrangement not distichous............................. 4. *P. andina*
      DD. Staminate flowers solitary or few in axils, not spicate: shrubs.
        E. Tip of leaf distinctly mucronate......................... 5. *P. nivalis*
        EE. Tip not evidently mucronate............................ 6. *P. alpina*
    CC. Apex of leaves distinctly tapering-acute.
      D. Arrangement of leaves on old plants distichous or 2-ranked: tree. 7. *P. ferruginea*
      DD. Arrangement not distichous except perhaps on young plants or new shoots.
        E. Plant a shrub: leaves thin and lax....................... 8. *P. acutifolia*
        EE. Plant a tree: leaves rigid, stiff.
          F. Staminate flowers sessile or essentially so: nut obtuse..... 9. *P. Totara*
          FF. Staminate flowers stalked: nut acute....................10. *P. Hallii*
  BB. Foliage not yew-like, the leaves being larger and longer, upwards of 1 inch long.
    C. Seed (drupe) not on an enlarged receptacle or thickened stalk: leaves narrow and long-acuminate............................11. *P. gracilior*
    CC. Seed sitting on a greatly enlarged thickened receptacle or stalk.
      D. Pistillate flowers subtended by 2 little leaves or bracts below the receptacle.
        E. End of leaves a sharp firm point or spine.................12. *P. spinulosa*
        EE. End of leaves not spinescent-pointed.
          F. Midrib not marked above, somewhat depressed in a groove or valley: bracts or leaves beneath receptacle long and attenuate...13. *P. neriifolia*
          FF. Midrib very prominent and raised on upper surface: bracts under receptacle very small.........................14. *P. macrophylla*
      DD. Pistillate flowers not bracted beneath receptacle.
        E. Midrib of leaf indistinct above: leaves not much if any exceeding 2 inches in length.............................15. *P. elongata*
        EE. Midrib prominent above.
          F. Length of leaves under 2 inches.......................16. *P. nubigena*
          FF. Length exceeding 2 inches............................17. *P. saligna*

1. **Podocarpus dacrydioides.** KAHIKA. Lofty forest tree sometimes more than 100 feet and trunk 5 feet diameter: leaves of mature trees ⅛ inch or less long and scale-like all around the twig, those on young trees twice as large and linear-falcate and distichous: staminate and pistillate flowers solitary and terminal: seed (or fruit)

a nut about ⅙ inch long, black, on red fleshy stalk. New Zealand, in swampy places.—*Podocarpus dacrydioides*, A. Richard, Essai d'une Flore de la Nouvelle-Zelande, 358 (1832).

2. **P. Nagi.** NAGI. Fig. 5. Distinct-looking tree with bright attractive stiffish foliage, the leaves being very broad, to 90 feet in its native country, with spreading or ascending-spreading branches; the trunk with smooth brownish-purple bark peeling off in thin gray flakes; branchlets opposite or sometimes alternate, green: leaves opposite, 2-ranked by a twist of the short petiole, elliptic-lanceolate to lanceolate, sometimes ovate, acute, narrowed at base, 2–3 inches long and about ¾ inch broad, many-nerved, bright green and usually lustrous above, slightly paler beneath, sometimes somewhat glaucescent: staminate flowers cylindric, about 1 inch long, in clusters of 3–5; fertile flowers solitary or in pairs: seed globose, little over ½

5. Podocarpus Nagi. About one-half natural size.

inch across, plum-like, dark purple, bloomy, on a but slightly thickened peduncle. Southern Japan, known as Nagi; hardy only in southern California and Florida and special places along Gulf Coast.—*Podocarpus Nagi*, Makino in Bot. Mag. Tokyo, xvii, 113 (1903); *P. Nageia*, R. Brown ex Mirbel in Mem. Mus. Par. xiii, 75 (1825); *Nageia japonica*, Gaertner, De Fructibus et Seminibus, i, 191 (1788); *Myrica Nagi*, Thunberg, Flora Japonica, 76 (1784).

3. **P. spicata.** MATAI. Forest tree to 80 feet, with upright crowded branches, the branches of young plants long and drooping: leaves of mature plants 2-ranked, to ½ inch long, very narrow, rounded at apex but perhaps apiculate (with minute point in center), glaucous underneath: staminate flowers many in axillary spikes; pistillates in few-flowered spikes: seed (or fruit) globose, nearly or quite black, fleshy, to ⅓ inch diameter, receptacle not evident. New Zealand.—*Podocarpus spicata*, R. Brown ex Bennett, Plantæ Javanicæ Rariores, 40 (1838).

4. **P. andina.** A small tree or shrub: leaves crowded, slightly 2-ranked, linear, ½–¾ inch long, very narrow, obtusish or mucronate, dark green and with a slightly raised midrib above, with a distinct midrib and 2 stomatiferous glaucous bands beneath: seed subglobose, usually solitary on a slender drooping stalk, dark bluish-black and about ½ inch across. Chile.—*Podocarpus andina*, Poeppig ex Endlicher,

Synopsis Coniferarum, 219 (1847); *Prumnopitys elegans*, Philippi in Linnaea, xxx, 731 (1860).

5. **P. nivalis.** Erect or prostrate bush to 8 feet, the branches often rooting: leaves close together, very thick, spreading or recurved, to ⅔ inch long and nearly ⅛ inch broad, obtuse, the midrib conspicuous underneath: staminate flowers few terminating slender axillary peduncles; pistillates solitary in axils: seed a small oblong nutlet on a fleshy red stalk and 2 projections or points at its tip. New Zealand, in subalpine regions.—*Podocarpus nivalis*, Hooker, Icones Plantarum, t. 582 (1843).

6. **P. alpina.** Shrub, usually very low but sometimes to 12 feet or more, with squarrose densely leaved branches: leaves spreading, thick, less than ½ inch long and than ⅛ inch broad, apex rounded, midrib prominent underneath: staminate flowers few on axillary peduncles; pistillates short-peduncled or nearly sessile: seed ovoid, bright red, less than ¼ inch long, pointed, on a broad receptacle. Tasmania and New South Wales.—*Podocarpus alpina*, R. Brown ex Mirbel in Mem. Mus. Par. xiii, 75 (1825).

7. **P. ferruginea.** MIRO. Forest tree to 80 feet and trunk to 3 feet diameter: leaves 2-ranked and close together, to ¾ inch long on old trees and nearly ⅛ inch broad, margins recurved, apex more or less acute: staminate flowers sessile and solitary; pistillates solitary or twin: seed drupe-like, ¾ inch long, reddish-purple and glaucous, the receptacle not expanded. New Zealand.—*Podocarpus ferruginea*, Don ex A. Cunningham in Ann. Nat. Hist. i, 212 (1838).

8. **P. acutifolia.** Branching shrub, sometimes to 30 feet: leaves rather lax, spreading, to 1 inch long, less than ⅛ inch broad, acuminate and very sharp-pointed, midrib not distinct: staminate flowers solitary or a few together in axils; pistillates very small, solitary or rarely twin, axillary: seed small, ovoid, on a fleshy red stalk. Southern New Zealand.—*Podocarpus acutifolia*, T. Kirk in Trans. N. Zeal. Inst. xvi, 370 (1883).

9. **P. Totara.** TOTARA. Very large tree, to 80, or occasionally to 100 feet or more, tall; bark reddish-brown, fibrous, separating in long shreds, on old trees thick and deeply furrowed; branches spreading with distichous ramification: leaves spreading in two ranks, short-petioled, linear to linear-lanceolate, ½–1 inch long and ⅛ inch broad more or less, acute and pungent, dull green above and plane or slightly grooved, paler beneath and with indistinct midrib: staminate catkins axillary, cylindric, ½–¾ inch long: fruit-body axillary, short-stalked, consisting of 1 or 2 subglobose seeds often slightly narrowed at the apex and about ½ inch long, with a red, swollen, rarely shriveled receptacle at the base. New Zealand. Totara is a vernacular name for the tree.—*Podocarpus Totara*, D. Don ex Lambert, A Description of the Genus Pinus, ed. 2, 189 (1832); *P. Totarra*, A. Cunningham in Ann. Nat. Hist. i, 212 (1838).

10. **P. Hallii.** Much like *P. Totara* and perhaps a variety of it with thin papery bark, leaves somewhat longer, seed acute rather than blunt, staminate flowers on evident stalks, young plants weak and branches often flexuous. New Zealand; named for J. W. Hall of Shortland.—*Podocarpus Hallii*, T. Kirk in Forest Flora of New Zealand, 13 (1889); *P. Totarra* var. *Hallii*, Pilger in Engler, Das Pflanzenreich, iv, pt. 5, 84 (1903).

11. **P. gracilior.** Tree to 60 feet or more, the young branches slender and long or more or less whorled: leaves 2–3 inches on old trees or to 4 inches on sterile shoots, to

nearly ¼ inch broad, stiff, gradually long-acuminate: staminate flowers 1–3 in axils; pistillate provided with scales: seed (fruit) about ⅓ inch long, hard, subtended by scales or bracts. Tropical Africa.—*Podocarpus gracilior*, Pilger in Engler, Das Pflanzenreich, iv, pt. 5, 71 (1903).

12. **P. spinulosa.** Shrub or small tree, known by its coriaceous spine-tipped leaves which are 1½ to about 3 inches long and ⅛ inch or more broad, with midrib prominent above: staminate flowers on axillary short branchlets, catkin-like; pistillate on short peduncles and subtended by 2 or 3 bracts or scales: seed dark blue, glaucous. Australia.—*Podocarpus spinulosa*, R. Brown ex Mirbel in Mem. Mus. Par. xiii, 75 (1825).

13. **P. neriifolia.** Tree to 70 feet, much-branched: leaves scattered or sometimes indistinctly whorled, 3–6 inches long, or longer on young plants, about ½ inch broad, long-acuminate, slightly glaucous underneath, the midrib above only slightly raised and in a valley or longitudinal depression: staminate flowers solitary or 2–3 and sessile; pistillate solitary: seed ovoid, about ½ inch long on a fleshy receptacle. China to New Guinea.—*Podocarpus neriifolia*, D. Don ex Lambert, A Description of the Genus Pinus, ii, 21 (1824).

14. **P. macrophylla.** In one or another of its forms, the most frequently seen in this country: tree to 50 feet in height, with horizontally spreading branches and pendent branchlets; the trunk with gray shallowly fissured bark: leaves alternate, pinkish when unfolding, more or less spreading, narrowly lanceolate, narrowed toward the apex and acute or obtusish, at the base gradually narrowed into a short petiole, bright green and lustrous and with a distinct midrib above, paler below, 3–4 inches long and more than ⅓ inch broad: staminate flowers fascicled, sessile, about 1 inch long: seed ovoid, ⅓–½ inch long, borne on a fleshy purplish-violet receptacle. Japan. Introduced to this country in 1862 by Dr. G. R. Hall. A tree of somber aspect, hardy as far north as South Carolina and perhaps farther.—*Podocarpus macrophylla*, D. Don ex Lambert, A Description of the Genus Pinus, ii, 22 (1824); *P. longifolia*, Hort. ex Gordon, Pinetum, 278 (1858).

Var. **Maki.** Plate VI. Branches upright: leaves more upright, linear-lanceolate, obtuse or obtusish, 1¾–3 inches long and ⅕–¼ inch broad: seed globose-ovoid, ⅓ inch long or slightly longer. Japan, where Maki is a vernacular name. Said to be tenderer than the type. Two variegated forms of this variety are in cultivation.—*Podocarpus macrophylla* var. *Maki*, Siebold in Jaarb. Nederl. Maatsch. Aanmoed. Tuinb. (Naaml.) 35 (1844); *P. chinensis*, Sweet, Hortus Britannicus, 371 (1827); *P. japonica*, Siebold, l. c.; *P. macrophylla* var. *chinensis*, Maximowicz in Mel. Biol. vii, 562 (1870); *P. Makoyi*, Blume, Rumphia, iii, 215 (1847).

Var. **appressa.** Bush-like with spreading branches: leaves less than 1½ inches long, the midrib indistinct above.—*Podocarpus macrophylla* var. *appressa*, Matsumura, Index Plantarum Japonicarum, ii, 16 (1905).

15. **P. elongata.** Tree to 70 feet but often dwarf, with branches very leafy: leaves spreading, coriaceous, narrowly linear-lanceolate, to 2 inches long and sometimes about ⅛ inch broad, gradually narrowed to apex and very acute, midrib indistinct above: staminate flowers solitary and sessile in axils; pistillates solitary and stalked: seed globose, about ⅓ inch across, on a short fleshy stalked receptacle. South Africa; in two or three forms.—*Podocarpus elongata*, L'Héritier ex Persoon, Synopsis Plantarum, ii, 580 (1807).

16. P. nubigena. Shrub in cultivation but becoming a tree, with short branches nearly opposite or whorled: leaves crowded, spreading, linear-lanceolate, to 1¾ inches long and upward of ⅛ inch broad, acute and mucronate, midrib conspicuous above, under side bearing 2 glaucous lines: staminate flowers clustered; pistillates solitary and stalked: seed ovoid, about ⅓ inch long on a very short-stalked fleshy receptacle. Chile.—*Podocarpus nubigena*, Lindley in Paxt. Flow. Gard. ii, 162 (1851-2).

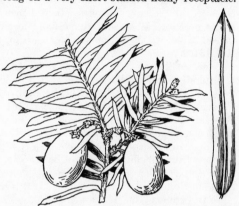

17. P. saligna. Much-branched tree to 60 feet or more: leaves spreading, linear-lanceolate and perhaps falcate or curved, to 4 inches long and to ¼ inch or more broad, gradually long-acuminate, midrib prominent above: staminate flowers aggregated on apex of branchlets; pistillates solitary, stalked: seed oblong, on broad receptacle. Chile, Peru.—*Podocarpus saligna*, D. Don ex Lambert, A Description of the Genus Pinus, ii, 20 (1824); *P. chilina*, L. C. Richard in Ann. Mus. Par. xvi, 297 (1810), *nomen; P. andina*, Hort.

6. Cephalotaxus drupacea. Separate leaf about twice natural size.

6. CEPHALOTAXUS. PLUM-YEW. Evergreen diœcious Asian trees and shrubs something like very large-leaved yews in foliage but bearing a drupe-like large seed resembling Torreya; branchlets opposite, with a resin-canal in the center of the pith: leaves linear, pointed, with a prominent midrib above and with 2 broad glaucous bands beneath, arranged in 2 rows, with a resin-duct in the middle: staminate flowers in 1–8-flowered short-stalked clusters; fertile consisting of a small cone with several bracts, each bearing 2 naked ovules: seed inclosed in a fleshy envelope, drupe-like, about 1 inch long, reddish- or greenish-brown. Cephalotáx-us: Greek, head, and *Taxus*; a taxus-like plant with the flowers in heads or clusters. Six species from Assam to China and Japan.—*Cephalotaxus*, Siebold & Zuccarini ex Endlicher, Genera Plantarum, Suppl. ii, 27 (1842).

The plum-yews make low trees or straggling bushes, attractive for variety in conifer plantations. In sheltered places they are fairly hardy as far north as western New York and Massachusetts although better suited to more southern locations. Plum-yews are propagated by means of seeds and also by cuttings of upright terminal shoots and cions set on seedlings or on *Taxus baccata*.

A. Foliage of loosely 2-ranked leaves that are not spine-pointed.
  B. Leaves 2 inches or less long, semi-erect, abruptly or suddenly short-pointed.1. *C. drupacea*
  BB. Leaves mostly exceeding 2 inches, nearly horizontal, gradually tapering to
      thin point...2. *C. Fortuni*
AA. Foliage of closely-set stiff leaves that are spine-pointed, 1 inch or less long....3. *C. Oliveri*

1. **Cephalotaxus drupacea.** JAPANESE PLUM-YEW. Fig. 6. Short-leaved shrub or small bushy tree, rarely to 30 feet tall in its native country, with wide-spreading branches usually light green when young; bark of trunk gray and fissured into narrow detachable strips: leaves about 1 inch long, abruptly pointed, narrow and straight, often upturned: staminate flowers very short-stalked: seed (or fruit) usually obovate, narrowed at the base, purplish, about 1 inch long. Japan; hardy in sheltered places as far north as Massachusetts, usually forming a shapeless wide-spreading bush.— *Cephalotaxus drupacea*, Siebold & Zuccarini, Floræ Japonicæ Familiæ Naturales, ii, 108 (1846).

Var. **fastigiata.** SPIRAL PLUM-YEW. Of columnar habit, with upright branches and spirally arranged leaves. Cultivated in Japan; tenderer than the type and hardy as far north as New York.—*Cephalotaxus drupacea* var. *fastigiata*, Schneider in Silva-Tarouca, Unsere Freiland-Nadelhölzer, 161 (1913); *C. pedunculata* var. *fastigiata*, Carrière, Production et Fixation des Variétés, 44 (1865); *Podocarpus koraiana*, Endlicher, Synopsis Coniferarum, 217 (1847).

Var. **nana.** Shrub with upright or ascending stems 1–6 feet tall and spreading by suckers: fruit subglobose, ¾ inch long, edible. North and central Japan.—*Cephalotaxus drupacea* var. *nana*, Rehder in Journ. Arnold Arb. iv, 107 (1923); *C. nana*, Nakai in Bot. Mag. Tokyo, xxxiii, 193 (1919).

Var. **pedunculata.** HARRINGTON PLUM-YEW. Young branches dark green: leaves to 2 inches long, narrowed into a sharp point: male flowers in branched heads on a stalk ½–¾ inch long. Known only as a cultivated plant in Japan.—*Cephalotaxus drupacea* var. *pedunculata*, Miquel in Ann. Mus. Lugd.-Bat. iii, 169 (1867); *C. pedunculata*, Siebold & Zuccarini, Floræ Japonicæ Familiæ Naturales, ii, 108 (1846); *C. Harringtonia*, K. Koch, Dendrologie, ii, II, 102 (1873).

Var. **sinensis.** Shrub to 12 feet: leaves linear-lanceolate, tapering to a sharp point. Central and western China.—*Cephalotaxus drupacea* var. *sinensis*, Rehder & Wilson in Sargent, Plantæ Wilsonianæ, ii, 3 (1916).

2. **C. Fortuni.** CHINESE PLUM-YEW. Long-leaved irregular branched shrub or in its native country a tree to 30 feet tall with slender spreading branches often pendulous at the ends, the trunk usually dividing near the ground into 2 to 5 ascending stems with reddish-brown bark peeling off in large irregular flakes leaving pale markings: leaves 2–3 inches long, tapering gradually into a sharp point, usually falcate, dark green and shining above: seed short-ellipsoidal, about 1¼ inches long, purplish. China; hardy as far north as New York and usually forming a rather irregular shrub with handsome dark green and lustrous foliage. Introduced to England by Robert Fortune.—*Cephalotaxus Fortuni*, Hooker in Bot. Mag. t. 4499 (1850).

3. **C. Oliveri.** Shrub with flat stiffish branches and rigid closely-set leaves in two opposite ranks, to 1 inch long and ⅙ inch or less broad, and spiny-pointed, truncate at base: seed ovoid, 1¼ inch long on stalk ½ inch long. Western China; yet little known in cultivation.—*Cephalotaxus Oliveri*, Masters in Bull. Herb. Boiss. vi, 270 (1898).

7. **TORREYA.** TORREYA. Evergreen North American and East Asian small to large trees with yew-like foliage and seed or nut much like that of Cephalotaxus but sessile, diœcious or seldom monœcious with fissured bark,

whorled branches, and subopposite branchlets; winter-buds with few decussate deciduous scales: leaves 2-ranked, linear or linear-lanceolate, spiny-pointed, without distinct midrib above and with 2 narrow glaucous bands beneath becoming fulvous with age, with a resin-duct in the middle; when bruised the foliage of some species emits a pungent or fetid odor: staminate flowers ovoid or oblong, composed of 6–8 whorls of stamens, surrounded at the base by bud-scales; fertile flowers consisting of a solitary ovule surrounded at the base by a fleshy aril and several scales: fruit-body drupe-like, consisting of a rather large seed, with thick woody shell entirely covered by a thin fleshy aril, ripening the second season; albumen ruminate; cotyledons 2, remaining under ground in germination. Torrèy-a or Tór-reya: for John Torrey, distinguished American botanist, 1796–1873. Six closely related species in North America and in eastern Asia; occasionally grown as ornamental evergreens for their handsome foliage and interesting habit.—*Torreya*, Arnott in Ann. Nat. Hist. i, 130 (1838); *Tumion*, Greene in Pittonia, ii, 194 (1891).

The oriental torreyas are hardier than the two native, standing in favorable places as far north as Massachusetts but not thriving in the interior so far north; the native species are adapted somewhat beyond their natural ranges and *T. californica* may survive as a small plant even in southern New England. Torreyas are not often seen in cultivation. They are propagated by seed, and slowly by cuttings of straight terminal shoots.

KEY to the species of Torreya:

A. Fresh foliage emitting strong or fetid odor when crushed.
  B. Leaves short, 1¼ inches or less long.
    c. Apex of leaf acute: two-year-old branches yellowish-green or yellowish-brown. . . . . .1. *T. taxifolia*
    cc. Apex produced into a thin spine: two-year-old branches reddish-brown.2. *T. nucifera*
  BB. Leaves long, commonly more than 1¼ inches. . . . . .3. *T. californica*
AA. Fresh foliage not noticeably aromatic when bruised.
  B. Leaves abruptly spine-pointed, slightly convex above. . . . . .4. *T. grandis*
  BB. Leaves gradually pointed, flat or nearly so above and 2 grooves along rib.5. *T. Fargesii*

1. **Torreya taxifolia.** FLORIDA TORREYA. STINKING-CEDAR. Plate IV. Tree to 40 feet, with spreading slightly pendulous branches, forming a rather open pyramidal head; bark brown, tinged orange: leaves linear, acuminate, rounded at base and subsessile, dark or dark yellowish-green above, with shallow white bands beneath, ¾–1½ inches long: seed (or fruit) obovoid, dark purple, 1–1¼ inches long. Florida. Discovered in 1833. Hardy at least as far north as South Carolina.—*Torreya taxifolia*, Arnott in Ann. Nat. Hist. i, 130 (1838).

2. **T. nucifera.** JAPANESE TORREYA. Fig. 7. Tree usually 30 feet, but occasionally 80 feet high, with spreading branches, forming a compact head, sometimes shrubby; bark grayish-brown: leaves lanceolate, acuminate, rigid and spiny-pointed, very dark green above, with 2 white impressed bands beneath, ¾–1½ inches long and ⅛–⅙ inch broad: seed obovoid-oblong, about 1 inch long, green, faintly tinged and striped with

purple. Southern and central Japan. First introduced to this country probably about 1860. A handsome tree with dark green lustrous leaves, hardy as far north as Massachusetts. The seeds are edible; the strong and close-grained wood is durable in water and is used in Japan for making water-pails and for cabinet-work.—*Torreya nucifera*, Siebold & Zuccarini in Abh. Bayr. Akad. Wissensch.iv, 3, 234(1846).

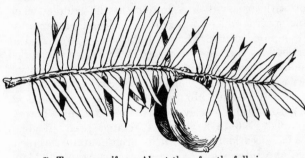

7. Torreya nucifera. About three-fourths full size.

3. **T. californica.** CALIFORNIA-NUTMEG. Tree to 70 or occasionally 100 feet, with spreading slightly pendulous branches, forming a pyramidal or, in old age, round-topped head; bark grayish-brown, tinged with orange: leaves linear, slightly falcate, acuminate, lustrous and dark green above, with narrow impressed bands beneath, 1–2½ inches long: seed oblong-oval or oval, light green streaked with purple, 1–1½ inches long. California; hardy as far north as Philadelphia. A handsome tree with slender spreading branches, but usually shrubby in the East.—*Torreya californica*, Torrey in N. York Journ. Pharm. iii, 49 (1852); *T. Myristica*, Hooker f. in Bot. Mag. t. 4780 (1854).

4. **T. grandis.** CHINESE TORREYA. Tree occasionally to 80 feet high, sometimes shrubby: leaves linear-lanceolate, with a slender spiny point, ½–1¼ inches long and ⅛ inch broad, bright green and lustrous above, with 2 white impressed bands beneath: seed obovoid-oblong, mucronate, measuring 1–1¼ inches long, brownish. Eastern China; hardy as far north as Massachusetts in sheltered positions.—*Torreya grandis*, Fortune ex Gordon, Pinetum, 326 (1858); *T. nucifera* var. *grandis*, Pilger in Engler, Das Pflanzenreich, iv, pt. 5, 107 (1903).

5. **T. Fargesii.** A Chinese species bearing the name of R. P. Farges, collector, little known, much like *T. grandis* but leaves darker green, rather longer and gradually pointed, flat or nearly so above and bearing 2 grooves along midrib: seed more globose and the albumen deeply ruminate or wrinkled.—*Torreya Fargesii*, Franchet in Journ. de Bot. xiii, 264 (1899); *T. grandis*, Rehder & Wilson in part.

CHAPTER III

THE TRUE CONE-BEARERS—PINES, AND KEY

T HE conifers constitute the natural family Pinaceæ. All of them are woody durable plants, ranging from low shrubs to the greatest trees of the earth. They tend strongly to a single continuous trunk that makes no main branches, producing a simple very tall bole, as firs, spruces, hemlocks, sequoias. Some of the groups, however, abound in strong side-branching and make arresting picturesque subjects in age, as pines and true cedars. While the foliage of most of them is evergreen, the individual leaves are not perpetual but shed after three or more years as one may see by tracing back the branchlets to different ages; and the mat of needles under the tree attests to this leaffall. The pines are trees of commanding importance as timber, and other groups are also major forest trees. They are of prime value in shelter-belts. In habit and shape of tree, in foliage, bark, spring-growth, and cones, the cone-bearers are singularly attractive as ornamentals; and the short-lived staminate cones (Plates IV, VII), although seldom noted, are interesting objects. The resinous and aromatic odors are important assets, and a pleasing contrast to the scents of flowers. The conifers stand apart in the plant-world as subjects at once singular to the horticulturist. Fortunately, they are of simple cultural requirements in places in which the various kinds are hardy.

PINACEÆ. Comprises resinous woody plants, mostly trees, usually evergreen, widely distributed over the earth but little developed in torrid regions, most extensive family of gymnosperms, differing from the Taxaceæ in technical characters (see page 18): plants diœcious or monœcious: leaves alternate, opposite, whorled or fascicled, from scale-like to long-linear: flowers under scales combined into catkin-like spikes or sometimes in small heads: mature seed-bearing body a dry hard durable cone or in one group (Juniperus) the scales cohering and fleshy; seeds often with flat thin wings. Upwards of thirty genera, most of which are represented by species in cultivation in North America. They are major horticultural subjects.

KEY to the genera of Pinaceæ, artificially arranged for convenience.

I. Genera of evergreen conifers, foliage persisting so that the plant
   never becomes bare.
   Group 1, the pines: leaves long and needle-like, 2 or more (exception
      in *P. monophylla*) together in a fascicle sheathed at base: cones not
      shattering, the scales being persistent......................... 1. PINUS, 39
   Group 2, the spruces and firs: leaves linear or needle-like but not
      greatly elongated (not often much exceeding 1 inch) and not in
      sheathed fascicles and not clustered: cones often shattering at ma-
      turity, each scale subtended by a bract.
      A. Trees with cones upright on the branch.
         B. Cone shattering, bracts sometimes projecting beyond the
            scales: leaves grooved above, or seldom 4-angled........ 2. ABIES, 78
         BB. Cone persistent (not shattering), the bracts much shorter
            than the scales: leaves keeled above................... 3. KETELEERIA, 95
      AA. Trees with cones pendulous, or deflexed or slanting on the branch.
         B. Cone showing forked bracts that project beyond the scales:
            branchlets not rough from persisting leaf-bases.......... 4. PSEUDOTSUGA, 96
         BB. Cone without bracts projecting beyond the scales: branchlets
            rough or knobby from persistent leaf-bases.
            C. Leaves usually stiff, mostly 4-sided or angled, sessile..... 5. PICEA, 99
            CC. Leaves usually distinctly flat, short, narrowed at base to a
               short petiole...................................... 6. TSUGA, 122
   Group 3, the sequoias, cryptomerias, etc.: leaves various but scat-
      tered, except in No. 17, sometimes of two kinds, one set being scale-
      like and others yew-like: scales of cone not provided with subtend-
      ing bracts, not shattering: seeds 2 or more to each scale.
      A. The leaves distinct and separate, never grown together at bases
         or in whorls.
         B. Cone-scales peltate, standing like shields on the cone: leaves
            of two kinds.
            C. Branchlets deciduous first or second year: leaves also de-
               ciduous on most species: 2 seeds under each cone-scale.10. TAXODIUM, 137
            CC. Branchlets and leaves not deciduous: 5–7 seeds under each
               scale..12. SEQUOIA, 139
         BB. Cone-scales not peltate, flattened and appressed on the cone,
            overlapping.
            C. Foliage of one kind, leaves either scale-like or yew-like:
               3–several seeds under each cone-scale.
               D. Leaves awl-shaped...............................13. CRYPTOMERIA, 141
               DD. Leaves lanceolate and flat, 1–2 inches long...........14. CUNNINGHAMIA, 143
               DDD. Leaves small, mostly scale-like and appressed.........15. ATHROTAXIS, 144
            CC. Foliage of two kinds, scale-like on fruiting branches, awl-
               like elsewhere: 2 seeds to a scale....................16. TAIWANIA, 145
      AA. The main or conspicuous leaves elongated (2½ inches or more
         long at full growth), closely contiguous at base and whorled;
         other leaves scale-like and usually not recognized..........17. SCIADOPITYS, 146
   Group 4, the araucarias, etc.: leaves scale-like and appressed all
      around the branch or else flat but not needle-like: cones large,
      shattering: seed solitary to each scale.
      A. Leaves crowded, scale-like and 4-angled, or flat and yew-like and
         broad at base: cone-scales opposite......................18. ARAUCARIA, 147
      AA. Leaves not crowded nor scale-like nor 4-angled but flat and
         parallel-veined, mostly ½ inch or more broad.............19. AGATHIS, 150
   Group 5, the junipers: cones small berry-like bodies, the cohering
      scales becoming fleshy: leaves opposite or in 3's, scale-like or short-
      needle-shaped..30. JUNIPERUS, 184

Group 6, the cypresses and arbor-vitæ: leaves and the scales of cones
small and mostly globose: foliage of small often scale-like leaves:
seeds 1–many to each cone-scale.
  A. Leaves opposite and scale-like, mostly appressed, but sometimes
    short-needle-like in young plants or on new shoots.
    B. Cone-scales peltate, therefore standing squarely before the
      observer.
      c. Seeds many with each cone-scale, the large cone commonly
        maturing the second year: branchlets seldom flattened:
        leaves with minutely fimbiate edges..................20. CUPRESSUS, 152
      cc. Seeds 5 or fewer with each scale, the cone maturing first
        season: branchlets flattened: leaf-edges entire........21. CHAMÆCYPARIS, 157
    BB. Cone-scales not peltate, but flattened, appressed and over-
      lapping: branchlets flattened.
      c. Scales of cone 8 or more (perhaps sometimes 6 in No. 24).
        D. The cones oblong with 1–5 seeds to the fertile scales...22. THUJA, 167
        DD. The cones nearly or quite globose with 3–5 seeds to each
          fertile scale: branchlets conspicuously flattened and
          sometimes ⅓ inch broad.......................23. THUJOPSIS, 175
      cc. Scales 6 or less, only the upper pair fertile and bearing
        2 seeds each......................................24. LIBOCEDRUS, 176
  AA. Leaves usually whorled, scale-like or linear: cone-scales mostly
    valvate (edge to edge), opposite or whorled.
    B. Scales all fertile and manifestly valvate.
      c. Number of scales 6–8 and unequal: leaves in 3's or 4's.
        D. The cone on a short thick peduncle or stalk without
          bracts...25. CALLITRIS, 178
        DD. The cone with many scale-like bracts at base.........26. ACTINOSTROBUS, 180
      cc. Number of cone-scales only 4 and equal or nearly so.
        D. Branchlets terete (cylindric), not jointed: leaves oppo-
          site, or alternate on strong shoots................27. WIDDRINGTONIA, 180
        DD. Branchlets flattened and jointed: leaves in 4's........28. TETRACLINIS, 182
    BB. Scales partly fertile, the lower ones sterile and slightly im-
      bricate: leaves in 3's...............................29. FITZROYA, 183
Group 7, the true cedars, large trees: leaves needle-like but not
elongated (as in pines) and clustered except on young shoots: cones
tardily shattering or falling in pieces....................... 7. CEDRUS, 128
II. Genera of deciduous conifers, the foliage falling annually so that the
  plant becomes bare in winter.
  A. Leaves regularly disposed along the branchlets, not in fascicles:
    scales of cone without subtending bracts.
    B. Cone-scales peltate, appearing shield-like to the observer,
      very irregular.......................................10. TAXODIUM, 137
    BB. Cone-scales not peltate, long and obovate: leaves dimorphic.11. GLYPTOSTROBUS, 139
  AA. Leaves (aside from those on new axial growths) clustered on
    short lateral spurs: bracts present in the cones.
    B. Cones not shattering, the scales being persistent: cones erect
      or not pendulous.................................... 8. LARIX, 131
    BB. Cones shattering or falling in pieces after maturity: cones
      hanging... 9. PSEUDOLARIX, 136

1. **PINUS.** PINE. Stately evergreen monœcious trees, also dwarf forms,
of some eighty species in the northern hemisphere, extending from the high
North to uplands in the tropics, of immense value for timber and any number
of them planted in windbreaks and for ornament and general interest.

Branches commonly whorled or in tiers: winter-buds covered with imbricated more or less resinous scales: leaves of two kinds but the short primary spirally arranged ones seen only on seedlings or infrequently on shoots from

older branches and as dry scales, the secondary being the only ones known to the general observer and in this treatment called the leaves or needles of pines; secondary or main leaves long and mostly very slender, terete or triangular in cross-section, contained in a short sheath at the base (sheath deciduous in some species), except in *P. monophylla* and *P. quadrifolia* (in this treatment) 2, 3, or 5 in each bundle (Figs. 8, 9, 10, 31): staminate flowers in yellow, orange or scarlet catkin-like spikes (Plates IV, VII, Fig. 11 showing another genus) arising in spring at tip of old shoot or at base of the continuing new shoot of the season, soon becoming dead and dry and perhaps persisting more or less through the early summer, composed of spirally-arranged 2-celled anthers under scales (Fig. 12): pistillate flowers in lateral or subterminal short dense greenish or purplish spikes that become the seed-bearing cones, each scale covering 2 ovules (Fig. 13): cone subglobose to cylindric, sometimes very large and woody, with persistent woody overlapping scales; seed small, or large and nut-like, in most species with a long thin wing (Fig. 14). Upland plants, frequently on poor thin soils, under favorable conditions usually making clear stands of great extent; prime forest trees; the most extensive genus of the gymnosperms, member of the subfamily Abietineæ.—*Pinus* (pì-nus), Linnæus, Species Plantarum 1000 (1753); the classical name.

8. The three leaves of Pinus rigida, showing sheath still intact in young cluster at right but partly broken away in old cluster. (×½)

In some kinds of pines the cones mature the first year, in others the second, and still others in the third year after blooming and pollinizing. Cones of certain species, as often in *P. clausa*, do not discharge the seeds for three or four years; and sometimes the cone persists

9. Pinus resinosa, showing the two-leaved sheaths, young at the right, old at left. (× 2)

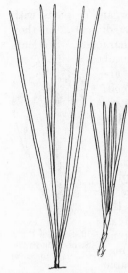

until it is overgrown and covered by the woody tissue of the enlarging branch. Some kinds of cones do not open to set free the seeds, but commonly the scales separate and liberate them, in which cases the cone is sometimes said to be dehiscent.

Twig-bearing in pines is described by Rehder: "The shoot which develops in spring from the terminal winter-bud (spring-shoot) produces in most species only one internode with one whorl of branchlets and is therefore called uninodal and bears the cones at the end of the shoot (subterminal), while in other species the spring-shoot produces two or more often incomplete whorls of branchlets (multinodal shoots) and bears the cones partly in the middle of the shoot (lateral)."

It is usually impossible to make positive identification of pines without mature cones. The differences are in size, shape, and density of

10. Pinus Strobus, with five leaves in sheath. (× ½)

cones as well as in the character of scales composing them. The end or exposed part of the scale is usually enlarged and more or less rhombic, termed the *scale-end* or *apophysis* (Fig. 15); on the scale-end is commonly a point or boss called an *umbo*. These terms reappear in the descriptions.

However much the planter may desire an offhand way of recognizing the different species of pines, wild and planted, he will not find it. Long experience in propagating and planting enables a person to name the species with which he deals by acquaintance-ship, but this will not aid him greatly in identifying other kinds. The distinguishing of the kinds in any important growing collection requires the habit of close observation and particularly the presence in the hand of foliage and cones, and then patience to compare with keys and descriptions. It is impossible to make a key without exceptions;

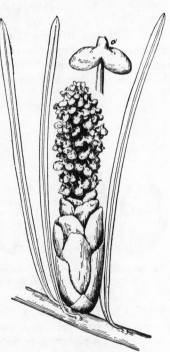

11. Staminate catkin or cone of a conifer; *a*, anther. Both enlarged.

and the use of a key presupposes a knowledge of the organs or parts with which it deals. The best keys are naturally the most difficult, for they require a study of covered rather than superficial characters. Students

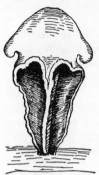

accustomed to the study of anatomical details should consult the excellent arrangement by Dr. W. M. Harlow (Tech. Publ. 32, N. Y. State College of Forestry, Syracuse), "The identification of the pines of the United States, native and introduced, by needle structure."

The pines are standard ornamental subjects. They are particularly adapted to parks and to large private estates to establish boundaries and when the planter desires trees that increase in character with the years, developing strong and striking aspects at full maturity. They are long-lived durable

12. Discharged anther of a pine. Enlarged.

13. Seeds of Pinus Strobus under the scale. (× about 2)

trees. With the dividing of estates and the fashion for compact verdure, the pines have unfortunately taken a somewhat subordinate place in planting, yet they are indispensable on ample areas for long-time landscape effect, for shade and shelter, and are a pleasing contrast to the urge for "immediate

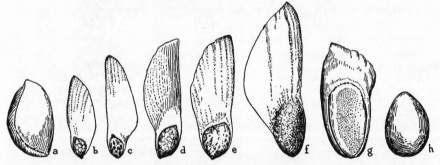

14. Seeds of pines, somewhat enlarged. *a*, P. koraiensis; *b*, sylvestris; *c*, rigida; *d*, nigra caramanica; *e*, ponderosa; *f*, canariensis; *g*, Torreyana with detachable wing; *h*, edulis.

effect" and for transitory things. They impart elements of strength and permanence to a private or public property. When well placed and with age they impart a picturesque note to estates.

Pines are of simple requirements and many of them are hardy in the northern states and Canada. They are rugged subjects. There is much variety amongst them in size, foliage, color, and habit of growth; and the cones are always decorative. Propagation is simple by means of seeds; and horticultural varieties and rare or seedless kinds are grafted on related stocks, the white or soft pines usually on seedlings of *Pinus Strobus* and the hard or red pines on *P. sylvestris* or *P. nigra*.

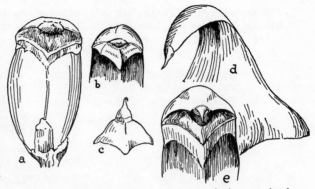

15. Scale-ends or apophyses on cones of pines, variously enlarged. *a*, Pinus nigra; *b*, resinosa; *c*, pungens; *d*, Coulteri; *e*, ponderosa.

SPECIES OF PINES IN THIS TREATMENT

Numerals following names (in parentheses) indicate the usual number of leaves or needles in a fascicle.

Subgenus **DIPLOXYLON.** Hard, Red, or Pitch pines: bracts at base of leaf-fascicles decurrent or running down the stem (Fig. 16, left): sheath of fascicle usually persistent: leaves serrulate or rough on edges: wood hard, mostly dark, commonly strongly resinous. Spring shoots uninodal or multinodal (uninodal in the following species unless otherwise stated in the text).

1. nigra (2)
2. leucodermis (2)
3. resinosa (2)
4. Thunbergii (2)
5. densiflora (2)
6. taiwanensis (2)
7. Massoniana (2)
8. Mugo (2)
9. sylvestris (2)
10. tabulæformis (2; 3)
11. insularis (3; 2)
12. echinata (2 or 3)
13. glabra (2)
14. pungens (2)
15. virginiana (2)
16. clausa (2)
17. halepensis (2; 3)
18. Pinaster (2)
19. contorta (2)
20. Banksiana (2)
21. muricata (2)
22. ponderosa (3; 2)
23. Jeffreyi (3)
24. palustris (3)
25. Tæda (3)
26. caribæa (2; 3)
27. rigida (3)
28. serotina (3; 4)
29. attenuata (3)
30. radiata (3; 2)
31. Roxburghii (3)
32. canariensis (3)
33. Sabiniana (3)
34. Coulteri (3)
35. Torreyana (5)
36. Pinea (2)

Subgenus **HAPLOXYLON**. Soft or White pines: bracts at base of fascicles on young growth not decurrent (Fig. 16, right): sheath of leaf-fascicle commonly soon deciduous or falling: leaves often or commonly smooth on edges: wood soft, with little resin, not deeply colored: uninodal.

37. cembroides (3; 2)
38. monophylla (1; 2)
39. edulis (2; 3)
40. quadrifolia (4; 1–5)
41. Bungeana (3)
42. Balfouriana (5)
43. aristata (5)
44. koraiensis (5; 3)
45. Cembra (5)
46 Armandi. (5)

47. albicaulis (5)
48. flexilis (5)
49. Lambertiana (5)
50. Ayacahuite (5)
51. parviflora (5)
52. Peuce (5)
53. nepalensis (5)
54. monticola (5)
55. Strobus (5)

KEY to Pinus, divided primarily on leaf-number:

 I. One-leaved pine (a solitary short stiff leaf in each sheath)............38. *P. monophylla*
 II. Two-leaved pines (prevailingly 2 leaves or needles in each sheath or fascicle).
    A. Bracts on young shoots not decurrent or running down the stem:
        leaf-sheath deciduous. (No. 37 may be sought here)............39. *P. edulis*
   AA. Bracts on young shoots manifestly decurrent and leaf-sheath persistent.
      B. Wing of seed very short...................................36. *P. Pinea*
     BB. Wing long and conspicuous.
        c. Cones deciduous, falling off as a whole after maturity, or at least
           the scales opening and discharging then.
          D. Bark of branches 2–4 years old prominently covered with
             scales, which are the decurrent base of bracts, each scale
             loosening or peeling off separately as a more or less rectangular piece.
             E. Branchlets brown or dark.
                F. Leaves usually less than 6 inches long.............. 1. *P. nigra*
                FF. Leaves 8 or more inches long.......................26. *P. caribœa*
             EE. Branchlets grayish-white: bark of trunk light gray....... 2. *P. leucodermis*
             EEE. Branchlets yellow or orange.
                 F. Developed or winter-buds very resinous.............. 3. *P. resinosa*
                 FF. Developed or winter-buds not resinous............... 4. *P. Thunbergii*
          DD. Bark of 2–4-year-old branches devoid of exfoliating scales.
             E. Branchlets glaucous or with a "bloom"................. 5. *P. densiflora*
             EE. Branchlets not glaucous, tawny-red: like *P. densiflora*.... 6. *P. taiwanensis*
             EEE. Branchlets not glaucous, various.
                 F. Length of leaves 4 inches or more................... 7. *P. Massoniana*
                 FF. Length of leaves 3–4 inches.......................12. *P. echinata*
                 FFF. Length of leaves 3 inches or less.
                   G. With cones practically sessile: shrub-like........... 8. *P. Mugo*
                   GG. With stalked cones: trees.
                     And bluish-green foliage........................ 9. *P. sylvestris*
                     And dark green foliage........................13. *P. glabra*
       cc. Cones persisting, and frequently not opening for three or more years.
         D. Shape of cone symmetrical (developed on all sides).
             E. Foliage somewhat glaucous...........................10. *P. tabulœformis*
             EE. Foliage not glaucescent.

F. Length of leaves short, 3½ inches or less.
  G. Prickle of cone-scales a very stout curved spine.....14. *P. pungens*
  GG. Prickle of cone-scales slender from a broad base.
    And cones opening at maturity.................15. *P. virginiana*
    And cones usually remaining for three or more years.16. *P. clausa*
  FF. Length of leaves medium, to 4 or 5 inches.
    G. Umbo or projection of cone-scales obtuse..........17. *P. halepensis*
    GG. Umbo sharp, sometimes deciduous................12. *P. echinata*
  FFF. Length of leaves long, 5–8 inches....................18. *P. Pinaster*
DD. Shape of cone lopsided, one side usually not fully developing.
  E. Length of leaves less than 4 inches.
    F. Scales of cone prickly............................19. *P. contorta*
    FF. Scales not prickly................................20. *P. Banksiana*
  EE. Length of leaves more than 4 inches: cone very prickly...21. *P. muricata*
III. Three-leaved pines.
  A. Bracts below leaf-fascicles, on young shoots, plainly decurrent: leaf-sheaths persisting.
    B. Wing of seed jointed and falling away as a whole.
      C. The wing thin and membranous.
        D. Cones deciduous, scales opening at maturity.
          E. Leaves under 4 or at most 5 inches long.
            And glaucescent.....................................10. *P. tabulæformis*
            And not glaucescent although bluish-green............12. *P. echinata*
          EE. Leaves 5 inches or more long.
            F. Branchlets glaucous: cone very long.................23. *P. Jeffreyi*
            FF. Branchlets not glaucous, yellowish- to orange-brown.
              G. Buds whitish....................................24. *P. palustris*
              GG. Buds brown.
                H. Cone sessile or practically so.
                  And subterminal..........................22. *P. ponderosa*
                  And lateral..............................25. *P. Tœda*
                HH. Cone short-stalked............................26. *P. caribœa*
        DD. Cones persistent for three years or more, scales opening tardily if at all.
          E. Shape of cone symmetrical, scales on all sides developing.
            F. With curved prickles (perhaps deciduous in No. 28).
              G. Leaves 5 inches or less long......................27. *P. rigida*
              GG. Leaves 6 inches or more long.....................28. *P. serotina*
            FF. Without curved prickles...........................10. *P. tabulæformis*
          EE. Shape of cone lopsided.
            With stout prickles..............................29. *P. attenuata*
            With minute prickles.............................30. *P. radiata*
      CC. The wing thick and heavy: leaves 6 inches or more long.
        D. Leaves slender: wing about half as long as seed...........33. *P. Sabiniana*
        DD. Leaves stout and stiff: wing about 1 inch long............34. *P. Coulteri*
    BB. Wing of seed long, not detaching: leaves very long.
      C. End of cone-scale elongated and recurved..................31. *P. Roxburghii*
      CC. End of cone-scale stout-conical and not recurved............32. *P. canariensis*
      CCC. End of cone-scale not prolonged, tip in a depression.........11. *P. insularis*
  AA. Bracts on young shoots not decurrent or running down the stem: leaf-sheath deciduous.
    B. Leaves mostly 1½ inches or less long, entire on edges..........37. *P. cembroides*
    BB. Leaves 2 inches or more long, and serrulate...................41. *P. Bungeana*
IV. Four-leaved pine..40. *P. quadrifolia*
V. Five-leaved pines (leaves or needles 5 in each fascicle).
  A. Bracts on shoots, subtending leaf-fascicles, clearly decurrent: cone broad and heavy, with short thick wing on seeds................35. *P. Torreyana*

16. Twigs of pine, showing leaf-scales decurrent in P. rigida at left and not so or deciduous in P. Strobus. Somewhat enlarged.

1. **Pinus nigra**, known also as *P. Laricio*. AUSTRIAN PINE. Plate VII. Fig. 15a. Rugged hardy pine of various natural and horticultural forms, of rather dark heavy aspect, in its native state a tree to 100 or occasionally 150 feet tall and sometimes a girth of 20 feet, with stout spreading branches in regular whorls forming a symmetrical pyramid, in old age sometimes broad and flat-topped; bark on old trees deeply fissured into irregular longitudinal scaly plates, pale brown beneath the deciduous scales; branchlets usually yellowish or light brown; winter-buds ovoid or oblong-ovoid, light brown, resinous: leaves 2 in a sheath, stiff, acute, dark green, 3–6½ inches long: conelet with mucronate scales; cones sessile, ovate, yellowish-brown, glossy, solitary or clustered, deciduous at maturity, usually 2–4 inches long; end of mature scale depressed, conspicuously keeled; umbo flattened, obtuse or with a very short prickle; seeds gray, ¼ inch. From Austria to Dalmatia and Rumania. The typical form (sometimes called var. *austriaca*) is hardy as far north as southern Ontario and New England.—*Pinus nigra*, Arnold, Reise nach Mariazell, 8 (1785); *P. Laricio*, Poiret in Lamarck Encyclopédie Méthodique, v, 339

(1804); *P. austriaca,* Hoess in Flora viii, Beibl.115 (1825); *P. nigricans,* Host in Sauter Vers. Geogr. Bot. Schild. Umg. Wiens, 23 (1826); *P. Laricio* var. *austriaca,* Loudon, Arboretum et Fruticetum Britannicum, iv, 2201 (1838); *P. nigra* var. *austriaca,* Ascherson & Graebner, Synopsis der Mitteleuropaischen Flora, ed. 1, i, 213 (1897).

Var. **calabrica.** CORSICAN PINE. Tall tree to 150 feet high, with shorter ascending branches forming a narrower head; bark gray; branchlets reddish-brown: leaves lighter green, 4–6 inches long, less crowded and variously curved: cones with the upper and middle scale-ends keeled. Southern Europe.—*Pinus nigra* var. *calabrica,* Schneider in Silva Tarouca, Unsere Freiland-Nadelhölzer, 261 (1913); *P. Laricio* var. *corsicana,* Loudon, Arboretum et Fruticetum Britannicum, iv, 2201 (1838); *P. nigra* var. *Poiretiana,* Ascherson & Graebner, Synopsis der Mitteleuropaischen Flora, ed. 1, i, 214 (1897).

Var. **caramanica.** CRIMEAN PINE. Fig. 14d. Tall tree, with long and stout branches: leaves dark green and glossy: cones light brown, about 4 inches long, with the upper and middle scale-ends obtusely keeled. Western Asia.—*Pinus nigra* var. *caramanica,* Rehder, Manual of Cultivated Trees and Shrubs, 61 (1927); *P. Pallasiana,* Lambert, A Description of the Genus Pinus, ed. 2, i (1824); *P. nigra* var. *Pallasiana,* Ascherson & Graebner, Synopsis der Mitteleuropaischen Flora, ed. 1, i, 214 (1897).

Var. **cebennensis.** CEVENNES PINE. Fig.17. Well-marked variety of looser and thinner habit than the other forms of *P. nigra,* with very slender leaves: tree to 60 feet tall; branchlets orange-colored: leaves to 6½ inches long: cones small, only about 2 inches long. Southwestern France, Pyrenees.—*Pinus nigra* var. *cebennensis,* Rehder in Journ. Arnold Arb. iii, 208 (1922); *P. pyrenaica,* Lapeyrouse, Histoire Abrégée des Plantes des Pyrénées, Suppl. 146 (1818), in part; *P. Salzmanni,* Dunal in Mem. Acad. Montp. (Sect. Sci.)ii, 81 (1851); *P. monspeliensis,* Salzmann ex Dunal, l. c., 83; *P. Laricio tenuifolia,* Parlatore in DeCandolle, Prodromus, xvi, II, 387 (1868); *P. cebennensis,* Hort. ex Gordon, Pinetum, ed. 2, 239 (1875); *P. horizontalis,* Hort. ex Rehder in Bailey, Cyclopedia

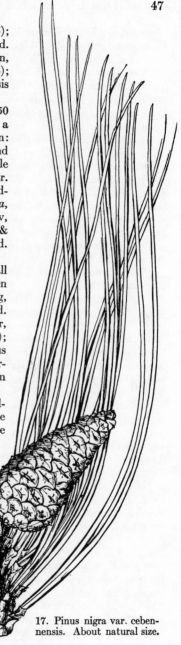

17. Pinus nigra var. cebennensis. About natural size.

of American Horticulture, iii, 1355 (1901); *P. nigra* var. *leptophylla*, Ascherson &
Graebner, Synopsis der Mitteleuropaischen Flora, ed. 2, i, 333 (1912); *P. nigra* var.
tenuifolia, Schneider in Silva Tarouca, Unsere Freiland-Nadelhölzer,262 (1913).

Var. **globosa**. Very dense and broad.—*Pinus nigra* var. *globosa*, Hort.

Var. **Hornibrookiana**. Plate IX. A low somewhat spreading shrub-like plant
originating as a "witches-broom" on Austrian pine in the Rochester parks and named
in compliment to Murray Hornibrook, author of "Dwarf and Slow-Growing Conifers":
branches many and stout, erect or nearly so, beset with crowded stiff sharp leaves
2 inches or more long.—*Pinus nigra* var. *Hornibrookiana*, Slavin; *P. nigra* forma
Hornibrookiana, Slavin.

Var. **monstrosa**. A monstrous form of columnar habit, with few branches in
widely separated whorls and the branchlets irregular and contorted; leaves shining
dark green, stiff, about 6 inches long; type in the Rochester parks.—*Pinus nigra* var.
monstrosa, Slavin; *P. nigra* forma *monstrosa*, Slavin.

Var. **pendula**. Branches pendulous.—*Pinus nigra* var. *pendula*, Rehder; *P. Laricio*
var. *pendula*, Beissner.

Var. **prostrata**. Branches prostrate.—*Pinus nigra* var. *prostrata*, Rehder; *P. Laricio*
var. *prostrata*, Beissner.

Var. **pygmæa**. Dwarf globose form.—*Pinus nigra* var. *pygmæa*, Rehder; *P. Laricio*
var. *pygmæa*, Rauch.

Var. **pyramidalis**. A rather narrow form with ascending curved branches and
shining bluish-green leaves reaching 5 inches: type plant in the Rochester (New York)
parks.—*Pinus nigra* var. *pyramidalis*, Slavin; *P. nigra* forma *pyramidalis*, Slavin.

2. **P. leucodermis**. GRAYBARK or BOSNIAN PINE. A mountain or alpine pine sometimes considered to be a form of *P. nigra* (*Laricio*), suggesting *P. Cembra* in general
habit, not often seen in cultivation: tree to 60 feet tall, of regular pyramidal habit;
bark light gray, broken into angular plates; branchlets glaucous when young, grayish-
white the second and third year; winter-buds oblong-ovoid, not resinous, the scales
brown with white tips or almost grayish-white: leaves 2, more or less appressed and
incurved toward the branch, stiff, 1½–2½ inches long, pungent or obtusish, bright
green: cone ovoid, about 3 inches long, similar to that of *P. nigra* but dull brown,
scarcely lustrous, deciduous at maturity. Balkan Peninsula.—*Pinus leucodermis*,
Antoine in Oester. Bot. Zeitschr. xiv, 366 (1864); *P. Laricio* var. *leucodermis*, Christ in
Flora, l, 81 (1867); *P. nigra* var. *leucodermis*, Rehder in Bailey, Standard Cyclopedia
of Horticulture, v, 2641 (1916).

3. **P. resinosa**. RED or NORWAY PINE. Figs. 9, 15b, 18. A major timber pine,
forming extensive forests, and also an important ornamental conifer of great hardiness:
majestic tree sometimes surpassing 100 feet in height, with regular straight bole
2–3 feet or seldom 5 feet in diameter in forest conditions, in the open with stout
spreading and sometimes pendulous branches forming a broad pyramidal head when
young and an open round-topped one in old age; bark of trunk divided by shallow
fissures; branchlets orange; winter-buds ovoid, acuminate, light brown, resinous:
leaves 2 together, slender and flexible, acute, dark green and lustrous, 4–6 inches long:
conelet with obtuse scales; cones subsessile, conic-ovoid, light brown, 1½–2½ inches
long, deciduous second year; scale-end flattened, conspicuously keeled, obtuse,
with small dark unarmed umbo, maturing and shedding seeds first autumn, decidu-

ous but likely to persist till following year: seeds dark brown, ⅛ inch long. Newfoundland to Manitoba, south to the mountains of Pennsylvania, to Michigan,
Wisconsin, and Minnesota.—*Pinus resinosa*, Aiton, Hortus Kewensis, iii, 367 (1789).

Var. **globosa.** A dwarf
form of globose habit, discovered about 1910 in New
Hampshire.—*Pinus resinosa*
var. *globosa*, Rehder in The
Cultivated Evergreens, 314
(1923); *P. resinosa* forma
globosa, Rehder in Journ.
Arnold Arb. iii, 41 (1922).

4. **P. Thunbergii.** JAPAN-
ESE BLACK PINE. Plate VIII.
A picturesque tree in its
native country, making a
broad head with irregular
horizontal branches, in cultivation sometimes known
erroneously as *P. Massoniana*,
distinguished by its white
buds and stiff rather short
leaves: tree to 100 feet or
even more high, with spreading often somewhat pendulous
branches; bark blackish-gray,
early fissured into elongated
irregular plates; branchlets
orange-yellow; winter-buds
oblong, grayish- or silvery-
white, with fimbriate scales,

18. Pinus resinosa.
About natural size.

free at the tips: leaves 2, stiff, sharply pointed, bright green, 2–5 inches long: cones
short-stalked, conic-ovate, grayish-brown, 2–3 inches long, sometimes clustered,
deciduous at maturity; scale-end flattened, with small depressed umbo, obtuse or
with a minute prickle; seed grayish-brown, ¼ inch long. Japan; hardy as far north
as New England and southern Ontario. Carl Peter Thunberg, for whom this pine is
named, was a Swede, successor to Linnæus at Upsala, who traveled in the Orient
1775-8.—*Pinus Thunbergii*, Parlatore in DeCandolle, Prodromus, xvi, II, 388 (1868);
P. Massoniana, Siebold & Zuccarini, Flora Japonica, ii, 24 (1842), not Lambert.

Var. **oculus-draconis** (Dragon-eye). Leaves marked with 2 broad yellow bands
similar to the variety of the same name of *P. densiflora.*—*Pinus Thunbergii* var.
oculus-draconis, Mayr.

Related species is **P. luchuensis** of the Lu-Chu Islands south of Japan: bark of
upper part of tall trunk smooth, thin, gray: leaves in pairs, 6 inches or somewhat more
long: cones ovate-conic, symmetrical, about 2 inches long.—*Pinus luchuensis*, Mayr
in Bot. Centralbl. lviii, 149 (1894).

5. **P. densiflora.** JAPANESE RED PINE. Plate X. Picturesque pine in Japan, known in a number of garden forms, confused in horticulture with *P. Massoniana*, of rapid growth when young: tree to 100 feet, with spreading branches forming rather broad head; bark orange-red, thin and scaly, at the base of old trunks thicker, grayish and fissured into oblong plates; branchlets orange-yellow, somewhat glaucous; winterbuds oblong-ovoid, chestnut-brown: leaves 2 in a sheath, slender, acute, bright bluish-green, 3–5 inches long: cones short-stalked, conspicuously mucronate when young, conic-ovoid to oblong, dull tawny yellow, somewhat oblique at the base, about 2 inches long, deciduous at maturity or sometimes persisting; scale-end flattened and slightly ridged, those near the base sometimes elongated; umbo small, with a short prickle, or obtuse; seed grayish-yellow, ¼ inch long. Japan; hardy north to southern Ontario and New England.—*Pinus densiflora*, Siebold & Zuccarini, Flora Japonica, ii, 22 (1842); *P. Massoniana*, Hort. ex Masters in Journ. Linn. Soc., Bot. xviii, 503 (1881), not Lambert.

Var. **albo-terminata.** Tips of leaves yellowish-white.—*Pinus densiflora* var. *albo-terminata*, Hort.

Var. **aurea.** Foliage yellow.—*Pinus densiflora* var. *aurea*, Mayr.

Var. **globosa.** JAPANESE GLOBE PINE, the Bandaisho of the Japanese. A dwarf form of globose habit.—*Pinus densiflora* var. *globosa*, Mayr.

Var. **oculus-draconis** (Dragon-eye). Each leaf marked with 2 yellow bands, and therefore the tufts of leaves, if seen from above, show alternate yellow and green rings, hence the name. There is a similar var. of *P. Thunbergii.*—*Pinus densiflora* var. *oculus-draconis*, Mayr.

Var. **pendula.** A form with pendulous or prostrate branches.—*Pinus densiflora* var. *pendula*, Mayr.

Var. **umbraculifera.** JAPANESE UMBRELLA PINE, the Tanyosho of the Japanese. Dwarf dense form, growing ultimately to 12 feet tall, with many upright-spreading branches forming an umbrella-like head.—*Pinus densiflora* var. *umbraculifera*, Mayr; *P. densiflora* var. *tabulæformis*, Hort.

6. **P. taiwanensis.** FORMOSA PINE. Much like *P. densiflora* but cone more oblong-ovate and bearing an elevated umbo which is not reflexed: branchlets tawny-red: leaves 2, sharp-pointed, about 3½ inches long, close together near the ends of branches: cones conic-oblong, about 2 inches long and 1½ inches broad. Formosa. Little known as a cultivated plant; has been started on Long Island but apparently not now growing there; seeds are offered in the United States.—*Pinus taiwanensis*, Hayata in Journ. Coll. Sci. Tokyo, xxx, 307 (1911).

7. **P. Massoniana.** A tender warm-temperate pine probably not in cultivation outside special collections but inserted here because the name has been applied to *P. densiflora* and *P. Thunbergii*; much like *densiflora* but has longer leaves (5–8 inches), longer cone (to nearly 3 inches) which is nut-brown and somewhat shining, in characters of conelet, and not glaucous branchlets; from *Thunbergii* by the absence of exfoliating scales on 2–4-year-old branchlets, longer leaves and longer more tapering cones of different color. There are differences also in leaf-structure. Southeastern China. This pine bears the name of Francis Masson, 1741–1805, a British collector.— *Pinus Massoniana*, Lambert, A Description of the Genus Pinus, i, 17 (1803); the true *Massoniana*. This is *P. sinensis*, Lambert, Genus Pinus, ed. 8vo. i, 47 (1832), but

P. sinensis of Mayr and others is *P. tabulæformis;* see Rehder in Journal of the Arnold Arboretum, vii, 22.

8. **P. Mugo** (known also as *P. montana* and *P. Mughus*). Mugo or Swiss Mountain Pine. Fig. 19. Small European pine, mostly dwarf or bushy but sometimes a tree to 40 feet and then much like *P. sylves-*

tris but differing from that species in darker color (not blue-green) of foliage, nearly or quite sessile cone which has more or less prickly umbos or points, and also in anatomical leaf-characters: as ordinarily seen in cultivation, *P. Mugo* (or *Mughus*) is a dense bush-like subject with stiff compact upright branches, a durable plant of slow growth, ordinarily under 10 or 12 feet high and without a bare trunk even when it has come to full coning; scales of winter-buds appressed; branchlets usually of dark brownish color: leaves 2, bright green, acutish, stout, crowded, ¾-2 inches long: conelet nearly sessile with mucronate scales: cones tawny-yellow to brown, conic or conic-ovoid, 1-1½ inches long, symmetrical, cinnamon-brown and deciduous at maturity; scale-end keeled or ridged, with prickle-like umbo. Mountain pine from Spain and central Europe to the Balkans; greatly variable in habit and in cones, and the nomenclature confused. The Mugo pine is one of the most dependable dwarf conifers for

19. Pinus Mugo var. pumilio with young cone. (× ½)

park and lawn planting; hardy northward into Canada.

This pine is mostly known in literature as *P. montana*, and the dwarf commonly planted forms as *montana* var. *Mughus*. The binomial *P. montana* starts with Philip Miller's great Gardeners Dictionary in 1768. Long before that time, however, this pine had been known as Mugo, apparently a Swiss-Italian vernacular or place-name: thus it is so called by Matthioli in 1586, and Miller quotes it from old Bauhin. It transpires, however, that the plant had been botanically named and described by Turra as early as 1764 as *Pinus Mugo*, and under rules of priority this name must hold; this has the advantage also of continuing the old vernacular.

Aside from stature forms, there are four races differing in the form and armature of cones. The name *P. Mugo* may be adopted in the sense of covering or including all these forms (a general botanical custom in parts of continental Europe), and each of the four kinds may be given a varietal name under it, as *P. Mugo* var. *Mughus*, var. *pumilio*, var. *rotundata*, var. *rostrata;* in this method, there is no one form that can be called *P. Mugo*. Under the practice of most writers in English, however, the specific name is interpreted as a designation of a particular form, which can be taken as the type; in this case the forms become *P. Mugo* (*P. Mugo* var. *Mughus*), var. *pumilio*, var. *rotundata*, var. *rostrata*, the varieties being three.—*Pinus Mugo*, Turra, Floræ Italicæ Prodromus, 67 (1764); *P. montana*, Miller, Gardeners Dictionary, ed. 8, no. 5 (1768); *P. Mughus*, Scopoli, Flora Carniolica, ed. 2, ii, 247 (1772); *P. montana* var. *Mughus*, Willkomm, Forstliche Flora, 177 (1875); *P. Mugo* var. *Mughus*, Zenari in Bull. Soc. Bot. Ital. 65 (1921).

Many forms of the Mugo pine have received Latin names but for our purposes we may display the three main varieties or races of horticultural importance as follows, all of them known in a state of nature, and two more recent variations:

Var. **pumilio**. BUSH PINE. Cones symmetrical, subglobose to ovoid, before maturity glaucous and usually violet-purple, ripe yellowish- or dark brown. Usually shrubby and upright. Mountains of Germany to the Alps and Balkan Peninsula.—*Pinus Mugo* var. *pumilio*, Zenari in Bull. Soc. Bot. Ital. 65 (1921); *P. pumilio*, Haenke, Jirasek. u. a. Beob. Riesengeb. 68 (1791); *P. carpatica*, Hort. ex Gordon, Pinetum, 180 (1858); *P. montana* var. *pumilio*, Willkomm, Forstliche Flora, 175 (1875).

Var. **rotundata**. Cones oblique and asymmetrical, conical or ovoid, 1½–2 inches long, spreading or bent downward, with the lower and occasionally the middle scales on the outer side ending in a short and blunt slightly reflexed pyramidal end. Usually a tree to 30 feet tall, with several stems. Mountains of Germany, Carpathian Mountains, and Alps.—*Pinus Mugo* var. *rotundata*, Hoopes, Book of Evergreens, 91 (1868); *P. rotundata*, Link in Abh. Akad. Berl. 168 (1827); *P. obliqua*, Sauter in Reichenbach, Flora Germanica Excursoria, 159 (1830); *P. montana* var. *rotundata*, Willkomm, Forstliche Flora, 174 (1875).

Var. **rostrata** (or *uncinata*). Cones asymmetrical and very oblique, conic-ovoid, 2–2½ inches long, directed downward; the scales on the outer side strongly developed, their much-elongated pyramidal ends terminating in hook-like processes directed toward the base of the cone (rostrate or beaked). Usually in nature a tree with a single stem, sometimes to 80 feet tall. Pyrenees to western Alps.—*Pinus Mugo* var. *rostrata*, Hoopes, Book of Evergreens, 91 (1868); *P. uncinata*, Ramond ex DeCandolle, Flore Française, iii, 726 (1805); *P. montana* var. *rostrata*, Antoine, Die Coniferen, 12 (1840).

Var. **compacta**, HILL MUGO PINE, Plate IX, of American cultivation is considered a form of var. *pumilio*, with dense almost globose shape and slender bright green leaves. —*Pinus Mugo* var. *compacta*, D. Hill.

Var. **Slavinii**. A very low compact but spreading form with erect branchlets and short bluish-green leaves, originated in the Rochester, New York, parks under B. H. Slavin.—*Pinus Mugo Mughus* forma *Slavinii*, Hornibrook.

9. **P. sylvestris.** SCOTS or SCOTCH PINE. Figs. 14b, 20. One of the best known of the pine trees, very hardy, represented in cultivation by many forms and important commercially, known by its blue-green attractive foliage and usually the red or reddish-brown aspect of the upper trunk. There are dwarf and stature forms in gardens and parks, but in nature it is a tree to 70 or occasionally 120 feet tall, with spreading often somewhat pendulous branches, pyramidal when young, with broad and round-topped often picturesque head in old age; bark on the upper part of the stem bright red in usual forms, thin and smooth, peeling off in papery flakes, thick toward the base, grayish- or reddish-brown and fissured into irregular longitudinal scaly plates; branchlets dull grayish-yellow; winter-buds oblong-ovoid, brown, resinous, the scales free at the apex: leaves 2 in a sheath, rigid, acute, twisted, bluish-green,

1½–3 inches long: conelet reflexed with minutely mucronate scales; cones short-stalked, conic-oblong, grayish- or reddish-brown, 1½–2½ inches long, not always symmetrical, deciduous at maturity; scale-ends little thickened, slightly keeled, only those near the base elongated; umbo small, obtuse; seed dark gray, ⅙ inch long. Norway, Scotland to Spain, western Asia and northeastern Siberia; naturalized in some places on the New England coast.—*Pinus sylvestris*, Linnæus, Species Plantarum, 1000 (1753).

Regional or geographical forms in Europe, known in forests, are:

Var. **engadinensis** of the higher mountains of Tyrol. Slow-growing pyramidal tree with grayish-green thick and rigid leaves 1–1½ inches long.—*Pinus sylvestris* var. *engadinensis*, Heer in Verh. Schweiz Naturf. Ges. xlvi, 181 (1862).

Var. **lapponica** of northern Europe. Of more narrow-pyramidal habit: leaves broader and shorter, remaining green on the branches for four to seven years: cones more yellowish.—*Pinus sylvestris* var. *lapponica*, Fries, Summa Vegetabilium Scandinaviæ, i, 58 (1846); *P. lapponica*, Mayr, Fremdländische Wald- und Parkbäume für Europa, 348 (1906); *P. Frieseana*, Ascherson & Graebner, Synopsis der Mitteleuropaischen Flora, ed. 2, i, 345 (1912).

Var. **rigensis**. A form with very red bark and straight tall stem.—*Pinus sylvestris* var. *rigensis*, Loudon, Arboretum et Fruticetum Britannicum, iv, 2157 (1838).

20. Pinus sylvestris. (× ½)

Var. **scotica** is similar to var. *rigensis* but the bark is redder and the leaves more glaucous and shorter, about 1½ inches long.—*Pinus sylvestris* var. *scotica*, Beissner in Jäger & Beissner, Ziergehölze, ed. 2, 488 (1884).

Many horticultural sorts of *P. sylvestris* are described and named, the most significant of which in North America are probably the following:

Var. **argentea**. Leaves light bluish-green and of silvery hue.—*Pinus sylvestris* var. *argentea*, Steven.

Var. **aurea**. The young leaves golden-yellow, changing the second year to green; of slow growth and rather dense habit.—*Pinus sylvestris* var. *aurea*, Beissner.

Var. **fastigiata.** With ascending branches forming a narrow pyramidal head.—
Pinus sylvestris var. *fastigiata*, Carrière; *P. sylvestris* var. *pyramidalis*, Hort.

Var. **nana.** Low and compact with stout twisted leaves usually not much if any exceeding 1 inch long.—*Pinus sylvestris* var. *nana*, Carrière; *P. sylvestris* var. *pygmœa*, Hort.

Var. **pendula.** With pendulous branches.—*Pinus sylvestris* var. *pendula*, Lawson.

Var. **pumila.** Dwarf globose bush.—*Pinus sylvestris* var. *pumila*, Beissner.

Var. **Watereri.** Dense broadly columnar form with short steel-blue leaves.—
Pinus sylvestris var. *Watereri*, Beissner, for Waterer, British nurserymen; *P. Wateriana*, Hort.

10. **P. tabulæformis** (incorrectly known as *P. sinensis*). CHINESE PINE. Fig. 21.
Confused often with *P. Thunbergii* and *P. densiflora*, both of which are Japanese, but
differing in leaf-anatomy, in frequently bearing 3 leaves and in its persistent cones

often lopsided or oblique: from *Thunbergii* particularly in the light brown rather than white buds, from *densiflora* in marked changing color characteristics of cone: *P. tabulæformis* (*table-form*, from its habit under some conditions of making a low gnarled flat crown) in its native place makes a tree to 70 feet tall; bark of trunk dark gray, fissured, red on the limbs; branchlets pale orange-yellow or pale grayish-yellow, slightly glaucous while young; winter-buds oblong, light brown, lustrous, slightly or not resinous: leaves 2–3, oftener 2, stiff, glaucescent, with rough margins, 2–6 or 7 inches long: cones subsessile, ovoid, 1½–2½ inches long, persistent for several years, pale yellow-brown but changing to dark brown; scale-ends rhombic, prominently keeled, with an obtuse or mucronate umbo; seeds brown, mottled or whitish, over ¼ inch long, with the wing ¾ inch long. Northern to central and western China; introduced in 1919 by E. H. Wilson to the Arnold Arboretum where it has proved hardy in sheltered positions.—*Pinus tabulæformis*, Carrière, Traité Général des Conifères, ed. 2, 510 (1867); *P. leucosperma*, Maximowicz in Bull. Acad. Sci. St. Petersb. xvi, 558 (1881); *P. funebris*, Komarov in Act. Hort. Petrop. xx, 177 (1901); *P. Henryi*, Masters in Journ. Linn. Soc. xxvi, 550 (1902); *P. sinensis*, Mayr, Fremdländische Wald- und Parkbäume für Europa, 349 (1906), in part, not Lambert; *P. Wilsonii*, Shaw in Sargent, Plantæ Wilsonianæ, i, 3 (1911).

21. Pinus tabulæformis. Nearly natural size.

Var. **densata.** Leaves usually 2, 3–5 inches long, stiff: cones ovoid, 2–2½ inches long, oblique, with their posterior scale-ends tumid and prominent and umbo more or less reflexed. Western China.—*Pinus tabulæformis* var. *densata*, Rehder in Journ. Arnold Arb. vii, 23 (1926); *P. densata*, Masters in Journ. Linn. Soc., Bot. xxxvii, 417 (1906); *P. prominens*, Masters, l. c.; *P. sinensis* var. *densata*, Shaw in Sargent, Plantæ Wilsonianæ, ii, 17 (1914).

Var. **yunnanensis.** YUNNAN PINE. Leaves oftener 3, slender, 4–10 inches long: cones 2½–3½ inches long; scale-ends flat; umbo small; seed with wing nearly 1 inch long: bark divided into ample plates. Southwestern China (Yunnan); probably a distinct species, but apparently not in cultivation in North America.—*Pinus tabulæformis* var. *yunnanensis*, Shaw in Sargent, Plantæ Wilsonianæ, ii, 17 (1916); *P. yunnanensis*, Franchet in Journ. de Bot. xiii, 253, (1899).

The true *P. sinensis* of Lambert, which is apparently not in cultivation, has been misinterpreted and is now considered to be *P. Massoniana;* see No. 7.

P. mongolica is a trade name, and plants growing in this country have not produced mature cones; it is probably *P. tabulæformis.*

11. **P. insularis.** BENGUET PINE. Forest tree, making pure stands, with wide-spreading horizontal branches, bark on old trunks of close irregular heavy plates: leaves in 3's or only seldom 2, very slender and pliable, 5–10 inches long, bright green: conelets mucronate; cones ovate-conic, 2–4 inches long, symmetrical or oblique, very persistent, the scale-ends shining brown, low-pyramidal and ridged, umbo with a sharp deciduous cusp or point. Philippines in the mountains, northern Burma; a tree is growing under glass at the New York Botanical Garden; at the Institute of Forest Genetics, Placerville, California, seedlings have been killed when not covered. It may stand in the warmest parts of the United States.—*Pinus insularis*, Endlicher, Synopsis Coniferarum, 157 (1847).

Very like *P. insularis* is **P. Merkusii,** TENASSERIM PINE, of the Philippines and southward, differing with only 2 leaves in a fascicle and narrow-cylindrical cones 2–3

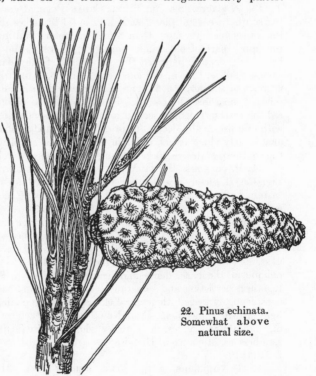

22. Pinus echinata.
Somewhat above
natural size.

inches long; has been introduced but probably too tender for the United States.— *Pinus Merkusii,* Junghuhn & De Vriese in Plantæ Novæ et Minus Cognitæ Indiæ Batavæ Orientalis, 5 (1845); bears the name of Governor Merkus of the Dutch East Indies.

12. **P. echinata.** SHORTLEAF or YELLOW PINE. Fig. 22. Large attractive tree to 75 or more feet, recorded as sometimes 120 feet tall and 4 feet diameter, with a relatively short pyramidal or broad-ovoid head, the spring shoots somewhat pruinose or with bloom and multinodal; branches in regular whorls, often pendulous; bark broken into large irregular plates covered with small appressed light cinnamon-red scales; winter-buds oblong-ovoid, brown: leaves 2, sometimes in 3's, slender, acute, dark bluish-green, 3–5 inches long: cones short-stalked or almost sessile, conic-oblong, dull brown, 1½–2½ inches long, maturing second autumn; scale-end flattened; umbo little elevated, with short straight or curved slender prickle which is soon deciduous; seeds ⅕–¼ inch long. Long Island to Missouri, Florida, and Texas; hardy as far north as eastern Massachusetts. A pine of uniform character, covering a large area as far west as Oklahoma. It reaches its greatest development southward and southwestward. —*Pinus echinata,* Miller, Gardeners Dictionary, ed. 8, no. 12 (1768); *P. mitis,* Michaux, Flora Boreali-Americana, ii, 204 (1803).

13. **P. glabra.** SPRUCE PINE. CEDAR PINE. Pyramidal large dark green tree of the southern coastal plain, with horizontal branches, becoming 100 or even 120 feet tall and sometimes more than 3 feet diameter; multinodal; bark of young trees and the upper part of old trunks smooth, pale gray, the lower part shallowly fissured; branchlets slender, light red tinged purplish, finally dark reddish-brown; winter-buds conic-cylindric, brown, resinous scales with pale fimbriate interlaced margins: leaves 2, soft and slender, 1½–3 inches long, marked with numerous rows of stomata: cones reflexed, on short stout stalks, broadly ovoid to oblong-ovoid, 1½–2½ inches long, reddish-brown, ripening second autumn; scale-ends slightly thickened or flat, armed with minute usually deciduous prickles. South Carolina to middle Florida and Louisiana, largely along rivers, occurring singly or as small woods or groves; hardy only in the southern states.—*Pinus glabra,* Walter, Flora Caroliniana, 237 (1788).

14. **P. pungens.** TABLE-MOUNTAIN PINE. HICKORY or POVERTY PINE. Plate X. Fig. 15c. Coarsely-grained tree of small or medium dimensions, of the east-south-eastern United States, 20–30 feet but sometimes 60 feet, with usually short trunk as well as short horizontal branches, forming a broad open often flat-topped head; multinodal; bark dark brown, thick, broken into irregular plates covered with thin scales, on the upper part of trunk and on the branches separating into thin loose scales; branchlets light orange; winter-buds oblong, obtuse, dark chestnut-brown: leaves 2, stout, twisted, sharply pointed, dark green, 1¼–2½ inches long: cones conic-ovoid, oblique at the base, dense and heavy, light brown, 2½–3½ inches long, mostly 3 together, persisting and sometimes closed for many years; scale-ends pyramidal and conspicuously keeled, the conical elongated umbo ending in a stout curved spine; seed light brown, ¼ inch long. From New Jersey and eastern Tennessee to northern Georgia, on mountains, ridges, and rocky slopes; infrequently planted.—*Pinus pungens,* Lambert ex Michaux f., Histoire des Arbres Forestiers de l'Amérique Septentrionale, i, 61 (1810).

15. **P. virginiana.** SCRUB PINE. JERSEY PINE. Mostly a small pine, 30–40 feet

high with open straggly top but in southern Indiana reaching 100 feet and 3 feet diameter, bearing grayish-green leaves in rather scattered or well-separated clusters; branches slender and horizontal or somewhat pendulous, in remote and irregular whorls, multinodal, forming a broad open pyramidal or sometimes flat-topped head; bark of trunk shallowly fissured into plate-like sections covered with thin appressed dark brown scales, smooth on the branches; branchlets usually pale green at first, becoming purple, more or less glaucous; winter-buds oblong, dark brown: leaves 2 stiff, twisted, spreading, acutish, 1½–3 inches long: cones nearly or quite sessile, maturing second autumn but often persisting after that, conic-oblong, reddish-brown, 1½–2½ inches long; scale-end little elevated, with a broad depressed-pyramidal umbo ending in a short recurved persistent prickle; seed pale brown, ¼ inch long. Southern New York and New Jersey to northeastern Mississippi and Alabama, in poor sandy or rocky soils; abundant in old fields in Maryland and Virginia; hardy as far north as Massachusetts; infrequently planted, but useful on thin poor land.— *Pinus virginiana*, Miller, Gardeners Dictionary, ed. 8, no. 9 (1768); *P. inops*, Aiton, Hortus Kewensis, iii, 367 (1789).

16. **P. clausa.** SAND PINE. Scrubby pine of sands, often of dunes, far south, little planted and not hardy in northern parts, sometimes bush-like but a tree to 15–25 feet and occasionally thrice the latter height, often branched to the ground, frequently forming dense groves; branches slender and spreading, multinodal; bark on the branches and on the upper part of the trunk smooth and ashy-gray, on the lower part deeply fissured into oblong plates covered with red-brown scales; branchlets red-brown; winter-buds oblong, obtuse, little or not resinous: leaves 2, slender and flexible, acute, dark green, 2–3 inches long: cones short-stalked, often oblique at the base, conic-ovoid, dark reddish-brown, 2–3½ inches long, dense and hard, remaining closed for three or four years after ripening and sometimes becoming enveloped by the growing wood of the branch; scale-end depressed-pyramidal, conspicuously keeled; umbo with a short stout spine. Florida and Alabama, mainly near the coast but attaining largest size in central peninsular Florida.—*Pinus clausa*, Vasey ex Sargent, Rept. 10th Census U. S. ix, 199 (1884); *P. inops* var. *clausa*, Engelmann in Bot. Gaz. ii, 125 (1877).

17. **P. halepensis.** ALEPPO PINE (as the Latin name signifies). An important Eurasian pine much planted in the Mediterranean regions, being recommended for seasides, little known in North America: tree to 60 feet tall, with short branches forming an open round-topped head with thin verdure; bark gray, smooth for a long time, finally fissured and exposing the reddish-brown inner bark; branchlets slender, yellowish- or light greenish-brown, frequently multinodal; winter-buds small, cylindric, not resinous: leaves 2, only seldom in 3's, slender, light green, 2½–4 inches long, mostly in tufts toward end of branchlets: cones short-stalked, spreading or deflexed, usually 1–3 at a place, conic-ovate or conic-oblong, reddish or yellowish-brown, unarmed, 2½–3½ inches long, persistent; scale-end flattened, with a transverse line and slightly or not elevated obtuse umbo; seed ¼ inch long. Portugal to northern Italy, Algeria to Afghanistan; planted in California; in the East probably not hardy north of the southern states; of small ornamental value.—*Pinus halepensis*, Miller, Gardeners Dictionary, ed. 8, no. 8 (1768); *P. alepensis*, Poiret in Lamarck, Encyclopédie Méthodique, v, 338 (1804); *P. pityrusa*, Steven in Bull. Soc. Nat. Mosc. i, 49 (1838).

Var. **brutia.** Leaves 4–7 or rarely 8 inches long, more rigid, bright or dark green:

cones sessile, not deflexed, usually in whorls of 2–6, with rugose depressed knobs. Southern Europe and western Asia.—*Pinus halepensis* var. *brutia*, Henry in Elwes & Henry, Trees of Great Britain and Ireland, v, 1100 (1910); *P. brutia*, Tenore, Catalogus Plantarum Horti Regii Neapolitani, Appx. i, 75 (1815); *P. pyrenaica*, David in Ann. Soc. Hort. Paris, 186 (1833); *P. eldarica*, Medwejew in Act. Hort. Tiflis, vi, II, 21 (1902).

Pinus oocarpa, P. patula, and P. Greggii belong in the *P. halepensis-radiata* relationship, of the Mexican region, introduced but perhaps not now in cultivation unless under test. P. oocarpa is known by the very persistent egg-shaped cone (whence the name *oocarpa*) which hangs on a long peduncle, the body 4–10 inches long: leaves 3, 4, or 5 in a fascicle, erect, sometimes 12 inches long: tree to 50 feet: ranges to Guatemala.—*Pinus oocarpa*, Schiede in Linnaea, xii, 491 (1838). P. patula has slender hanging foliage, upper part of trunk red, leaves mostly in 3's, to 12 inches long: cones persistent, sessile, 3 or 4 inches long: tree to 60 feet: probably planted in California.—*Pinus patula*, Schlechtendal & Chamisso in Linnaea, vi, 354 (1831). P. Greggii (Dr. Josiah Gregg, botanical explorer) is much like *P. patula* but the bark on the upper part of the trunk is smooth and gray: leaves 3, to 4 inches long: cones to nearly 5 inches long, persistent, sessile: tree to 50 feet.—*Pinus Greggii*, Engelmann ex Parlatore in DeCandolle, Prodromus, xvi, II, 396 (1868).

18. P. Pinaster. CLUSTER PINE. MARITIME PINE. A great tree in the Mediterranean area, said to reach 120 feet in height and 14 feet in girth, widely employed in various countries for dune-planting and afforestation and as a source of resin and turpentine; in cultivation it makes an attractive tree of rapid growth, with a regular pyramidal crown; branches spreading, sometimes pendulous, multinodal; bark deeply fissured into narrow longitudinal ridges covered with small scales; branchlets bright reddish-brown; winter-buds oblong-oval, brown, not resinous: leaves 2, stiff, acute, usually twisted, glossy green, 5–9 inches long: cones short-peduncled, clustered, conic-oblong, light brown and glossy, 4–7 inches long, persistent; scale-end pyramidal, conspicuously keeled with prominent triangular acute umbo: seed grayish-brown, ⅓ inch long. Portugal to Greece, Algeria; probably not reliably hardy outside the middle states but stands along Long Island Sound. Varieties are known in Europe. *Pinaster* is Latin for a wild pine.—*Pinus Pinaster*, Aiton, Hortus Kewensis, iii, 367 (1789); *P. maritima*, Poiret in Lamarck Encyclopédie Méthodique, v, 337 (1804).

Var. Hamiltonii, LORD ABERDEEN PINE, has shorter leaves and larger cones.—*Pinus Pinaster* var. *Hamiltonii*, Gordon; *P. Hamiltonii*, Tenore.

19. P. contorta. SHORE PINE. WESTERN SCRUB PINE. Scrubby low maritime pine with short trunk but making a tree to 20, occasionally to 30 feet tall, with rather stout branches forming a round-topped compact or open head with dense

23. Pinus contorta var. latifolia.
Natural size.

foliage; bark deeply and irregularly divided into small oblong plates covered with appressed dark red-brown scales tinged with purple or orange; branchlets light orange or orange-brown, multinodal; buds ovoid, dark chestnut-brown, resinous: leaves 2, stiff, twisted, acutish, dark green, 1–2 inches long: cones ovoid or conic-ovoid, very oblique at the base, often remaining closed for several years after maturity, 1–2 inches long, light yellowish-brown and lustrous, scales of the upper side with elevated pyramidal apex, the dark umbo ending in a slender incurved spine. Alaska along the coast to north-central California; little planted and not hardy northward in the East.—*Pinus contorta*, Loudon, Arboretum et Fruticetum Britannicum, iv, 2292 (1838); *P. Bolanderi*, Parlatore in DeCandolle Prodromus, xvi, II, 379 (1869); *P. contorta* var. *Bolanderi*, Vasey, Rept. U. S. Dept. Agr. xviii, 177 (1875).

Var. **latifolia.** LODGE-POLE PINE. Plate XLV. Fig. 23. A taller tree of pyramidal habit, to 80 or occasionally to 150 feet tall, with orange branchlets, lighter green leaves 1½–3½ inches long, and with less oblique cones; bark thin, close, light orange-brown, covered with thin loosely appressed scales. The commonest coniferous tree of the northern Rocky Mountains, and is in the Black Hills; it often forms forests of great extent. It contributes an important part in the regeneration of the forests of the mountain region. In the East it is hardy to New England and southern Ontario. By some authors the Lodge-pole pine is considered to be a distinct species.—*Pinus contorta* var. *latifolia*, Engelmann in Rept. U. S. Geogr. Surv. W. 100th Merid. vi, 262 (1878); *P. Murrayana*, Balfour, Rept. Botany Oregon Expedition, 2 (1853); *P. Boursieri*, Carrière, Traité Général des Conifères, 298 (1855); *P. contorta* var. *Murrayana*, Engelmann in S. Watson, Botany of California, ii, 126 (1880).

20. **P. Banksiana.** JACK PINE. Fig. 24. A scrubby northern pine, covering great areas of barren lands, coning at an early age, sometimes a bush-like low tree but exceptionally to 70 feet tall; branches slender, spreading, forming a broad open head; bark dark brown, slightly tinged with red, divided into irregular narrow ridges covered with thick appressed scales; branchlets yellowish- to purplish-brown, multinodal; winter-buds oblong-ovoid, light brown, very resinous: leaves 2, short and stiff, twisted, spreading, flat or slightly concave on inner face, about $\frac{1}{12}$ inch broad, acute or obtusish, dark or bright green, about 1 inch long: cones conic-oblong, usually curved and deformed, pale yellow-brown and lustrous, unarmed, 1½–2 inches long, remaining on the tree twelve to fifteen years; scale-end flattened, with a transverse line and a small dark obtuse umbo; seed black, ⅜ inch long. From Nova Scotia to Athabasca and Mackenzie rivers south to northern New York, Wisconsin, Minnesota and northern Illinois and Indiana. Hardiest of the American pines and valuable for colder regions, particularly for planting on dry and sandy soil; old trees are often picturesque but the species is little prized as an ornamental subject. The species is dedicated to Sir Joseph Banks, 1743–1820, familiar name in natural science.—*Pinus Banksiana*, Lambert, A Description of the Genus Pinus, 7 (1803); *P. divaricata*, Gordon, Pinetum, 163 (1858).

21. **P. muricata.** BISHOP PINE. PRICKLY-CONE PINE. A small or medium-sized coastal or maritime pine of the Pacific region, forming a rather dense close rounded crown or head in age but pyramidal when young, with hard close-grained wood; bark on lower part of trunk broken into irregular plates covered with thin loose dark brown scales tinged with red, on the upper part and on the branches broken into thin loose scales; branchlets orange-brown; winter-buds cylindric, dark chestnut-brown, very

resinous; multinodal: leaves 2, stiff, usually twisted, acute, dark green, 4–7 inches long: cones usually clustered, oblong-ovoid, oblique at the base, chestnut-brown, 2–3½ inches long; scales of the upper side with elongated conical apex terminated by a dark triangular spiny umbo pointing backward; scales of the lower side more flattened, with slender straight spines; the cones usually remain closed for several years after maturity; seed almost black, ¼ inch long. California, near the sea, from Mendocino County to Mexico (Lower California) usually in widely detached groves southward; hardy only in California and the southern states; not much planted. — *Pinus muricata*, D. Don in Trans. Linn. Soc., xvii, 441 (1837).

22. **P. ponderosa.** WESTERN YELLOW PINE. BULL PINE. Figs. 14e, 15e, 25. A characteristic massive timber pine of the western mountain and mesa country making open or park-like forests and groves, of many forms and several botanical varieties variously interpreted by authors, recorded as attaining an age of 500 years and a height of more than 200 feet: usually 100–150 feet tall and diameter of 5–8 feet, with stout spreading and often pendulous branches usually ascending at the ends and forming a narrow spire-like head; bark very variable, dark brown or nearly black to cinnamon-red, fissured into rounded ridges or on old trees into large plates, separating into thick cinnamon-red scales; branchlets orange-brown, fragrant when broken; winter-buds oblong-ovoid or ovoid, resinous: leaves 3, acute, dark or yellowish-green, 5–11 inches long: cones almost sessile, often in clusters, ovoid-oblong, light reddish or yellowish-brown and lustrous, 3–6 inches long; scale-end depressed-pyramidal or flattened, with a broadly triangular umbo terminated by a stout usually recurved prickle; lower scales with more elongated apex; seed ¼ inch long. British Columbia to Lower California; hardy in sheltered positions as far north as Massachusetts; often

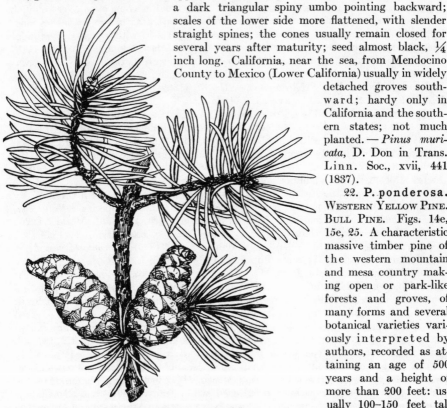

24. Pinus Banksiana. (× ¾)

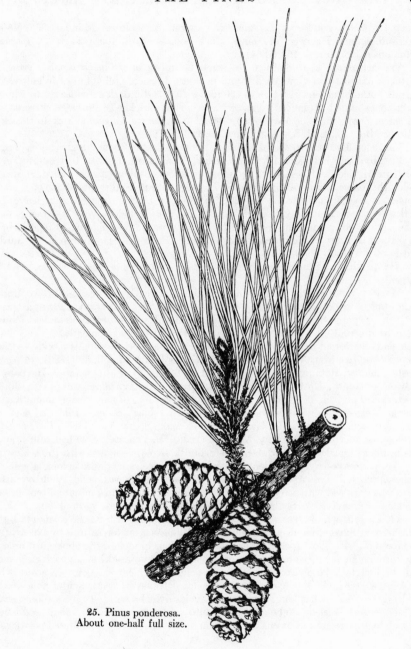

25. Pinus ponderosa.
About one-half full size.

planted.—*Pinus ponderosa*, Douglas in Lawson, Agricultural Manual, 354 (1836); *P. Benthamiana*, Hartweg in Journ. Hort. Soc. Lond. ii, 189 (1847); *P. apacheca*, Lemmon in Erythea, ii, 103 (1894).

Var. **arizonica**, kept distinct by some botanists as *Pinus arizonica*, grows in southern Arizona and New Mexico and northern Mexico, probably not in cultivation outside botanic gardens, is a tree to 100 feet with 3–5 stiff dark green leaves to 7 inches long: cones about 2 inches long, with recurved prickles.—*Pinus ponderosa* var. *arizonica*, Shaw, Pines of Mexico, 24 (1909); *P. arizonica*, Engelmann ex Rothrock in Wheeler, Bot. Rept. U. S. Geogr. Surv. vi, 260 (1878).

Var. **scopulorum**. ROCKY MOUNTAIN YELLOW PINE. ROCK PINE. The eastern or Rocky Mountain extension of *P. ponderosa*, from South Dakota to western Texas, northern Mexico, and westward, by some authors considered to be a distinct species under the name *Pinus scopulorum* or *P. brachyptera:* smaller in all parts than *P. ponderosa* itself, usually to 75 feet tall, with nearly black furrowed bark: leaves 3–6 inches long, sometimes in 2's: cones smaller, ovoid or rounded-ovoid, 2–4 inches long. Somewhat hardier than the type.—*Pinus ponderosa* var. *scopulorum*, Engelmann in S. Watson, Botany of California, ii, 126 (1880); *P. scopulorum*, Lemmon in Garden and Forest, x, 183 (1897).

Var. **pendula**. Branches pendulous.—*Pinus ponderosa* var. *pendula*, H. W. Sargent.

Mexican pines related to *P. ponderosa* but apparently not planted in the United States unless in botanic collections, are **P. Montezumæ**, MONTEZUMA PINE, a tree to 100 feet or more with fascicles usually 5-leaved but sometimes more or less, bluish-green or green, 5–12 inches long: cones conic-ovoid to long-conic, 2–12 inches long; scale-ends depressed-pyramidal to nearly flat, with a short deciduous prickle.—*Pinus Montezumæ*, Lambert, A Description of the Genus Pinus, ed. 3, i, 39 (1832); *P. macrophylla*, Lindley, Botanical Register, xxv, Misc. 63 (1839); *P. Gordoniana*, Hartweg ex Gordon in Journ. Hort. Soc. Lond. ii, 79 (1847); *P. Grenvilleæ*, Gordon in Journ. Hort. Soc. Lond. ii, 77 (1847). Var. **Hartwegii**, a form of the higher mountains of central Mexico with short leaves and small nearly black cones.—*Pinus Montezumæ* var. *Hartwegii*, Engelmann in Trans. St. Louis Acad. Sci. iv, 177 (1880); *P. Hartwegii*, Lindley, Botanical Register, xxv, Misc. 62 (1839). **P. Teocote**, to 90 feet tall; branchlets pruinose (or glaucous); winter-buds cylindric-ovoid, resinous, with the scales free at the tips: leaves rigid, 3, about 4–8 inches long: cones cylindric-ovoid, about 2½ inches long, dull brown or slightly shining, soon falling; scale-ends slightly raised, transversely ridged with ashy-gray usually depressed umbo and a minute often obsolete prickle.—*Pinus Teocote*, Schlechtendal & Chamisso in Linnaea, v, 76 (1830).

23. **P. Jeffreyi**. JEFFREY PINE. Fig. 26. Distinguished from *P. ponderosa* by its bluish-green foliage, glaucous branchlets, and long cones: forest tree to 120 or even 180 feet tall, with short spreading or often pendulous branches, the uppermost ascending, forming an open pyramidal and sometimes narrow spire-like head; bark cinnamon-red, broken into large irregular plates; young branchlets glaucous, fragrant when broken; winter-buds oblong-ovoid, not resinous: leaves 3, stout, acute, pale or dull bluish-green, 5–8 inches long: cones conic-ovoid, light brown, 5–12 inches long; scale-end depressed, keeled; umbo elongated into a slender recurved spine; seed about ½ inch long. Oregon to Lower California, in mountains; hardy in sheltered positions as

far north as Massachusetts. A distinct and ornamental pine of symmetrical habit when young, leaves longer than in most other hardy species. This pine bears the name of John Jeffrey of Edinburgh, who collected in North America in the last century.— *Pinus Jeffreyi*, Murray, Rept. Botany Oregon Expedition, 2 (1853); *P. ponderosa* var. *Jeffreyi*, Vasey, Rept. U. S. Dept. Agr. xviii, 179 (1875).

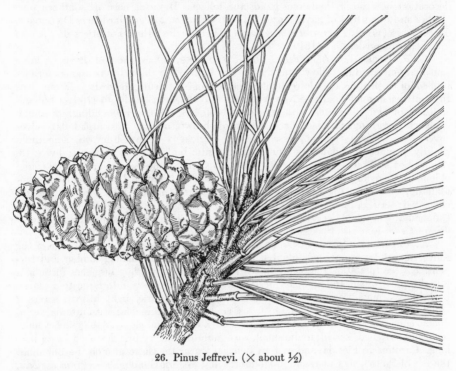

26. Pinus Jeffreyi. (× about ½)

Farther south, in New Mexico, Arizona, northern Mexico, **P. leiophylla** is distinguished by the deciduous leaf-sheaths, small cones (2 inches or less long) maturing third year: leaves in 3's, slender, 4 inches or less long.—*Pinus leiophylla*, Schlechtendal & Chamisso in Linnaea, vi, 354 (1831). *P. chihuahuana*, Engelmann in Wislizenus, Memoir of a Tour to Northern Mexico, 103 (1848) is by some persons regarded as a synonym, by others as a variety, and still others as an independent species.

24. **P. palustris.** LONGLEAF PINE. SOUTHERN PINE. Plate XI. Important timber, resin, and turpentine pine of the southeastern and southern United States, sometimes planted in or near its native regions: tree to 100 or 120 feet tall, with ascending branches forming an oblong open head; bark light orange-brown, separating into large appressed papery scales; branchlets orange-brown, occasionally multinodal; winterbuds white, oblong: leaves 3, crowded, forming tufts at the end of branchlets, dark

green, 8–18 inches long, with internal resin-ducts: cones almost sessile, cylindric, dull brown, 6–10 inches long; scale-end flattened; umbo dark brown, with triangular reflexed short spines; seed almost ½ inch long. Virginia to Florida, Mississippi and Texas, mostly of low sandy regions along the coasts but also extending into higher lands in Alabama. Branches are shipped in great quantities to the northern cities for decoration because of their long handsome foliage. It yields hard or southern pine lumber and quantities of naval stores.—*Pinus palustris*, Miller, Gardeners Dictionary, ed. 8, no. 14 (1768); *P. australis*, Michaux f., Histoire des Arbres Forestiers de l'Amérique Septentrionale, i, 64 (1810).

25. **P. Tæda.** LOBLOLLY PINE. OLD-FIELD PINE. FRANKINCENSE PINE. A large southern pine yielding yellow pine timber and lumber for the markets and sometimes tapped for turpentine, only infrequently planted for ornament and hardy as far north as the southern or milder parts of New York: tree to 100, occasionally to 170 feet tall and to 3 feet or more diameter, with spreading branches, the upper ascending, forming a compact round-topped head; bark bright red-brown, fissured into broad flat ridges covered with large thin appressed scales; branchlets yellowish-brown, sometimes slightly pruinose or glaucous, multinodal; winter-buds oblong, resinous: leaves 3, slender but stiff, acute, bright green, 6–9 inches long: cones sessile, spreading, conic-oblong, light reddish-brown, 3–5 inches long; scale-end flattened or depressed-pyramidal; umbo small, with stout and short triangular recurved spine, lower scales not elongated; seed ⅓ inch long. New Jersey to Florida and Texas and to Arkansas and Oklahoma; known under many local names. In Latin, *tæda* is a pitch-pine tree.—*Pinus Tæda*, Linnæus, Species Plantarum, 1000 (1753).

26. **P. caribæa.** SLASH PINE. SWAMP PINE. A coastal and sand-plains pine of the southern country, sometimes planted in its native regions, yielding lumber and turpentine: tree to 100 or 120 feet tall, with horizontally spreading branches forming a round-topped broad and compact head; bark separating freely into large thin scales; branchlets orange-brown, multinodal; winter-buds cylindric, light brown: leaves 2 and 3 in a fascicle, dark green and lustrous, acute, 8–12 inches long, with internal resin-ducts: cones short-peduncled, conic-oblong, dark brown and glossy, 3–6½ inches long; scale-end flattened, keeled; umbo small, with minute recurved prickles; seed ⅙–¼ inch long. Carolina to Florida, and eastern Louisiana near the coast, also on the Bahamas, the Isle of Pines near Cuba, and in Honduras and eastern Guatemala.—*Pinus caribæa*, Morelet in Rev. Hort. Cote d'Or, i, 105 (1851); *P. cubensis*, Grisebach in Mem. Amer. Acad., n. s. viii, 530 (1863); *P. bahamensis*, Grisebach, Flora British West Indies, 503 (1864); *P. Elliottii*, Engelmann in Trans. St. Louis Acad. Sci. iv, 186 (1880); *P. heterophylla*, Sudworth in Bull. Torr. Bot. Club, xx, 45 (1893).

27. **P. rigida.** PITCH PINE. Figs. 8, 14c, 16, 27. Characteristic northeastern pine growing mostly on poor and rocky lands or sometimes in swamps, of irregular shape and dark foliage, not often planted for ornament: tree to 80 feet tall, with horizontally spreading branches forming an open irregular pyramid; bark of old trunk deeply and irregularly fissured into broad flat ridges covered with dark red-brown scales, often tinged purple, on young stems thin and broken into plate-like scales; branchlets light brown, multinodal; winter-buds ovoid or ovoid-oblong, chestnut-brown: leaves 3, stiff and spreading, dark green, 2–5 inches long: cones almost sessile, twin or often in clusters, ovoid, light brown, 2–4 inches long; scale-end little elevated; umbo triangular,

ending in a slender recurved prickle; seed dark brown, ¼ inch long, its wing ¾ inch long. Maine to Ontario and Ohio, south to northern Georgia. Of rapid growth when young and valuable for colonizing on dry and rocky soil; old trees are often picturesque. It sprouts readily from stumps when cut down or partly destroyed by fire, often with odd leafage, but the sprouts are short-lived and do not develop into trees.—*Pinus rigida*, Miller, Gardeners Dictionary, ed. 8, no. 10 (1768).

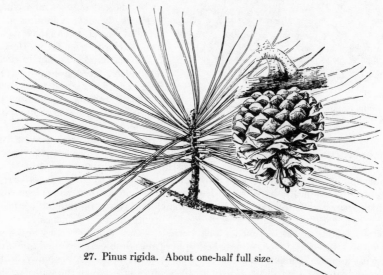

27. Pinus rigida. About one-half full size.

28. P. serotina. BLACK PINE. POND PINE. By some authors considered to be a variety of *P. rigida*, from which it differs in longer leaves and sheaths, less prickly cones, more southern range, and more paludose habitat: usually a tree 40–50 feet or sometimes to 80 feet tall, with stout often contorted branches forming an open round-topped head; bark shallowly fissured into small plates; branchlets dark orange, later dark brown, multinodal: leaves 3, rarely 4, slender, 6–8 inches long: cones ovoid, 2–2½ inches long, with slender incurved mostly deciduous prickles; seed ⅛ inch long. New Jersey to Florida and central Alabama in low flat lands or sandy and peaty swamps and sour bogs. Little known in cultivation, and probably not hardy north of the Middle Atlantic states.—*Pinus serotina*, Michaux, Flora Boreali-Americana, ii, 105 (1803); *P. rigida* var. *serotina*, Loudon, Arboretum et Fruticetum Britannicum, iv, 2242 (1838).

29. P. attenuata. KNOB-CONE PINE. Prevailingly a rather small tree of dry low mountain slopes in the Pacific region, little known as a horticultural subject and then usually a bushy tree with dull and thin foliage: tree usually only 20 but sometimes to 100 feet tall, with slender horizontal branches ascending at the ends, forming a broad pyramid, with open round-topped head in old age; bark of young stems and branches thin and smooth, pale brown, at base of old trunks dark brown and shallowly fissured into large loose scales; young branchlets slender, dark orange-brown, multinodal;

winter-buds oblong-ovoid, dark brown: leaves 3, slender, acuminate, pale yellowish or bluish-green, 3–7, usually 4–5 inches long: cones short-stalked, usually in clusters, very long-persistent, elongated-conical, 3½–6 inches long, upper scales with pyramidal apex and prominent sharply pointed and recurved umbo, lower scales with depressed

28. Pinus radiata.
(× about ¼)

apex and small prickly umbo; seed ¼ inch long. Oregon and California; to be planted only in mild climates. —*Pinus attenuata*, Lemmon in Garden and Forest, v, 65 (1892); *P. californica*, Hartweg in Journ. Hort. Soc. Lond. ii, 189 (1847), not Loisel.; *P. tuberculata*, Gordon in Journ. Hort. Soc. Lond. iv, 218 (1849), not Don.

30. **P. radiata.** Monterey Pine. Fig. 28. Picturesque as it grows on the Monterey Peninsula south of San Francisco and at San Simeon Bay to the southward, the only native stations; planted for ornament, especially near the coast, and for reforestation in New Zealand and Australia: tree to 100 or to 140 feet under favorable conditions in cultivation, with stout spreading branches forming an irregular open round-topped head; bark thick, deeply furrowed into broad flat ridges covered with thick appressed scales, dark red-brown; branchlets brown, multinodal; winter-buds ovoid, bright chestnut-brown: leaves 3, acute, bright green, 4–6 inches long: cones short-stalked, conic-ovoid, 3–7 inches long, persistent and closed for many years, upper scales with elevated, rounded, almost hemispherical and obscurely keeled apex; umbo small, with minute, straight or recurved prickle, lower scales with almost flattened apex; seed black, ¼ inch long. Hardy on the eastern side only in the southern states. A handsome species with bright green foliage and of rapid growth when young.— *Pinus radiata*, D. Don in Trans. Linn. Soc. xvii, 442 (1837); *P. insignis*, Douglas ex Loudon, Arboretum et Fruticetum Britannicum, iv, 2265 (1838); *P. montereyensis*, Hort.

Var. **binata**, on Santa Rosa Island, California, and Guadalupe Island, Mexico, has stouter leaves in fascicles of 2, scale-tips of pistillate flowers deflexed; probably not in cultivation.—*Pinus radiata* var. *binata*, Lemmon, Handbook of West American Cone-bearers, 42 (1895).

31. **P. Roxburghii.** Chir Pine. Asian forest and timber pine: tree to 100 feet tall or more, with round-topped symmetrical head; bark thick, to 2 inches, deeply fissured into large plates; branchlets light yellow-brown; winter-buds oblong, light chestnut-brown, not resinous, with fringed not recurved scales: leaves 3, slender, pendulous, light green, 8–12 inches long: cones short-stalked, conic-ovoid, 4–7 inches long; scale-end elongated-pyramidal, compressed, more or less recurved; umbo obtuse; seed ¾–1 inch long, edible. Himalayas from Bhutan to Afghanistan on the outer slopes and foothills. Cultivated in California, and not hardy in the East north of the southern states. As a young plant it is very ornamental with its long drooping light green leaves. This conifer is usually known as *P. longifolia* of William Roxburgh, author of botanical works on India and Bengal, but that name had been used previously for another pine, and to avoid confusion Sargent renamed the plant *P. Roxburghii.*—*Pinus Roxburghii*,

Sargent, Silva of North America, xi, 9 (1897); *P. longifolia,* Roxburgh ex Lambert, A Description of the Genus Pinus, i, 29 (1803), not Salisbury.

32. P. canariensis. CANARY PINE. Figs. 14f, 29. Picturesque long-leaved pine of the Canary Islands, long known in cultivation in mild climates: tree to 80 feet tall, with slender branches forming a broad round-topped head; stem and branches usually with scattered short leafy branch-lets; dark reddish, slightly fissured into irregular scales; branchlets yellowish, pruinose when young; winter-buds ob-long, not resinous, with reflexed conspicuously white-fringed scales brown in the middle: leaves 3, slender, spreading and pendulous, light green and lustrous, 9–12 inches long: cones cylindric-ovoid, 4–8 inches long; scale-end low-pyramidal, irregularly 4-sided, light brown and glossy, with big obtuse umbo pointing backward as scales spread; seed ½ inch long. Cultivated in California where it grows faster than the native *P. radiata,* even in dry and rocky situations. Not hardy east-ward in the open north of the southern states.—*Pinus canari-ensis,* C. Smith in Buch, Beschr. Canar. Ins. 159 (1825).

29. Pinus canariensis.
(× ½)

33. P. Sabiniana. DIGGER PINE. Long-leaved large-coned edible-seeded pine of the central valley of California, usually of medium size: tree to 50 or sometimes 80 feet tall, usually divided into several stems with short crooked branches, the lower ones pendent, the upper ones ascending, forming a round-topped head; bark thick, dark brown, deeply and irregularly fissured into thick ridges covered with small ap-pressed scales; branchlets stout, glaucous, multinodal: leaves 3, slender, flexible, pale bluish-green, 8–12 inches long: cones pendent on about 2-inch-long stalks, oblong-ovoid, light red-brown, 6–10 inches long; scale-end pyramidal, sharply keeled, narrowed into a stout incurved spiny hook, the lower scales much reflexed and armed with a spur-like incurved spine; seed ¾ inch long, its wing about half as long as seed. Head of Sacramento Valley, south to Los Angeles County; seeds eaten by the Digger Indians. Named for Joseph Sabine (1770–1837), Secretary of the Horticultural Society of London, who grew this pine in his garden in England. Hardy probably as far north as the Middle Atlantic states; little planted.—*Pinus Sabiniana,* Douglas in Trans. Linn. Soc. xvi, 747 (1833).

34. P. Coulteri. COULTER PINE. BIG-CONE PINE. Fig. 15d. Pine of western California of open loose habit, becoming picturesque, bearing very large woody heavy prongy cones: tree to 80 feet tall, with stout branches, pendulous below and ascending above, forming a loose pyramidal head; bark dark brown or nearly black, deeply di-vided into broad rounded ridges covered with thin appressed scales, multinodal; winter-buds oblong-ovoid, resinous: leaves 3, stout, acuminate, dark bluish-green, 6–12 inches long: cones short-stalked, pendent, cylindric-ovoid, yellowish-brown, 9–14 inches long; scale-end elongated-pyramidal, narrowed into the compressed spiny-tipped straight or incurved umbo; seed-wing broadest about the middle and nearly 1 inch long. Inner coast ranges from near San Francisco to Lower California; hardy only in southern states. Dedicated to Thomas Coulter, Irish botanist, died 1843, who collected in Mexico and California.—*Pinus Coulteri*, D. Don in Trans. Linn. Soc. xvii, 440 (1837); *P. macrocarpa*, Lindley, Botanical Register, xxvi, Misc. 61 (1840).

35. **P. Torreyana.** TORREY PINE. SOLEDAD PINE (first discovered in Soledad Cañon, San Diego County). Plate XII. Figs. 14g, 30. Small or medium-sized pine, rarest of the American species, known in two restricted localities in southwestern California: tree to 40 or under favorable conditions in cultivation to 90 feet tall, with spreading and sometimes ascending branches; bark deeply and irregularly fissured into broad flat ridges covered with appressed light red-brown scales; winter-buds conic-ovoid, pale brown, scales with appressed tips and white fimbriate interlaced margins; branchlets greenish or purplish, bloomy, glabrous: leaves 5, rigid, dark green, 8–13 inches long: cones broadly ovoid, 4–6 inches long, chocolate-brown; scale-end low-pyramidal; umbo elongated and reflexed with short spiny tip; seeds ¾ inch long, with a short wing about half as long as the seed, soon deciduous. Of irregular and picturesque habit in San Diego County by the sea and on Santa Rosa Island; often more vigorous when planted in southern California. This interesting but little cultivated pine bears the name of John Torrey (see *Torreya*, page 35).—*Pinus Torreyana*, Parry, Botany of the Mexican Boundary Survey, 210 (1859).

30. Pinus Torreyana before dehiscence. (× ¾)

36. **P. Pinea.** ITALIAN STONE PINE. PARASOL PINE. Picturesque tree in age, the trunk then mostly devoid of side-branches until toward the top and usually inclined or crooked, crowned with an unsymmetrical umbrella-like head: tree, sometimes becoming 80 feet tall; branchlets pale brown; winter-buds not resinous, with revolute scales: leaves 2 in a fascicle, rather stiff, 4–8 inches long: cone broad-ovoid to nearly globular, 4–6 inches long, solitary or 2–3 together, maturing third year; scale-ends somewhat pyramidal and radiately ridged, with flat blunt umbo; seeds usually numerous, to ¾ inch long, hard on exterior, flattened on outer surface, dark reddish- or purplish-brown, edible. Mediterranean region, where it is also much planted; seeds prized for food; hardy only in southern states and California. *Pinea* is classical Latin name for pine-nut.—*Pinus Pinea*, Linnæus, Species Plantarum, 1000 (1753).

37. **P. cembroides.** MEXICAN STONE PINE. Low tree, commonly not exceeding 20 feet, with spreading branches and rounded head; branchlets dark orange and at first pubescent: leaves usually 3 but sometimes 2, slender (not stout and stiff as in Nos. 1, 2, and 4), to 2 inches long, curved: cone nearly globose, about 1–2 inches broad and long; scale-end pyramidal and ridged, with broad blunt umbo; seed to ¾ inch long,

THE PINES
very narrowly winged. Mexico; extends northward into adjacent southern parts of New Mexico and Arizona. Little known as a planted tree outside the southwestern region. Pines Nos. 37–40 are by some authorities considered to be forms of one species (as disclosed in the synonymy, page 70), in which case Nos. 38, 39, and 40 become varieties of *P. cembroides* inasmuch as this is the oldest name in the group. While they seem to run together more or less, yet they appear distinct in the field and they occupy different ranges; and for horticultural purposes they may be entered separately. They yield edible seeds much gathered by Indians.—*Pinus cembroides*, Zuccarini in Abh. Akad. Wiss. Muench. i, 392 (1832); *P. osteosperma*, Engelmann in Wislizenus, Memoir of a Tour to Northern Mexico, 89 (1848).

To the Cembroides group belong two Mexican species, both small bushy trees. They are probably not now in cultivation and could be expected to be hardy only in the southern states and southern California. **P. Pinceana.** Leaves entire, in clusters of 3: cones cylindric.—*Pinus Pinceana*, Gordon, Pinetum, 204 (1858); named in honor of Mr. Pince of Exeter (England). **P. Nelsonii.** Fascicles with 3 partly connate serrulate leaves and a persistent sheath: cones cylindric.—*Pinus Nelsonii*, Shaw in Gard. Chron., ser. 3, xxxvi, 122 (1904); named for E. W. Nelson, who collected it in Mexico in 1898.

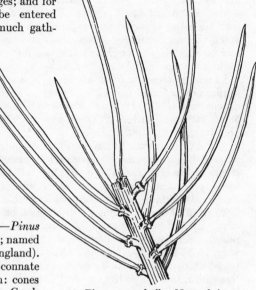

31. Pinus monophylla. Natural size.

38. **P. monophylla.** ONELEAF PINYON or PINE. Fig. 31. Rugged small low-branched flat-topped tree to 50 feet: leaf solitary in a sheath (sometimes 2), about 2 inches long, stiff, terete and striate, glaucous-green, mostly curved, very sharp-pointed, sheaths soon deciduous, bracts decurrent: cone to 2 inches long, very broad, scales woody and concave, scale-ends thick and angular with a downwardly pointing obtuse umbo; seed about ½ inch long, with prominent wing. Mountain slopes and table-lands, western Utah, Nevada and northern Arizona, southern California east of Sierras, northern Lower California; hardy in western New York and to Massachusetts.—*Pinus monophylla*, Torrey in Fremont's Report of an Exploring Expedition to the Rocky Mountains, 319 (1845); *P. Fremontiana*, Endlicher, Synopsis Coniferarum, 183 (1847); *P. cembroides* var. *monophylla*, Voss in Mitteil. Deutsch. Dendrol. Ges. xvi, 95 (1907).

39. **P. edulis.** PINYON. NUT PINE. Plate XIII. Fig. 14h. Small rugged broad-topped tree to 50 feet but usually lower and bushy-branched near the base, with

mostly 2 (sometimes 3) dark green sharp-pointed stiff leaves mostly under 1½ inches long: cone subglobose, very like that of No. 38 but usually smaller, umbo less pronounced. Wyoming to west Texas, Colorado, Arizona, Mexico, in foothills. Leaf-structure is usually different from that in *P. monophylla*. Hardy in western New York and Massachusetts. Named for the eatable large seed (edù-lis: *edible*).—*Pinus edulis*, Engelmann in Wislizenus, Memoir of a Tour to Northern Mexico, 88 (1848); *P. cembroides* var. *edulis*, Voss in Mitteil. Deutsch. Dendrol. Ges. xvi, 95 (1907); *Caryopitys edulis*, Small, Flora of Southeastern United States, 29 (1903).

40. **P. quadrifolia.** FOURLEAF PINYON. Small tree but reaching probably 50 feet, with spreading branches and eventually a flat crown, the branchlets pubescent when young: leaves commonly 4 but sometimes fewer or as many as 5, short, commonly less than 1½ inches long, very stiff and incurved, strongly angled, blue-green on the back: cone nearly globular, to 2 inches across, scale-end much thickened and ridged, the umbo prominent; seeds about ½ inch long, very short-winged. Southern California, Lower California.—*Pinus quadrifolia*, Parry ex Parlatore in DeCandolle, Prodromus, xvi, II, 402 (1868); *P. Parryana*, Engelmann in Amer. Journ. Sci., ser. 2, xxxiv, 332 (1862), not Gordon; *P. cembroides* var. *Parryana*, Voss in Mitteil. Deutsch. Dendrol. Ges. xvi, 95 (1907).

41. **P. Bungeana.** LACEBARK PINE. Singular pine, known by flaky bark and white-patched bodies, commonly more or less bushy in cultivation and often with several trunks or leaders: tree to 80 or 100 feet tall, with long and slender branches; bark exfoliating in large thin irregular plates, leaving light gray particolored areas, on old trees chalky-white; young branches grayish-green, glabrous: leaves 3, rigid, acute, light green, 2–4 inches long, with stomata on the back: cones almost sessile, conic-ovate, light yellowish-brown, 2–3 inches long; scale-end much broader than high, ridged, with a triangular pointed and recurved umbo; seed dark brown, with narrow wing, ⅓–½ inch long. Northwestern China where it has been cultivated from ancient times; hardy as far north as western New York and Massachusetts. A slow-growing tree with rather sparse light green foliage. This tree bears the name of Alexander von Bunge, of St. Petersburg, productive author on the plants of northern and northeastern Asia; died 1890.—*Pinus Bungeana*, Zuccarini in Endlicher, Synopsis Coniferarum, 166 (1847).

The closely related Himalayan **P. Gerardiana**, CHILGHOZA PINE, has larger cones and longer oblong-cylindric edible seeds. It has been repeatedly introduced to Great Britain, but is at present very rare and probably not known in this country where it probably would be hardy only in the southern states.—*Pinus Gerardiana*, Wallich ex Lambert, A Description of the Genus Pinus, ed. 3, ii, t. 79 (1832).

42. **P. Balfouriana.** FOXTAIL PINE. Subalpine Californian pine, mostly of intermediate size, little planted: tree to 40 but sometimes 90 feet tall, narrow-pyramidal when young, irregular and open in old age; bark on stems and branches of young trees thin and smooth, milky-white, on old trees thick, dark red-brown, deeply divided into broad flat ridges covered with small appressed scales; branchlets dark brown, puberulous at first: leaves 5, crowded, incurved, and pressed against the branches, rigid, acute, dark green on the back, with conspicuous white lines on the ventral sides, 1–1½ inches long, remaining for ten to twelve years on the branches: cones pendulous, subcylindric, dark purplish-brown, 3½–5 inches long; scale-end flattened, the concave

oblong umbo with minute incurved prickle; seed ⅓ inch long, with adnate wing. California, on mountains in the north and again in the south; hardy in sheltered positions as far north as Massachusetts. This tree carries the name of John Hutton Balfour, died 1884, of the Royal Botanic Garden in Edinburgh, interested in an association for the introduction of North American plants.—*Pinus Balfouriana*, Murray in Rept. Botany Oregon Expedition, 1 (1853).

43. **P. aristata.** BRISTLE-CONE PINE. HICKORY PINE. Subalpine resinous-leaved small species of the western United States, sometimes regarded as a bristly-coned variety of *P. Balfouriana:* bushy, but sometimes to 50 feet tall, at other times a semi-prostrate shrub; branchlets light orange and almost glabrous: leaves 5, stout or slender, dark green, 1–1½ inches long, with white lines on the ventral sides, usually with conspicuous scattered exudations of resin: cones cylindric-ovoid, 3–3½ inches long; scale-end elevated; umbo with a slender incurved spine to ¼ inch long; seed ¼ inch long. Colorado, Utah, Nevada, Arizona, southern California; hardy as far north as Massachusetts. In cultivation usually a handsome low shrub with ascending branches densely clothed with appressed leaves.—*Pinus aristata*, Engelmann in Amer. Journ. Sci., ser. 2, xxxiv, 331 (1862); *P. Balfouriana* var. *aristata*, Engelmann in Rept. U. S. Geogr. Surv. W. 100th Merid. vi, 375 (1878).

44. **P. koraiensis.** KOREAN PINE. Plate XIV. Fig. 14a. The Korean nut pine is native also in certain mountains in the main island of Japan, and is frequently planted: pyramidal tree to 75 feet tall, exceptionally to 100 feet and to 10 feet in girth; bark gray or gray-brown, thin, peeling off in irregular flakes, red-brown beneath; branchlets with yellowish-brown pubescence; winter-buds oblong-ovate, acuminate, dark chestnut-brown: leaves 5, or sometimes 3, straight, dark green and glossy on the back, bluish-white on the inner sides, 2½–4 inches long: cones short-peduncled, conic-oblong, yellowish-brown, 4–6 inches long, indehiscent; scales rhombic-obovate, with recurved obtuse apex; seed over ½ inch long, brown, sharply edged, edible. Mountains of northeastern Asia; hardy as far north as southern Ontario and New England. A handsome tree of pyramidal habit and rather slow growth; one of the best hardy pines for small gardens. It often forks, and it becomes irregular in age.—*Pinus koraiensis*, Siebold & Zuccarini, Flora Japonica, ii, 28 (1842); *P. mandshurica*, Ruprecht in Bull. Phys. Math. Acad. Sci. St. Petersb. xv, 382 (1857).

45. **P. Cembra.** SWISS STONE PINE. Standard hardy pine for ornamental planting, in several forms, symmetrical and compact or dense in habit, of slow durable growth: tree to 70 or sometimes 120 feet tall, with spreading usually short branches forming a narrow dense pyramid, in old age often with very picturesque broad open round-topped head; bark greenish-gray and smooth on young trees, on old trunks reddish-gray and divided into thin scaly plates; branchlets coated with dense yellowish-brown tomentum; winter-buds globose-ovoid, long-acuminate: leaves 5, straight, dark green on back, bluish-white inside, 2–5 inches long, with medial resin-ducts: cones short-peduncled, ovate, obtuse, light brown, 2½–3½ inches long; scales broadly ovate, rounded at apex; scale-end much broader than high; seed ½ inch long, edible, germinating second year. Alps of central Europe and from northeastern Russia to Mongolia; hardy as far north as Saskatchewan. *Cembra* is a place-name in the Alps.—*Pinus Cembra*, Linnæus, Species Plantarum, 1000 (1753).

Var. **pumila,** perhaps to be regarded as a distinct species, *P. pumila,* DWARF

STONE PINE, is a shrub to 10 feet high, main branches usually prostrate: leaves 1¾–3 inches long, obscurely serrulate, with the resin-ducts usually marginal: cone ovoid, 1¼–1¾ inches long. Northeastern Siberia and high mountains of Korea and Japan.

It is probably as hardy as *P. Cembra* itself, but does not seem to thrive under cultivation. — *Pinus Cembra* var. *pumila*, Pallas, Flora Rossica, i, 5 (1784); *P. pumila*, Regel in Index Seminum quæ Hortus Botanicus Imperialis Petropolitanus, 23 (1858).

Var. **sibirica.** SIBERIAN STONE PINE. A form with shorter leaves and larger cones; of narrower habit and more vigorous growth.—*Pinus Cembra* var. *sibirica*, Loudon, Hortus Britannicus, 387 (1830); *P. sibirica*, Mayr, Fremdländische Wald- und Parkbäume für Europa, 388 (1906).

Var. **aurea.** Foliage yellowish. — *Pinus Cembra* var. *aurea*, Hort.

Var. **columnaris.** Of narrow habit.—*Pinus Cembra* var. *columnaris*, Beissner.

46. **P. Armandi.** CHINESE WHITE PINE. Plate XV. Fig. 32. East Asian tree to 60 feet tall, with wide-spreading horizontal branches; bark smooth, pale gray; branchlets glabrous in distinction from *P. koraiensis* and *P. flexilis*, but usually minutely glandular; winter-buds cylindric, chestnut-brown: leaves 5, slender and thin, drooping or wide-spreading, 3–6 inches long, serrulate, bright green, without stomata on the back, bent or knuckled near the base: cones peduncled and pendent, oblong-conical, 4–6 or sometimes 8 inches long, yellowish-brown; scales obovate, appressed, much thickened in the middle, with large broadly rhombic scale-end and small obtuse thickened umbo often slightly recurved; seeds pale reddish-brown, ovoid, compressed, ½ inch long, with a sharp edge all around. Central and western China; also southern Japan, Formosa. A handsome pine of rather loose habit with wide-spreading branches, hardy in Massachusetts. This pine has much the appearance of *P. nepalensis* but in that species the leaves are straight rather than bent near the base as well as longer, and the

32. Cone of Pinus Armandi, nearly full size.

young shoots are not glandular; cones usually longer in *excelsa* and seeds with prominent wings. Named in compliment to Père Armand David, missionary-botanist, who collected in China.—*Pinus Armandi*, Franchet in Nouv. Arch. Mus. Paris, ser. 2, vii, 95 (Pl. David. i, 284) (1885); *P. scipioniformis*, Masters in Bull. Herb. Boiss. vi, 270 (1898); *P. Mastersiana*, Hayata in Gard. Chron. xliii, 194 (1908); *P. Armandi* var. *Mastersiana*, Hayata in Journ. Coll. Sci. Tokyo, xxv, art. 19, 215 (1908).

47. **P. albicaulis.** WHITEBARK PINE. High mountain pine, sometimes constituting the timber-line, of western North America: middle-sized tree or sometimes bush-like, rarely 60 feet tall but usually not exceeding half that height, trunk often twisted or crooked, bearing wide-spreading branches; bark fissured into thin brown to creamy-white scales; branchlets glabrous or puberulous with scattered minute short hairs, brown to orange, tough and pliable: leaves 5, rigid, entire, $1\frac{1}{2}$–$2\frac{1}{2}$ inches long, dark green, with stomatic lines on the back, persistent for five to eight years: cone subsessile, ovoid or globose-ovoid, 2–3 inches long, dull purple, finally brown; scales much thickened, often with stout pointed umbo; seeds $\frac{1}{3}$–$\frac{1}{2}$ inch long. British Columbia and Alberta to California and Wyoming; probably hardy in the East as far north as Canada, but difficult in cultivation.—*Pinus albicaulis*, Engelmann in Trans. St. Louis Acad. Sci. ii, 209 (1863).

48. **P. flexilis.** LIMBER PINE. ROCKY MOUNTAIN WHITE PINE. Plate XIV. Mostly of middle size, with pliable soft branches closely set with dark green leaves not harsh to the hand: to 50, sometimes to 80 feet tall, with stout horizontal branches forming a narrow open pyramid, in old age with low broad round-topped head; bark dark brown or nearly black and deeply fissured on old trunks, on young stems and on the branches thin and smooth, gray to silvery-white; branchlets glabrous or minutely brown-tomentulose; winter-buds broadly ovoid, slender-pointed: leaves 5, firm, acute, dark green, $1\frac{1}{3}$–3 inches long, with stomata on the back: cones short-stalked, ovoid to cylindric-ovoid, light brown, 3–6, rarely 10 inches long; scales rounded at the apex, tipped with an obtuse dark umbo, the lower ones elongated and reflexed; seeds dark brown, mottled with black, $\frac{1}{3}$–$\frac{1}{2}$ inch long, with narrow wing. Mountains and highlands, Alberta to western Texas, west to Oregon and California, southward to Lower California. A desirable hardy pine for planting.—*Pinus flexilis*, James in Long's Expedition, ii, 34 (1823).

Var. **reflexa.** Tree to 100 feet tall: leaves slender, to 4 inches long, entire or remotely serrulate: cones 5–9 inches long, on longer stalks, with often thin reflexed scales. Arizona. Doubtful if in cultivation and probably not hardy North. This pine has been known as *P. strobiformis*, but that name is properly applied to a species of Arizona and Mexico closely allied to *P. Ayacahuite* and by some authors considered to be a variety of it.—*Pinus flexilis* var. *reflexa*, Engelmann in Rept. U. S. Geogr. Surv. W. 100th Merid. vi, 258 (1878); *P. reflexa*, Engelmann in Coult. Bot. Gaz., vii, 4 (1882); *P. strobiformis*, Sargent, Silva of North America, xi, 33 (1897), not Engelmann.

49. **P. Lambertiana.** SUGAR PINE. A very tall and long-coned Pacific soft or white pine, of slow growth in cultivation in the East: tree to 200 or 220 feet tall, with spreading somewhat pendulous branches forming a narrow open pyramid; old trees usually with flat-topped wide-spreading open head; bark on young stems and branches smooth and thin, dark green, on old trunks thick and deeply divided into plate-like ridges covered with large purple-brown or cinnamon-red scales; branchlets brown, pubescent;

winter-buds oblong-obovate, apiculate: leaves 5, stout, sharply pointed, dark bluish-green, 3–4 inches long, with conspicuous white lines on the back: cones on peduncles 2–3½ inches long, cylindric, often slightly curved, light brown, lustrous, 10–20 inches long; seed about ½ inch long, dark brown or nearly black. Mountain slopes, Oregon to Lower California, in the Coast ranges and the Sierras, long-lived and making great forests; hardy as far north as western New York and Massachusetts in sheltered positions. A handsome tree of pyramidal habit and with dark green foliage. This noble pine appropriately bears the name of Aylmer Bourke Lambert, 1761–1842, British botanist, author of the great work "A Description of the Genus Pinus." — *Pinus Lambertiana*, Douglas in Trans. Linn. Soc. xv, 500 (1827).

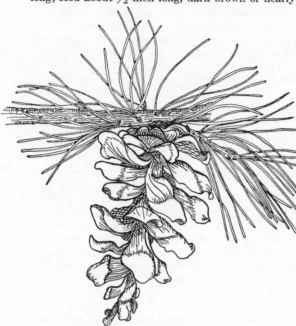

33. Pinus parviflora, showing an old opened cone.
About natural size.

50. **P. Ayacahuite.** MEXICAN WHITE PINE. Variable tall pine, particularly in the seeds, of mountain slopes: tree to 100 feet tall, with spreading slender branches; bark rough and scaly on old trees; branchlets yellowish-brown, finely pubescent: leaves 5, slender and somewhat pendulous, bluish-green, 4–6 inches long: cones stalked, pendent, cylindric-conical, gradually narrowed toward the apex, often slightly curved, brownish-yellow, 9–15 inches long; seeds about ½ inch long, gray-brown, mottled dark brown. Northern Mexico to Guatemala; hardy in sheltered places as far north as southern New England, probably more so when grown from seeds from the cooler parts of its range. *Ayacahui-te* is a vernacular name of this pine in Mexico.—*Pinus Ayacahuite*, Ehrenberg ex Schlechtendal in Linnaea, xii, 492 (1838); *P. Don-Pedrii*, Roezl, Catalogue des Graines de Conifères Mexicains, 31 (1857); *P. Loudoniana*, Gordon, Pinetum, 230 (1858); *P. Bonapartea*, Roezl in Gard. Chron. 358 (1858).

Two varieties (perhaps separate species) are probably not in cultivation:

Var. **brachyptera** has seeds larger and wing very short. Northern Mexico.— *Pinus Ayacahuite* var. *brachyptera*, Shaw, Pines of Mexico, 11 (1909); *P. strobiformis*, Engelmann in Wislizenus, Memoir of a Tour to Northern Mexico, 102 (1848).

Var. **Veitchii** has cones to 18 inches; seed dark brown with broad wing ½ inch long. Central Mexico.—*Pinus Ayacahuite* var. *Veitchii*, Shaw, Pines of Mexico, 10 (1909); *P. Veitchii*, Roezl, Catalogue des Graines de Conifères Mexicains, 32 (1857).

51. **P. parviflora.** JAPANESE WHITE PINE. Fig. 33. Short-leaved small-coned variable picturesque tree to 80 feet, of pyramidal habit, with slender horizontal branches; bark of young trees smooth, on older trees fissured into thin flaky scales, red-brown beneath; branchlets light greenish-brown, puberulous: leaves 5, crowded, rather stiff, usually twisted, forming brush-like tufts at the ends of the branchlets, bluish-green, ¾–1½ inches long: cones ovoid or oblong-ovoid, almost sessile, reddish-brown, 2–3 inches long, often persistent; seeds dark brown, hardly ½ inch long, with short wing. Japan and Formosa, on mountains. A handsome hardy pine with wide-spreading branches and dark green foliage. Much grown as dwarfs by the Japanese. The name *parviflora* was first applied to cultivated plants, probably grafted and dwarfed, with short leaves and cones. The wild plant, with longer leaves, larger cones and longer-winged seeds, was described as *P. pentaphylla* and these forms have sometimes been separated as *P. parviflora* var. *pentaphylla;* but Wilson, who critically studied this pine in Japan, found no real character to distinguish them and recognized only one botanical form.— *Pinus parviflora*, Siebold & Zuccarini, Flora Japonica, ii, 27 (1842); *P. pentaphylla*, Mayr, Monographie der Abietineen des Japanischen Reiches, 78 (1890); *P. parviflora* var. *pentaphylla*, Henry in Elwes & Henry, Trees of Great Britain and Ireland, v, 1033 (1909).

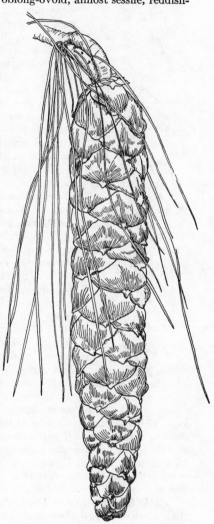

Var. **glauca.** A form with glaucous bluish foliage.—*Pinus parviflora* var. *glauca*, Beissner.

Var. **nana.** A less vigorous form with leaves shorter than the type.—*Pinus parviflora* var. *nana*, Beissner.

52. **P. Peuce.** MACEDONIAN WHITE PINE. Slow-growing tree of narrow or pyramidal form, attaining 50 feet in height, with ascending short branches forming a narrow dense pyramid; bark smooth on young trees, grayish-brown, ultimately fissured into small plates; branchlets greenish, glabrous, not glaucous; winter-buds ovoid: leaves 5, straight, bluish-green, 3–4 inches long, without stomata on back: cones short-stalked, cylindric, 3½–6 inches long, with obovate scales, deciduous; seed 4 lines long. Mountains of the Balkan peninsula; hardy as far north as New England and southern Ontario. Well adapted to small grounds, some-

34. Cone of Pinus nepalensis. (× ⅔)

what like *P. Cembra* in appearance. In Latin, *peuce* (peù-see) is an adopted word for a pine or pitch-pine tree.—*Pinus Peuce*, Grisebach, Spicilegium Floræ Rumelicæ et Bithynicæ, ii, 349 (1844); the specific name has been written *Peuke* but not so by the author of it; *P. excelsa* var. *Peuce*, Beissner, Handbuch der Nadelholzkunde, 286 (1891).

53. P. nepalensis. HIMALAYAN WHITE PINE. BLUE PINE. Fig. 34. Very tall relatively smooth-barked long-leaved handsome pine, in clear stands and mixed forests in its native region, with soft drooping grayish-green foliage, attaining 150 feet in height, with spreading and slightly ascending branches forming a broad open pyramid, with a rather loose open habit; bark grayish-brown, in small plates, with shallow fissures at maturity; branchlets greenish, glabrous, glaucous; winter-buds cylindric-obovoid, acute, pale brown: leaves 5, slender, flaccid, drooping, grayish- or bluish-green, 6–8 inches long: cones cylindric, 6–10 inches long on stalks 1–2 inches long; seeds brown, 4 lines long. Himalayas, from Bhutan to Afghanistan, up to 12,500 feet; hardy in sheltered positions as far north as Massachusetts, but suffers in very severe winters. —*Pinus nepalensis*, De Chambray, Traité Pratique des Arbres Résineux Conifères, 342 (1845); *P. excelsa*, Wallich ex Lambert, A Description of the Genus Pinus, ii, 5 (1824); not Lamarck; *P. Griffithii*, McClelland in Griffith Notulæ, iv, 17 (1854) et Icones Plantarum Asiaticarum, iii, t. 365 (1854).

Var. **zebrina** has leaves with yellow areas, giving the foliage a banded or zoned appearance.—*Pinus napalensis* var. *zebrina*, new comb.; *P. excelsa* var. *zebrina*, Croux.

54. P. monticola. WESTERN WHITE PINE. Plate XVI. Fig. 35. A forest timber pine, western representative of *P. Strobus*, differing in its stouter and stiffer leaves, in the longer cones with more rows of scales, and in a narrower and denser habit of growth: tree to 100 or sometimes 150 feet tall, with slender spreading somewhat pendulous branches forming a narrow open pyramid; bark of young stems smooth and thin, light gray, on old trees deeply divided into nearly square plates covered by small purple appressed scales; branchlets puberulous, yellowish- or reddish-brown; winter-buds ovoid, acute: leaves 5, stiff, bluish-green and glaucous, 1½–4 inches long, with few inconspicuous or no lines on the back: cones short-peduncled, cylindric, slender, slightly curved, 5–11 inches long, yellowish-brown; scales pointed by the slightly thickened sometimes recurved umbo; seed red-brown, mottled with black, ⅓ inch long. British Columbia to California, eastward to Montana; hardy as far north as Massachusetts.—*Pinus monticola*, Douglas ex Lambert, A Description of the Genus Pinus, ed. 2, iii, 27 (1837).

35. Pinus monticola.
(× ⅔)

55. P. Strobus. WHITE PINE. Plates IV, XVII. Figs. 10, 13, 16. Prime forest and timber tree of eastern North America, fast-growing, tractable and ornamental, planted in several forms: in nature it attains 100 feet and is reported more than twice that height and 6 feet in diameter; branches strongly ascending when young but becoming horizontal with maturity; in old age the head is usually broad and open and often very picturesque; bark on young stems thin and smooth, green tinged with red, on old trunks thick and deeply divided into broad connected ridges covered with small appressed purplish scales; branchlets greenish or light greenish-brown, glabrous or slightly puberulous; winter-buds ovoid, acuminate: leaves 5, variable in length, soft, bluish-green, 2–5 inches long: cones on stalks ½–1 inch long, cylindric, slender, often curved, 3–8 inches long, with oblong-obovate scales, maturing second season; seed red-brown, mottled with black, 3 lines long. Forming forests on sandy lands but distributed in other habitats, Newfoundland to Manitoba, south to Georgia, Illinois and Iowa. The word *Strobus* was anciently used for an unidentified incense-bearing tree, transferred by Linnæus to this pine. In England it is known as Weymouth pine, from Lord Weymouth who planted it on his estate 200 years or more ago; well known in Europe.—*Pinus Strobus*, Linnæus, Species Plantarum, 1001 (1753); *Strobus Weymouthiana*, Opiz in Lotos, iv, 94 (1854); *S. Strobus*, Small, Flora of Southeastern United States, 29 (1903).

Var. **prostrata**. A dwarf procumbent plant with diffuse branches trailing on the ground. This varietal name was proposed in England for a horticultural plant of American origin. Recently what is assumed to be the same form of the species in nature has been described as *P. Strobus* forma *prostrata* by Fernald and Weatherby (Rhodora, xxxiv, 168, 1932); it occurs on serpentine mountains of western Newfoundland, forming spreading and closely depressed fruiting carpets not more than 20–32 inches high, sprawling over areas 6–10 feet across. Of the var. *prostrata* Dallimore and Jackson (Handbook of the Coniferæ) state that it is prostrate in habit and that a plant may be seen in the rock-garden at Kew. Hornibrook (Dwarf and Slow-Growing Conifers) gives the history of var. *prostrata* as having been found by Rehder in the Arnold Arboretum, a plant being sent to Kew in 1893 where it is perfectly prostrate and hangs vertically over the face of a stone. It is stated that Beissner found a similar form in a garden in Germany. It is recorded by Bean (Trees and Shrubs Hardy in the British Isles); Silva Tarouca and Schneider (Freiland-Nadelhölzer) make it a subvariety of *Strobus*. Persons who know the white pine only as a great forest and timber tree are hardly prepared for such radical variation as expressed in the prostrate form.

Var. **aurea**. Foliage yellowish, at least on small trees or when the leaves are young.—*Pinus Strobus* var. *aurea*, Hort.

Var. **contorta**. An odd form from Rochester parks: leader and the somewhat ascending branches twisted, bearing tufts of leaves 2–3 inches long: cones about 1½ to nearly 2½ inches long.—*Pinus Strobus* var. *contorta*, Slavin; *P. Strobus* forma *contorta*, Slavin.

Var. **fastigiata**. A form with ascending branches forming a narrow-pyramidal or nearly columnar head.—*Pinus Strobus* var. *fastigiata*, Beissner; *P. Strobus* var. *pyramidalis*, Hort.

Var. **glauca**. Foliage light bluish-green.—*Pinus Strobus* var. *glauca*, Beissner.

Var. **nana**. A compact rounded or broad-conical bush with short leaves.—*Pinus Strobus* var. *nana*, Carrière; *P. Strobus* var. *densa*, Hort.

Var. **nivea**. Foliage silvery-white underneath, and leaves usually short.—*Pinus Strobus* var. *nivea*, Booth & Knight.

Var. **umbraculifera**. UMBRELLA WHITE PINE. Compact umbrella-shaped bush with short leaves.—*Pinus Strobus* var. *umbraculifera*, Knight.

CHAPTER IV

THE TRUE CONE-BEARERS—FIRS AND SPRUCES

THE firs, as modernly understood, bear their leaves in circular pits or depressions which are apparent on the branch when the leaves fall with age; but the leaves still persist on a young shoot when it is cut and dried. The true firs hold their cones upright or erect on the twig, as in Abies and the cones soon fall apart or in pieces; but in Pseudotsuga, which is more a fir than a spruce, the cones are hanging and they do not shatter. The spruces bear leaves on a short projection or sterigma, with which they articulate, and the leaves fall when a twig is cut and dried. The cones of spruces are hanging and they do not fall in pieces or shatter. The genera Picea and Tsuga comprise the spruces. There are good differences in the "looks" of these groups as they grow, to which the attentive planter soon becomes accustomed. These genera comprise the cultivated members of the subfamily Abietineæ, together with Pinus, Cedrus, Larix, and Pseudolarix. See key on pages 44–46.

The genera treated in this chapter are five:

2. Abies.
3. Keteleeria, page 95.
4. Pseudotsuga, page 96.
5. Picea, page 99.
6. Tsuga, page 122.

2. **ABIES.** FIR. Beautiful monœcious evergreen trees of substantial richly-foliaged aspect, often stately, symmetrically pyramidal or narrow-conical when young or of middle age but some of them becoming great forest trees with clear boles, trunk simple and mostly not forked, lateral branches whorled in tiers, nearly forty species in the northern hemisphere (as far south as Guatemala in the western hemisphere and as northern Africa and the Himalayas in the eastern) and most of them introduced to cultivation for ornament and many of them utilized as timber trees; distinguished from Picea, the spruces, in leaves mostly flat and relatively broad rather than

(78)

manifestly angled in cross-section, and not shedding when the twig is dried, scar left by falling leaf hollow and disk-shaped (Fig. 36a), cones erect instead of declined or pendulous and shattering at maturity; bark usually smooth,

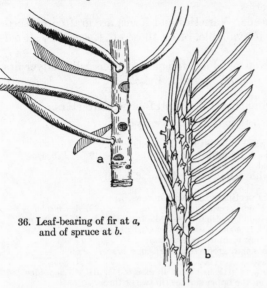

36. Leaf-bearing of fir at *a*, and of spruce at *b*.

thin on young trees, thick and furrowed at base of old trees; winter-buds with or without resin: leaves persistent for many years, linear to linear-lanceolate, entire, sessile, contracted above the circular base and leaving a circular scar as they fall, flattened, usually grooved and deep green and lustrous above, with 2 white or pale stomatic bands and keeled beneath, rarely 4-sided with stomata on all 4 sides, rounded and variously notched or pointed at the apex, spirally arranged but frequently appearing 2-ranked by a twist at their base, with 2 resin-canals which are either marginal or median (Fig. 37), and with 2, rarely 1, vascular bundles; the leaves on upper fertile branches crowded, more or less erect, often incurved or falcate, thickened or quadrangular, obtuse or acute: catkins axillary, appearing in early spring from buds formed the previous summer on branchlets of the year, surrounded by involucres of the enlarged scales of the flower-buds; staminate catkins pendent on branches above the middle of the tree; fertile catkins globular, ovoid or oblong, with numerous 2-ovuled imbricate scales, erect on the topmost branches: fruit an erect ovoid or oblong-cylindrical cone, its scales longer or shorter than their bracts, broad and rounded or truncate at the incurved apex, narrowed at base into a long stipe; seeds with large thin wing; cotyledons 4–10. Abies (à-bies) is the ancient Latin name of the silver-fir. —*Abies*, Hill, British Herbal, 509 (1756), at least as to name.

37. Resin-canals shown in cross-section of fir leaves, marginal above and median below, the central object being the midrib.

The firs are mostly slow-growing trees requiring a cool humid climate for best results, and often demand considerable attention before becoming well established. Mostly they are injured by dust and smoke and are therefore not well adapted to planting in the interior of cities. For this country, *Abies concolor* is the most widely adaptable species. The firs are not variable in cultivation as are many other classes of conifers, and only a few of the species yield named horticultural varieties.

Firs are propagated from seeds. Varieties and forms are grafted on seedlings of the particular species, if available, or on those of *A. concolor*, *A. balsamea*, and *A. alba*.

The species with very glaucous or bluish foliage are often called silver firs, as *A. alba, amabilis, concolor, Delavayi, grandis, Veitchii*.

KEY to species of Abies, primarily on leaf and foliage characters.

A. Leaves with stomatiferous lines on both surfaces and glaucous or grayish-green: buds resinous.
   B. Arrangement of short stiff and pointed leaves radial (standing in all directions or planes), the resin-ducts median or internal.........19. *A. Pinsapo*
   BB. Arrangement of leaves not radial.
      c. Buds completely covered with resin: leaves flat or distinctly flattened.
         D. Branchlets glabrous: leaves pectinate (in two flat rows, like a comb on either side the shoot); resin-ducts marginal.......29. *A. concolor*
         DD. Branchlets pubescent: leaves not pectinate; resin-ducts median.26. *A. lasiocarpa*
      cc. Buds only thinly resinous, with free sharp scales at base: leaves of upper ranks upwardly curving; resin-ducts marginal.
         D. The leaves on sterile shoots flat, grooved above: cone bracts much exserted and reflexed............................30. *A. nobilis*
         DD. The leaves 4-sided: cone bracts little or not at all exserted....31. *A. magnifica*
AA. Leaves lacking stomatiferous lines on the upper surface (in two or three species a few incomplete lines near the apex).
   B. Branchlets deeply grooved, particularly on two-year-old branches.
      c. Pubescence lacking on branchlets: leaves with internal resin-ducts.14. *A. homolepis*
      cc. Pubescence of branchlets brown, in the grooves: leaves with marginal resin-ducts...15. *A. spectabilis*
   BB. Branchlets not or slightly grooved.
      c. Under surface of leaves without conspicuous white or glaucous bands (sometimes fairly conspicuous in *A. chensiensis*).
         D. Apex of leaves acutish to spiny-pointed.
            E. Cones violet-purple: leaves of upper ranks partly recurved; resin-ducts marginal: winter-buds very resinous.........11. *A. recurvata*
            EE. Cones green: leaves spreading at nearly right angles or upper ranks directed forward; resin-ducts internal: winter-buds thinly resinous.......................................12. *A. holophylla*
         DD. Apex of leaves emarginate or bifid; resin-ducts marginal.
            E. Cones green: leaves more or less pectinate: buds not or slightly resinous.
               F. Leaves emarginate: branchlets glabrous...............10. *A. chensiensis*
               FF. Leaves sharply bifid (at least in young plants): branchlets slightly grooved, hairy in the grooves................13. *A. firma*
            EE. Cones purple: leaves of upper ranks directed forward, slender, often curved, bifid at apex: buds resinous..............16. *A. Pindrow*
      cc. Under surface of leaves with 2 white or glaucous stomatic bands.
         D. All branchlets more or less pubescent.
            E. Buds resinous.
               F. Foliage more or less pectinate (like teeth of comb).

G. Winter-buds very resinous.
  H. Leaves distinctly pectinate, $1\frac{1}{4}$–$2\frac{1}{2}$ inches long:
    branchlets soon glabrous and lustrous...........28. *A. grandis*
  HH. Leaves not all strictly pectinate, $\frac{1}{2}$–$1\frac{1}{4}$ inches long.
    I. Apex of leaves acute to obtusish; resin-ducts
      marginal.................................17. *A. religiosa*
    II. Apex of leaves truncate to emarginate; resin-ducts
      internal..................................25. *A. balsamea*
GG. Winter-buds slightly resinous: leaves very white be-
  neath, to $1\frac{1}{2}$ inches long, sharply bifid: branchlets
  slightly grooved............................... 6. *A. Faxoniana*
FF. Foliage not pectinate.
  G. Direction of leaves spreading upward and outward.
    H. Length of leaves $\frac{1}{2}$–$\frac{3}{4}$ inch; resin-ducts internal.
      I. Leaf with 8–12 lines of stomata in each band:
        bracts of cone much exserted................24. *A. Fraseri*
      II. Leaf with 4–8 lines of stomata in each band:
        bracts not or slightly exserted..............25. *A. balsamea*
    HH. Length of leaves about 1 inch; resin-ducts marginal
      (internal in No. 7).
      I. Branchlets soon glabrous, yellowish: buds thinly
        resinous.................................. 4. *A. koreana*
      II. Branchlets densely pubescent, brown: buds very
        resinous.
        J. Apex of leaves truncate or emarginate: bark
          smooth................................. 3. *A. Veitchii*
        JJ. Apex of leaves acutish to obtuse: bark flaky... 7. *A. squamata*
  GG. Direction of leaves forward.
    H. Width of leaves $\frac{1}{12}$ inch or more.
      I. Pubescence of branchlets pale, short: leaves
        about 1 inch long; resin-ducts marginal.......27. *A. amabilis*
      II. Pubescence of branchlets dense, rufous: leaves
        $\frac{1}{2}$–$\frac{3}{4}$ inch long; resin-ducts internal.......... 5. *A. Mariesii*
    HH. Width of leaves $\frac{1}{24}$–$\frac{1}{16}$ inch, to $1\frac{1}{2}$ inches long; resin-
      ducts internal.
      I. Branchlets smooth, minutely pubescent: leaves
        with 4–5 lines of stomata in each band....... 1. *A. sibirica*
      II. Branchlets slightly grooved, with hairs in the
        grooves: leaves with 7–8 lines of stomata in each
        band.................................... 2. *A. sachalinensis*
EE. Buds not resinous: leaves with marginal resin-ducts: cones
  green.
  F. Foliage not pectinate.
    G. Cone with hidden bracts: leaves spreading upward
      and outward.............................21. *A. cilicica*
    GG. Cone with exserted and reflexed bracts: leaves directed
      forward.................................22. *A. Nordmanniana*
  FF. Foliage pectinate: cone with exserted bracts............23. *A. alba*
DD. All branchlets glabrous (often slightly hairy in Nos. 8 and 9):
  resin-ducts marginal.
  E. Apex of leaves obtuse or emarginate, rarely acutish: branch-
    lets brown: cones purple or violet.
    F. Winter-buds resinous: leaves slender, $\frac{3}{5}$–1 inch long,
      emarginate.
      G. Leaves not or scarcely revolute; resin-ducts internal on
        fertile branches............................... 8. *A. Fargesii*
      GG. Leaves revolute at the margin; resin-ducts marginal.. 9. *A. Delavayi*

1. Abies sibirica. SIBERIAN FIR. A great forest tree of wide distribution in the northern regions on mountains of the Old World, covering extensive areas, but little known
in cultivation; although hardy the early growth is often injured by late frosts and the
tree becomes thin; to 100 feet tall; bark smooth; winter-buds globose, resinous; branchlets gray, minutely pubescent: leaves linear, slender, up to 1¼ inches long, rounded
and entire or bifid at apex, lustrous, bright green above, often with 2 or 3 short lines
of stomata near apex, with 2 narrow grayish bands beneath, crowded and directed
forward: cones cylindric, 2–3 inches long, bluish before maturity; scales about ⅗ inch
wide, with denticulate margin; bracts hidden, scarcely half as long as scale. Northern
Russia to Kamchatka, Altai Mountains, south to Turkestan and Manchuria.—*Abies
sibirica*, Ledebour, Flora Altaica, iv, 202 (1833); *A. Pichta*, Forbes, Pinetum Woburnense, 113 (1839); *A. Semenovii*, Fedtschenko in Bot. Centralb. lxxiii, 210 (1898).

A related species, **A. nephrolepis,** has been planted experimentally: bark of trunk
rough; branchlets more pubescent: leaves shorter: cones smaller; bracts longer.
Eastern Siberia, northern China.—*Abies nephrolepis*, Maximowicz in Bull. Acad. St.
Petersb. x, 486 (1866); *A. sibirica* var. *nephrolepis*, Trautvetter in Maximowicz in
Mem. Div. Sav. Acad. Sci. St. Petersb. ix, 260 (1859); *A. gracilis*, Komarov in Act.
Hort. Petrop., xx, 203 (1901). *A. nephrolepis* var. *chlorocarpa* has been listed.

2. A. sachalinensis. SAGHALIN FIR. A very large hardy tree of thin habit from the
northern part of farther Asia, not frequently planted, differing from *A. Veitchii* in the
longer less silvery more forward-pointing leaves, branchlets hairy only in the grooves,
rather larger and otherwise different cones; to 120 feet tall, with smooth light gray
bark; winter-buds small, very resinous; branchlets slightly grooved, pubescent in the
grooves: leaves similar to those of *A. sibirica*, but without stomata above and with
broader stomatic bands beneath and slightly broader and longer: cones about 3 inches
long, gradually narrowed toward the apex; scales with entire margin, densely pubescent
outside; bracts exserted and reflexed. Northern Japan, Saghalin, and Kurile Islands.
—*Abies sachalinensis*, Masters in Gard. Chron. xii, 588 (1879); *A. Veitchii* var.
sachalinensis, F. Schmidt in Mem. Acad. Sci. St. Petersb., ser. 7, xii, 175 (1868).

Var. **nemorensis** has cones smaller (about 2½ inches long) with bracts not showing.
—*Abies sachalinensis* var. *nemorensis*, Mayr, Monographie der Abietineen des Japa-
nischen Reiches, 42 (1890); *A. Wilsoni*, Miyabe & Kudo in Trans. Sapporo Nat. Hist.
Soc. vii, 132 (1919).

3. A. Veitchii. VEITCH FIR. Fig. 38. Japanese: one of the most ornamental of the
firs because of its foliage prominently white underneath and its pyramidal habit,
particularly attractive when young; to 80 feet tall, with smooth grayish bark; winter-
buds purplish, very resinous, the lateral almost united with the terminal one; branchlets brown, rather densely pubescent: leaves crowded, directed forward and more or
less upward, on the lower side of the branchlets pectinate, linear, ½–1 inch long,

truncate and notched at apex, lustrous dark green above, with 2 broad silvery-white bands beneath: cones cylindric, 1¾–2½ inches long, bluish-purple before maturity; bracts slightly exserted and reflexed; seeds with a broad short wing, scarcely as long as body. Central Japan, in mountains; discovered in 1860 on Fujiyama by John Gould Veitch, 1839–1870. Hardy as far north as Ontario and New England. — *Abies Veitchii*, Lindley in Gard. Chron. 23 (1861).

Var. nikkoensis. Cones small, perhaps not exceeding 2 inches, points of bracts only slightly visible. — *Abies Veitchii* var. *nikkoensis*, Mayr, Monographie der Abietineen des Japanischen Reiches, 39 (1890).

Var. olivacea. Cones green before maturity. — *Abies Veitchii* var. *olivacea*, Shirasawa in Bot. Mag. Tokyo, xxvii, 132 (1913).

38. Abies Veitchii. (× about ¾)

4. **A. koreana.** KOREAN FIR. Plate XX. A small to medium tree of pyramidal habit, yet little known in this country; to 50 feet; bark of older trees rough, fissured into irregular plates; branchlets sparingly pubescent, yellowish or silver-gray at first, becoming glabrous and purplish; winter-buds thinly resinous: leaves crowded, usually broader toward the apex, rounded and emarginate, or on young plants pointed, ⅓–¾ inch long, revolute at the margin, lustrous above, with whitish bands beneath: cones cylindric, 2–3 inches long and about 1 inch in diameter, violet-purple before maturity; scales about ¾ inch broad; bracts about as long as scales, slightly exserted and reflected. Korea, on mountains. Hardy and attractive.—*Abies koreana*, E. H. Wilson in Journ. Arnold Arb. i, 188 (1920).

5. **A. Mariesii.** MARIES FIR. Large tree in its native habitat in Japan, differing from *A. Veitchii* in the very soft-pubescent shoots, shorter very blunt leaves, and mostly larger cones, not much planted; to 80 feet tall, with smooth pale gray bark, rough at base of old trees; winter-buds subglobose, small, resinous; branchlets densely rusty-pubescent: leaves crowded, those of the middle ranks directed forward and nearly appressed, the lateral ones longer and spreading, linear, slightly broader above the middle, rounded or bifid at apex, ⅓–¾ inch long, lustrous above, with white bands beneath: cones ovoid to oblong-ovoid, narrowed toward the ends, 1¾–3½ inches long, dark purple before maturity; scales about 1 inch broad; bracts hidden; seed-wings twice as long as body. Mountains of Japan; hardy as far north as Massachusetts but not doing as well as *A. Veitchii*. It bears the name of its discoverer and introducer, Charles Maries.—*Abies Mariesii*, Masters in Gard. Chron. xii, 789 (1879).

6. **A. Faxoniana.** FAXON FIR. Very large Chinese fir, little planted and horti-

cultural experience lacking; to 120 feet tall; bark dark gray, furrowed; winter-buds ovoid, purple, very resinous; branchlets densely brown-pubescent, slightly grooved: leaves crowded, irregularly spreading in two ranks, the upper rows shorter, linear, obtuse to emarginate, rarely mucronate, slightly revolute at the margins, ½–1 inch long, lustrous dark green above, with white bands beneath; resin-ducts internal or marginal: cones ovoid-oblong, 2–3 inches long, violet-purple before maturity; scales about ¾ inch broad; bracts somewhat exserted, upright or reflexed; seed-wing scarcely as long as body. Western China, in forests at high elevations. This fir is named in compliment to the late Charles E. Faxon, American botanical artist.—*Abies Faxoniana*, Rehder & Wilson in Sargent, Plantæ Wilsonianæ, ii, 42 (1914).

7. **A. squamata.** FLAKY FIR. Very tall tree with prominent shaggy bark, little known in cultivation; to 120 feet tall; bark purplish-brown, exfoliating in thin flakes; winter-buds subglobose, reddish-brown, very resinous; branchlets densely brownish pubescent: leaves crowded and ascending, linear, often falcate, obtuse or acutish, ⅗–1 inch long, bluish-green above, with white bands beneath: cones oblong-ovoid, 2–2½ inches long, violet before maturity, resinous; scales about ⅗ inch wide; bracts slightly exserted. Western China, at great altitudes. Notable for its flaky bark which begins to peel on the primary branches when about six years old, the inner bark purplish-red even on young branches.—*Abies squamata*, Masters in Gard. Chron., ser. 3, xxxix, 299 (1906).

8. **A. Fargesii.** FARGES FIR. Promising tall Chinese fir with colored shoots and short thick branches, not yet sufficiently tested; to 100 feet tall; winter-buds resinous; branchlets glabrous, reddish-brown or purplish, slightly grooved and often hairy in the grooves: leaves on upper side of branchlets crowded, spreading at nearly right angles, the middle ranks upright or nearly reflexed, those below pectinate, linear, sometimes falcate, emarginate or bifid at apex, about 1 inch long, dark green and lustrous above, with white bands beneath: cones ovoid-oblong, 2–3 inches long; scales about ¾ inch wide; bracts slightly exserted and recurved. Central China. Named for R. P. Farges, explorer.—*Abies Fargesii*, Franchet in Journ. de Bot. xiii, 256 (1899).

Closely related to *A. Fargesii* is **A. sutchuenensis**, which differs chiefly in its stouter and shorter ascending leaves acute or obtuse, with distinct yellow petioles. Western China; probably not cultivated outside botanical collections.—*Abies sutchuenensis*, Rehder & Wilson in Sargent, Plantæ Wilsonianæ, ii, 48 (1914); *A. Fargesii* var. *sutchuenensis*, Franchet in Journ. de Bot. xiii, 256 (1899).

9. **A. Delavayi.** DELAVAY FIR. Large silver fir of China, of doubtful hardiness in the North; to 120 feet tall; bark gray, fissured in old trees; winter-buds resinous; branchlets usually glabrous, red-brown, lustrous, slightly grooved and often hairy in the grooves: leaves crowded, spreading at nearly right angles, those of the middle ranks much smaller, nearly upright, and often upturned, scarcely pectinate below, linear, emarginate at apex, ⅗–1 inch long, acute at the margin and usually strongly revolute, dark green above with wide bands beneath: cones cylindric-oblong, 2½—3 inches long, violet-black before maturity; scales about ¾ inch wide and entire at the margin; bracts slightly exserted. Western China, at high altitudes; collected by R. P. Delavay.—*Abies Delavayi*, Franchet in Journ. de Bot. xiii, 255 (1899); *A. Faberi*, Craib in Notes Bot. Gard. Edinb. xi, 278 (1919); *Keteleeria Fabri*, Masters in Journ. Linn. Soc., Bot. xxvi, 555 (1902).

A related species is **A. Beissneriana**. Tallest of the Chinese firs, to about 200 feet; bark fissured, dark gray; branchlets yellowish or grayish-yellow, rarely slightly puberulous: leaves crowded, linear-ligulate, nearly plane above and sometimes stomatiferous near apex, with pale or glaucescent bands beneath: cones peduncled; bracts hidden. Western China, in high mountains. Bears the name of Ludwig Beissner, author "Handbuch der Nadelholzkunde."—*Abies Beissneriana*, Rehder & Wilson in Sargent, Plantæ Wilsonianæ, ii, 46 (1914).

In this affinity seems to belong the fir **A. Forrestii**. Tree to 60 feet tall; branchlets brown, glabrous or slightly hairy: leaves pectinately arranged, ascending and forming a V-shaped groove, those of lower and upper ranks directed forward and upward and curving slightly backward, exposing the white under side, linear, to 1½ inches long, rounded or emarginate, with broad white bands beneath: mature cones not known. Southwestern China, at high altitudes; probably not cultivated in North America. Named for G. Forrest, botanical traveler in China.—*Abies Forrestii*, Craib ex Coltman Rogers in Gard. Chron., ser. 3, lxv, 150 (1919), in obs.; and in Notes Bot. Gard. Edinb. xi, 279 (1919).

10. **A. chensiensis.** SHENSI FIR. Tall distinct fir from the provinces of Shensi and Hupeh in central-northern China, promising for planting; to 120 feet tall; winter-buds ovoid, slightly resinous; branchlets glabrous, yellowish-gray, older ones dark gray: leaves horizontally spreading and more or less 2-ranked, linear, broader above the middle, ⅜–1½ inches long, usually rounded and emarginate at apex, rarely acutish, shining dark green above, with grayish-green or sometimes glaucescent bands beneath: cones ovoid-oblong, 3–4 inches long and nearly 2 inches in diameter, green while young, finally cinnamon-brown; scales about 1¼ inches wide, erose at the margin and tomentose outside; bracts hidden. China; hardy in eastern Massachusetts.—*Abies chensiensis*, Van Tieghem in Bull. Soc. Bot. France, xxxviii, 413 (1891).

11. **A. recurvata.** MIN FIR. Plate XVIII. Attractive Chinese silver fir particularly marked by the recurved or backwardly pointing sharp leaves specially on branchlets two or three years old; to 120 feet tall, with rough dark gray or reddish-brown bark; buds ovoid, very resinous; branchlets glabrous and lustrous, yellowish-gray: leaves spreading at nearly right angles on the middle ranks and partly more or less recurved, pectinate below, linear, ⅜–1½ inches long, shorter on fertile branches, acutish or sharply pointed, lustrous or bluish-green above, paler green beneath: cones oblong-ovoid, 2–4 inches long, violet-purple before maturity, finally grayish-brown; scales about ⅗ inch wide; bracts hidden. Western China, making extensive forests on mountains in the Min River region; hardy in western New York and eastern Massachusetts.—*Abies recurvata*, Masters in Journ. Linn. Soc., Bot. xxxvii, 423 (1906).

12. **A. holophylla.** NEEDLE FIR. MANCHURIAN FIR. Tall tree, to 100 feet or more, little planted, bearing long narrow pointed leaves; winter-buds slightly resinous; branchlets yellowish-gray, glabrous, slightly grooved: leaves spreading at nearly right angles outward and upward, pectinate below, linear, entire at apex and spiny-pointed in young plants, acute or obtusish in older trees, lustrous bright green above, with grayish or slightly whitish bands beneath: cones cylindric, 5–6 inches long, green when young, finally dull light brown; scales 1½–2 inches wide; bracts hidden. Manchuria and Korea. At the Arnold Arboretum it has proved hardy and promises to

become a handsome and distinct tree of pyramidal habit with bright green lustrous foliage.—*Abies holophylla*, Maximowicz in Bull. Acad. Sci. St. Petersb. x, 487 (1866).

13. **A. firma.** Momi Fir. A Japanese tree of primitive forests, little known in cultivation in the United States; to 120 feet tall; bark dark gray, soon becoming scaly, fissured on old trees; buds small, slightly resinous; branchlets brownish, slightly grooved, short-pubescent in the grooves: leaves pectinate, linear, broadest about the middle, with bifid pungent apex on young plants, obtuse and emarginate on older

39. Abies homolepis. ($\times$ $\frac{3}{5}$)

plants, up to 1½ inches long, lustrous dark green above, not keeled and with grayish bands beneath: cones cylindric, gradually narrowed toward the apex, 4–5 inches long, yellowish-green before maturity; bracts exserted, not reflexed. Japan, ascending to about 7,000 feet. It is hardy as far north as western New York and can be grown in sheltered positions in eastern Massachusetts, but will probably do better in the Middle Atlantic states.—*Abies firma*, Siebold & Zuccarini, Flora Japonica, ii, 15 (1842); *A. Momi*, Siebold in Verhandl. Batav. Gen. xii, 12 (1830), *nomen nudum; A. bifida*, Siebold & Zuccarini, Flora Japonica, ii, 19 (1842).

14. **A. homolepis.** Nikko Fir. Plate XVIII. Fig. 39. One of the best ornamental firs, now frequently planted in the eastern United States, with dark rich foliage on up-

turned branches and great purplish upstanding cones often on low branches; to 120 feet tall; bark scaly; winter-buds ovoid, resinous; branchlets deeply grooved, particularly on two- and three-year-old branchlets, grayish, glabrous: leaves spreading outward and upward, separated in the middle by a V-shaped depression, pectinate below, those of the outer ranks about 1 inch long, of the middle ranks shorter, linear, rounded and slightly bifid at apex, shining dark green above, with broad white bands beneath: cones cylindric, slightly narrowed at the ends, about 4 inches long, purple before maturity; scales about ⅖ inch wide, entire at the margin; bracts hidden. Japan, on mountains; hardy as far north as New England and southern Ontario, and it has proved, in the eastern states, one of the most satisfactory and ornamental firs.—*Abies homolepis*, Siebold & Zuccarini, Flora Japonica, ii, 17 (1842); *A. Tschonoskiana*, Regel in Index Seminum quæ Hortus Botanicus Imperialis Petropolitanus, 32 (1865); *A. brachyphylla*, Maximowicz in Bull. Acad. Sci. St. Petersb. x, 488 (1866).

Var. **Scottæ.** Dwarf Nikko Fir. Branch-sport on the grounds of Mrs. A. H. Scott near Media, Pennsylvania.—*Abies homolepis* var. *Scottæ*, McFarland (Horticulture, Dec. 15, 1932).

Var. **Tomomi.** More sparingly branched and with shorter leaves.—*Abies homolepis* var. *Tomomi*, Rehder in Journ. Arnold Arb. i, 53 (1919).

Var. **umbellata.** Cones green before maturity.—*Abies homolepis* var. *umbellata*, Wilson, Conifers and Taxads of Japan, 58 (1916); *A. umbellata*, Mayr, Monographie der Abietineen des Japanischen Reiches, 34 (1890); *A. umbilicata*, Hansen in Journ. Roy. Hort. Soc. xiv, 478 (1892).

A related species is **A. Kawakamii,** not planted. Branchlets deeply grooved, yellowish, pubescent in the grooves or nearly glabrous: leaves pointing forward, the upper ranks ascending and curved: cones 2–3 inches long. Formosa.—*Abies Kawakamii*, Hayata, Ic. Pl. Formos. ix, 108 (1920).

15. **A. spectabilis.** Upper Himalayan Fir. Immense tree in parts of the Himalayan region, 8,000 to 13,000 feet, not hardy northward; to 150 feet and more tall; bark scaly, rough; winter-buds large, subglobose, resinous; branchlets reddish-brown, deeply grooved, pubescent in the grooves: leaves arranged as in *A. homolepis*, but larger, 1–2⅓ inches long, rounded or bifid at apex, lustrous dark green above, with broad white bands beneath: cones cylindric, 6–7 inches long, violet-purple before maturity; scales about ¾ inch broad; bracts hidden or slightly exserted. Sikkim and Bhutan Himalaya. A handsome tree with wide-spreading branches forming a broad-pyramidal head; possibly it will stand as far north as the Middle Atlantic states.—*Abies spectabilis*, Spach, Histoire Naturelle des Végétaux, Phan. xi, 422 (1842); *A. Webbiana*, Lindley in Penny Cyclopædia, i, 30 (1833); *A. densa*, Griffith, Notulæ, iv, 19 (1854); *Pinus spectabilis*, D. Don, Prodromus Floræ Nepalensis, 55 (1825).

Var. **brevifolia.** Leaves shorter, not exceeding 1¼ inches, with grayish-white bands beneath. Northwestern Himalaya; somewhat hardier than the type, but probably will not thrive in most parts of New York.—*Abies spectabilis* var. *brevifolia*, Rehder in Journ. Arnold Arb. i, 54 (1919); *A. Webbiana* var. *brevifolia*, Henry in Elwes & Henry, Trees of Great Britain and Ireland, iv, 751 (1909).

16. **A. Pindrow.** Lower Himalayan or Pindrow Fir. A Himalayan species little known in North America, growing natively in altitudes of 6,000–10,000 feet; to 200 feet tall; bark smooth and gray on young trees, grayish-brown and fissured on

old trees; winter-buds large, resinous; branchlets smooth and glabrous, gray: leaves crowded above, the middle ranks directed forward, pectinate below, narrowly linear, narrowed into a bifid acute apex, entire in young plants, 1–2⅓ inches long, lustrous dark green above and with pale grayish bands beneath: cones cylindric, 4–5½ inches long, deep purple while young; scales 1¼ inches wide; bracts hidden. Western Himalaya: Kumaon to Kashmir; probably hardy as far north as Middle Atlantic states. Varieties are distinguished abroad.—*Abies Pindrow*, Spach, Histoire Naturelle des Végétaux, Phan. xi, 423 (1842); *A. Webbiana* var. *Pindrow*, Brandis, Forest Flora, 528 (1874); *Picea Pindrow*, Royle ex Loudon, Arboretum et Fruticetum Britannicum, iv, 2346 (1838); *Pinus Pindrow*, Royle, Illustrations of the Botany of the Himalaya Mountains, 354, t, 86 (1839). *Pindrow* is a vernacular name.

17. **A. religiosa.** SACRED FIR. Tall Mexican and Guatemalan fir in mountains above 4,000 feet, probably hardy only in the southern states and California, the branches employed in its native regions for decoration in religious festivals; to 150 feet tall; bark gray or grayish-brown, fissured into oblong plates; winter-buds globose-ovoid, resinous; branchlets brown, short-pilose: leaves pectinate, the middle ranks directed forward, linear, narrow, acute to obtusish, ⅔–1¼ inches long, dark green above, with white or grayish-white bands beneath: cones cylindric-oblong, 5–6 inches long and 2–2½ inches in diameter, dark violet-blue before ripening; bracts longer than the scale, reflexed.—*Abies religiosa*, Schlechtendal & Chamisso in Linnaea, v, 77 (1830); *A. hirtella*, Lindley in Penny Cyclopædia, i, 31 (1833).

18. **A. numidica.** ALGERIAN FIR. Small or medium attractive tree with stiffish branches, dense foliage of short and stout leaves, promising well for cultivation in the North; to 60 feet tall; bark gray, smooth; winter-buds ovoid, large, not or slightly resinous; branchlets glabrous and lustrous: leaves much crowded above, spreading outward and upward, on stronger branchlets more or less backward, on weaker ones with a V-shaped depression in the middle, pectinate below, stout, linear, often broadest above the middle, rounded at apex and slightly emarginate or entire, rarely acutish, ⅜–¾ inch long and 1/12 inch broad, dark green above, often only faintly grooved and usually stomatiferous near apex or on fruiting branches with several stomatic lines, with white bands beneath: cones cylindric, 5–7 inches long; scales 3¼ inches broad, with entire margin; bracts hidden. Northern Africa (Algeria), a region once known as Numidia; hardy as far north as New York and in sheltered positions to Massachusetts.—*Abies numidica*, De Lannoy ex Carrière in Rev. Hort., 106 (1866); *A. Pinsapo* var. *baborensis*, Cosson in Bull. Soc. Bot. France, viii, 607 (1861); *A. baborensis*, Letourneux, Cat. Arb. et Arbust. d'Algérie (1888).

A related species is **A. nebrodensis,** from Sicily, with resinous winter-buds and pubescent branchlets; it is in cultivation in Europe.—*Abies nebrodensis*, Mattei in Bull. Ort. Bot. Palermo, vii, 64 (1908).

A. maroccana from Morocco is probably not in cultivation.—*Abies maroccana*, Trabut in Bull. Soc. Bot. France, liii, 154 (1906).

19. **A. Pinsapo.** SPANISH FIR. Attractive tree for mild climates or protected places, long in cultivation in several forms and hybrids, known in its native region as Pinsapo; to 80 feet; bark smooth, fissured in old trees; winter-buds ovoid, resinous; branchlets glabrous, brownish: leaves spreading radially at nearly right angles, linear, thick and rigid, acute or obtusish, ⅜–¾ inch long, dark green and stomatiferous and slightly

convex above, with grayish bands beneath: cones cylindric, 4–5 inches long, purplish-brown; scales about 1 inch wide, with entire margin; bracts small, hidden. Southern Spain; hardy in sheltered positions as far north as Massachusetts. A handsome tree of striking appearance, thriving on limestone soil.—*Abies Pinsapo*, Boissier in Bibl. Univ. Genève, xiii, 167 (1838).

Var. **argentea.** Foliage silvery-white.—*Abies Pinsapo* var. *argentea*, Beissner.

Var. **glauca.** Foliage glaucous.—*Abies Pinsapo* var. *glauca*, Beissner.

Var. **pendula.** Branches drooping.—*Abies Pinsapo* var. *pendula*, Beissner.

A. Vilmorinii, an artificial hybrid between *A. cephalonica* and *A. Pinsapo*, is a handsome vigorous tree with spreading spiny-pointed leaves about 1 inch long; intermediate between the parents. Originated in 1868 in France by Vilmorin.—*Abies Vilmorinii*, Masters in Journ. Roy. Hort. Soc. xxvi, 108 (1901).

A. insignis, hybrid of *A. Nordmanniana* and *A. Pinsapo*, is a broad-pyramidal vigorous tree; winter-buds resinous: leaves crowded, the upper ranks pointing forward, thickish, lustrous bright green, usually obtuse at apex, about 1 inch long. Raised first in 1872 and repeatedly afterward; several forms have been distinguished: as var. **Beissneriana,** var. **Kentiana,** var. **Mastersiana,** and var. **speciosa.**—*Abies insignis*, Carrière apud Bailly in Rev. Hort., 230 (1890). *A. insignis* var. *Beissneriana*, Rehder (*A. Beissneriana*, Mottet). *A. insignis* var. *Kentiana*, Rehder (*A. Kentiana*, Mottet). *A. insignis* var. *Mastersiana*, Rehder (*A. Mastersiana*, Mottet). *A. insignis* var. *speciosa*, Rehder (*A. Nordmanniana speciosa*, Bailly).

20. **A. cephalonica.** GREEK FIR. Plate XIX. Handsome well-known fir with radially arranged pointed leaves lustrous above and white-banded underneath; to 100 feet; bark grayish-brown, smooth, fissured in old trees; winter-buds ovoid, reddish, resinous; branchlets lustrous, red-brown, glabrous: leaves radially spreading and slightly directed forward, the middle ranks above shorter, linear, stiff, gradually narrowed into a sharp point, $\frac{1}{2}$–1 inch long, shining deep green above, sometimes with a few stomata near apex, with white bands beneath, the margins obtuse: cones cylindric, 5–7 inches long and 1$\frac{3}{4}$–2 inches in diameter, brownish; scales with convex undulate or entire margin; bracts exserted and reflexed. Mountains of Greece, formerly making an extensive forest on the Ionian island of Cephalonia; hardy as far north as Massachusetts and western New York.—*Abies cephalonica*, Loudon, Arboretum et Fruticetum Britannicum, iv, 2325 (1838); *A. Reginæ-Amaliæ*, Heldreich in Gartenflora, ix, 313 (1860); *A. panachaica*, Heldreich in Gartenflora, x, 286 (1861).

Var. **Apollonis.** Branchlets yellowish: leaves more crowded above, only a few leaves below spreading downward and forward, thicker and broader, acute or sometimes obtusish.—*Abies cephalonica* var. *Apollonis*, Beissner, of Handbuch der Nadelholzkunde, 440 (1891); *A. Apollonis*, Link in Linnaea, xv, 528 (1841).

A. Borisii regis (King Boris), native of the Balkan region and named for King Boris, is related to *A. cephalonica*, but has closely pubescent branchlets and leaves not so sharp-pointed or even blunt.—*Abies Borisii regis*, Mattfeld in Notizbl. Bot. Gart. Berlin, ix, 235 (1925).

A. Bornmuelleriana of Asia Minor has glabrous branchlets and long blunt or emarginate leaves. Named for Joseph Bornmueller, Weimar, Germany.—*Abies Bornmuelleriana*, Mattfeld in Notizbl. Bot. Gart. Berlin, ix, 239 (1925). The last two are seldom if at all planted.

21. **A. cilicica.** Cilician Fir. Sturdy tree of narrow-pyramidal form with leaf arrangement of *A. Nordmanniana* but less densely foliaged, leaves narrower and spreading upward and outward, branches more slender, cones different; to 100 feet tall; bark ashy-gray, smooth, scaly in old trees; winter-buds small, with few keeled acute scales, free at the tips, not resinous; branchlets gray, with scattered short hairs: leaves spreading upward and forward, on weak shoots outward and upward and leaving a V-shaped depression in the middle, somewhat pectinate below, linear, slender,

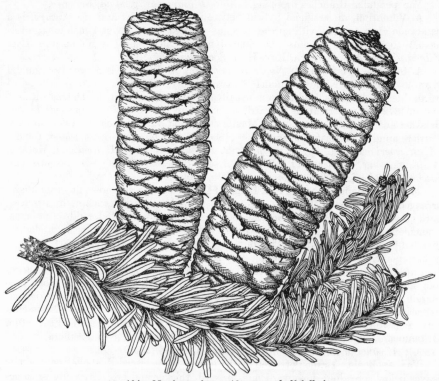

40. Abies Nordmanniana. About one-half full size.

rounded or acute and slightly bifid at apex, about 1 inch long, shining bright green above, with narrow white bands beneath: cones cylindric, 7–9 inches long, reddish-brown; scales 1¾–2 inches broad, with entire margin; bracts hidden. Asia Minor (Cilicia), northern Syria; hardy as far north as southern Ontario and New England. —*Abies cilicica*, Carrière, Traité Général des Conifères, 229 (1855).

22. **A. Nordmanniana.** Nordmann or Caucasian Fir. Fig. 40. Long known and desirable narrow-pyramidal and densely foliaged fir with horizontal or somewhat declined branches, the leaves looking forward, dark green; to 150 feet; bark grayish-

brown, slightly fissured in old trees; winter-buds ovoid, acute, with slightly keeled obtusish scales, not resinous; branchlets gray with scattered short hairs: leaves directed forward and densely covering the branchlets, pectinate below, linear, rounded and bifid at apex, $\frac{3}{4}$–$1\frac{1}{2}$ inches long, lustrous dark green above, with whitish bands beneath: cones cylindric, 5–6 inches long, reddish-brown; scales about $1\frac{1}{2}$ inches wide; bracts exserted and reflexed. Caucasus, Asia Minor, Greece; hardy as far north as southern Ontario and New England. Bears the name of Alexander Nordmann, Finnish botanist, who found it in the Caucasus in 1837.—*Abies Nordmanniana*, Spach, Histoire Naturelle des Végétaux, Phan. xi, 418 (1842).

Var. **aurea.** Foliage yellow.—*Abies Nordmanniana* var. *aurea*, Beissner.

Var. **tortifolia.** Leaves of the middle ranks above falcate and twisted, partly exposing the white under side.—*Abies Nordmanniana* var. *tortifolia*, Rehder.

23. **A. alba.** SILVER FIR. Familiar fir for ornament and forest planting in Europe, less satisfactory under usual American conditions, variable in cultivation, marked by its pectinate or comb-like leaves white underneath, non-resinous buds and cylindric cones; to 150 feet and more; bark grayish, scaly in old trees; winter-buds small, with few obtuse scales, not resinous; branchlets gray, with scattered short hairs: leaves pectinate, those of the upper and middle ranks pointing outward and upward, linear, rounded and bifid at apex, $\frac{3}{5}$–$1\frac{1}{4}$ inches long, lustrous dark green above, with white bands beneath: cones cylindric, 4–$5\frac{1}{2}$ inches long, green while young, finally reddish-brown; scales about 1 inch broad, tomentose outside; bracts exserted and reflexed. Mountains of central and southern Europe. Planted as far north as southern Ontario and New England but liable to damage in severe winters and requiring protection or sheltered situation. There are several varieties but few true dwarfs.—*Abies alba*, Miller, Gardeners Dictionary, ed. 8, no. 1 (1768); *A. pectinata*, DeCandolle, Flore Française, iii, 276 (1805); *A. Picea*, Lindley in Penny Cyclopædia, i, 29 (1833).

Var. **equi trojani.** Leaves attenuate toward the apex and slightly emarginate: cones oblong-cylindric; bracts much exserted. Asia Minor. This variety forms a transition to *A. cephalonica;* probably not in cultivation.—*Abies alba* var. *equi trojani*, Ascherson & Graebner, Synopsis der Mitteleuropaischen Flora, ed. 2, i, 290 (1913); *A. pectinata* var. *equi trojani*, Ascherson & Sintenis in Boissier, Flora Orientalis, v, 701 (1883).

Var. **columnaris.** Branches very short, of nearly equal length, forming a columnar head.—*Abies alba* var. *columnaris*, Rehder; *A. pectinata* var. *columnaris*, Carrière.

Var. **compacta.** Dwarf and dense.—*Abies alba* var. *compacta*, Rehder.

Var. **pendula.** Branches pendulous.—*Abies alba* var. *pendula*, Ascherson & Graebner; *A. pectinata* var. *pendula*, Carrière.

Var. **pyramidalis.** SENTINEL SILVER FIR. With ascending branches, forming a columnar head.—*Abies alba* var. *pyramidalis*, Voss; *A. alba fastigiata*, Ascherson & Graebner; *A. pectinata* var. *pyramidalis*, Carrière.

Var. **tortuosa.** Dwarf compact form with shining leaves.—*Abies alba* var. *tortuosa*, Rehder; *A. pectinata* var. *pumila*, Hort.

24. **A. Fraseri.** FRASER FIR. SOUTHERN BALSAM FIR. Plate XX. Interesting fir in a collection but usually not satisfactory as a cultivated subject; to 70 feet tall; bark smooth, reddish and scaly in old trees; winter-buds small, subglobose, very resinous; branchlets yellowish-gray, densely covered with short reddish hairs: leaves crowded,

spreading upward and forward, pectinate below, linear, rounded and bifid at apex, ⅗–1 inch long, shining dark green above, with broad white bands beneath: cones oblong-ovoid or ovoid, 1½–2¼ inches long, purple before maturity; scales about ¾ inch wide; bracts exserted and reflexed. Alleghany Mountains from West Virginia to North Carolina and Tennessee, making forests at 4,000 to 6,000 feet; hardy as far north as southern Ontario and New England; not particularly ornamental. The species bears the name of John Fraser, a collector who introduced it to Europe early in last century.—*Abies Fraseri*, Poiret in Lamarck Encyclopédie Méthodique, Suppl. v, 35 (1817).

Vars. *compacta* and *prostrata* are listed.

25. **A. balsamea.** BALSAM FIR. Well-known tree of northern swamps and hills, but not adaptable to ordinary grounds; to 70 feet tall; bark grayish-brown, scaly on old trees; winter-buds small, reddish, very resinous; branchlets ashy-gray, short-pubescent: leaves spreading upward, pectinate below, on weaker branchlets indistinctly pectinate above, linear, rounded and slightly bifid at apex, ⅗–1 inch long, lustrous dark green above and often with a few stomatic lines near apex, with narrow grayish-white bands beneath: cones oblong, 1½–2½ inches long, violet-purple before maturity; scales ⅗ inch wide; bracts usually inclosed (exserted in var. **phanerolepis**). Labrador to West Virginia, west to Minnesota and Iowa, mostly in swampy areas but sometimes on hillsides; at high elevations becomes a bush forming thickets. The exudations from the trunk provide Canada balsam, and oil of fir from the bark.—*Abies balsamea*, Miller, Gardeners Dictionary, ed. 8, no. 3 (1768). *Abies balsamea* var. *phanerolepis*, Fernald in Rhodora, xi, 203 (1909).

Var. **hudsonia.** HUDSON FIR. Dwarf form with dark green shorter and broader leaves, making a spreading bush only a few inches high.—*Abies balsamea* var. *hudsonia*, Sargent, Silva of North America, xii, 109 (1898); *A. hudsonia*, Bosc ex Knight & Perry, Synopsis of Coniferous Plants, 39 (1850); *A. Fraseri* var. *hudsoni*, Carrière, Traité Général des Conifères, 200 (1855); *A. balsamea* var. *hudsonica*, Veitch, Manual of the Coniferæ, 83 (1881); *Picea Fraseri* var. *hudsonia*, Knight & Perry, Synopsis of Coniferous Plants, 39 (1850). Interpreted as *A. balsamea* forma *hudsonia* by Fernald & Weatherby (Rhodora, xxxiv, 190, 1932): "The dwarf, prostrate extreme of *Abies balsamea* is certainly only a depressed *form*, a response to bleak habitats, quite parallel with the dwarf forms in *Picea* and other groups." It is to be determined whether all the plants cultivated as *hudsonia* are of the same origin or represent the wild habitat form.

Var. **macrocarpa.** Leaves longer and cones 3–3½ inches long. Wisconsin.—*Abies balsamea* var. *macrocarpa*, Kent in Veitch, Manual of the Coniferæ, ed. 2, 492 (1900).

26. **A. lasiocarpa.** ALPINE FIR. Plate XXII. Western high mountain tree more or less hardy in the East as far north as Canada but may not thrive and of little merit there as an ornamental subject; to 100 or even to 150 feet tall; bark smooth and silvery-gray, fissured in old trees; winter-buds small, ovoid, resinous; branchlets ashy-gray, with a short rufous pubescence: leaves much crowded, directed upward and forward, linear, rounded or acutish at apex, rarely emarginate, 1–1½ inches long, pale bluish-green, stomatiferous above and only slightly grooved, with broad pale bands beneath: cones oblong-cylindric, 2½–4 inches long, truncate or depressed at apex; scales ¾–1 inch wide; bracts hidden. Alaska to Oregon, Utah and northern New

Mexico.—*Abies lasiocarpa*, Nuttall in North American Sylva, iii, 138 (1849); *A. subalpina*, Engelmann in Amer. Naturalist, x, 555 (1876); *Picea bifolia*, A. Murray in Gard. Chron. iii, 106 (1875).

Var. **arizonica.** CORK FIR. Bark thick and corky, grayish-white: leaves emarginate at apex, with bluish-white bands beneath, the lower ranks pectinate, the upper ones directed forward. Northern Arizona and northern New Mexico, southern Colorado. —*Abies lasiocarpa* var. *arizonica*, Lemmon in Sierra Club Bull. ii, 167 (1897); *A. arizonica*, Merriam in Proc. Biol. Soc. Washington, x, 115 (1896).

Var. **compacta.** A dwarf compact form.—*Abies lasiocarpa* var. *compacta*, Rehder; *A. subalpina* var. *compacta*, Beissner.

27. A. amabilis. CASCADE FIR. Handsome great tree in the moist and cool conditions of the Pacific mountains but not satisfactory in dry exposed regions and in the East usually does not succeed; to 250 feet tall; bark silvery-white or pale, at the base of old trees thick and furrowed; winter-buds globose, very resinous; branchlets gray, densely pubescent: leaves crowded, the upper ranks directed forward, the lower ones spreading, pectinate below, linear, often broadest above the middle, truncate or bifid at the apex, about 1 inch long, shining dark green above, with broad white bands beneath: cones oblong, $3\frac{1}{2}$–6 inches long, purple before maturity, puberulous; scales 1–$1\frac{1}{4}$ inches wide; bracts hidden. British Columbia and Alberta to Oregon; hardy as far north as Massachusetts in sheltered positions.—*Abies amabilis*, Forbes, Pinetum Woburnense, 125 (1839).

28. A. grandis. GIANT FIR. Gigantic tree in its far western habitat, more or less hardy in special places as far north as New York but not reliable eastward as an ornamental; to 300 feet tall; bark smooth, brownish, fissured into thin plates and red-brown or grayish-brown at the base of old trees; winter-buds ovoid, resinous; branchlets olive-green, minutely pubescent: leaves pectinate, linear, rounded and bifid at apex, flexible, $1\frac{1}{4}$–$2\frac{1}{4}$ inches long, shining dark green above, with white bands beneath: cones cylindric, 2–4 inches long, green; scales 3 or 4 times as long as the hidden bracts. Vancouver Island to northern California, east to Montana, near the coast and in mountains.—*Abies grandis*, Lindley in Penny Cyclopædia, i, 30 (1833); *A. amabilis*, Murray in Proc. Roy. Hort. Soc. iii, 310 (1863); *A. Gordoniana*, Carrière, Traité Général des Conifères, ed. 2, 298 (1867).

29. A. concolor. COLORADO or WHITE FIR. Probably most satisfactory in eastern America of the native firs, thriving under many conditions, in several forms or varieties, conspicuous in its blue-green long spreading leaves and light colored bark; to 200 feet or more; bark smooth gray, on old trees fissured and scaly; winter-buds globose, resinous; branchlets yellowish-green, minutely pubescent or nearly glabrous: leaves irregularly arranged, mostly spreading outward and curving upward, some of the middle ranks above directed forward, linear, acute, or rounded at apex, $1\frac{1}{2}$–2 inches long, bluish-green, slightly convex and stomatiferous above, not grooved, convex and with pale bands beneath: cones cylindric, 3–5 inches long, narrowed at the ends, greenish or purplish before maturity; scales about 1 inch wide; bracts hidden. Colorado to southern and Lower California, northern continental Mexico and New Mexico; hardy as far north as southern Ontario and New England. Withstands heat and drought better than other firs.—*Abies concolor*, Lindley & Gordon in Journ. Hort. Soc. Lond. v, 210 (1850).

Var. **Lowiana.** PACIFIC WHITE FIR. To 250 feet, winter-buds smaller: leaves pectinately arranged, 2–3 inches long, rounded and bifid at apex, shallowly grooved above. Oregon and California; much tenderer than the type.—*Abies concolor* var. *Lowiana*, Lemmon, Handbook Western American Cone-bearers, ed. 3, 64 (1895); *A. Lowiana*, Murray in Proc. Roy. Hort. Soc. iii, 317 (1863); *A. lasiocarpa*, Masters in Gard. Chron. xiii, 8 (1880).

Var. **argentea.** Foliage silvery-white.—*Abies concolor* var. *argentea*, Niemetz.

Var. **aurea.** Foliage golden-yellow when young.—*Abies concolor* var. *aurea*, Beissner.

Var. **brevifolia.** Leaves short and thick.—*Abies concolor* var. *brevifolia*, Beissner.

Var. **conica.** Dwarf pyramidal form, Rochester (New York) parks: branches and branchlets crowded and horizontal, with leaves 1½ inches or less long.—*Abies concolor* var. *conica*, Slavin; *A. concolor* forma *conica*, Slavin.

Var. **globosa.** Of globose habit, with short branches.—*Abies concolor* var. *globosa*, Beissner.

Var. **violacea.** PURPLECONE WHITE FIR. Foliage bluish-white.—*Abies concolor* var. *violacea*, Beissner.

Var. **Wattezii.** Foliage first pale yellowish, changing to silvery-white.—*Abies concolor* var. *Wattezii*, Beissner.

30. **A. nobilis.** NOBLE FIR. Great tree of the Pacific region, hardy in sheltered positions eastward as far north as Massachusetts, but not likely to be satisfactory under general conditions; to 250 feet tall; bark reddish-brown, deeply fissured, smooth in young trees; winter-buds resinous, the outer scales narrow and acuminate; branchlets minutely rusty-pubescent: leaves crowded above, the lower ranks spreading outward, the middle ranks much shorter, appressed to the branchlets near the base, then curving upward, linear, rounded and entire or slightly emarginate at apex, 1–1½ inches long, bluish-green, stomatiferous and grooved above, with narrow pale bands beneath: cones cylindric-oblong, slightly narrowed toward the apex, 6–10 inches long, green before maturity, becoming purplish-brown; scales 1¼–1½ inches wide; bracts much exserted and reflexed. Washington to northern California, 2,000 to 5,000 feet.—*Abies nobilis*, Lindley in Penny Cyclopædia, i, 30 (1833).

Var. **glauca.** Foliage glaucous.—*Abies nobilis* var. *glauca*, Beissner.

Var. **argentea** is listed.

31. **A. magnifica.** RED FIR. Handsome western fir of good habit sometimes hardy to eastern Massachusetts, but usually not reliable in exposed places; to 200 feet tall; winter-buds and branchlets like those of the preceding species: leaves less crowded, quadrangular in sections, rounded and entire at apex, keeled and stomatiferous above, with pale bands beneath: cones cylindric-oblong, 6–9 inches long, pubescent, purplish-violet before maturity; scales 1¼–1½ inches wide; bracts hidden. Oregon to California in mountains 5,000 to 10,000 feet.—*Abies magnifica*, Murray in Proc. Roy. Hort. Soc. iii, 318 (1863); *A. nobilis* var. *magnifica*, Kellogg, Forest Trees of California, 35 (1882).

Var. **shastensis.** Bracts exserted and often reflexed, covering nearly half the scales. Oregon to California.—*Abies magnifica* var. *shastensis*, Lemmon in Bien. Rept. Calif. State Bd. For. iii, 145 (1890); *A. shastensis*, Lemmon in Garden and Forest, x, 184 (1897).

Var. **argentea.** Foliage bluish-white.—*Abies magnifica* var. *argentea*, Beissner.

Var. **glauca.** AZURE FIR. Foliage deep glaucous.—*Abies magnifica* var. *glauca*, Beissner.

32. **A. venusta.** BRISTLECONE FIR. Attractive and striking tree where it thrives but not hardy in the northeastern country; to 150 feet; the lower branches pendulous, the upper short, forming a head abruptly narrowed from a broad pyramidal base into a slender spire; bark smooth, brown, fissured at the base of old trees; winter-buds elongated, acute, ⅜–1 inch long, not resinous; branchlets greenish, glabrous: leaves pectinate, linear-lanceolate to linear, rigid, spiny-pointed, 1¼–2½ inches long, shining dark green above, not grooved, with broad white bands beneath: cones ovoid, 3–4 inches long, purplish-brown, resinous; bracts exserted, upright, ending in rigid spines 1–2 inches long, giving the cone a bristly appearance. Monterey County, California, at elevations of about 3,000 feet; outside California possibly hardy in the southern states.—*Abies venusta*, K. Koch, Dendrologie, ii, II, 210 (1873); *A. bracteata*, Nuttall, North American Sylva, iii, 137 (1849); *Pinus venusta*, Douglas, in Compan. Bot. Mag. ii, 152 (1836); *P. bracteata*, D. Don in Trans. Linn. Soc. xvii, 442 (1837).

3. **KETELEERIA.** Evergreen monœcious conifers of China and Formosa, probably three or four species, little planted in North America, allied to Abies or the firs and something like them in appearance, differing in the shiny foliage and in technical details such as the clustered rather than single staminate flowers, variable leaves ridged or flattish above and which do not shed when the twig is dried, cone-scales persistent (not shattering): trees with rough irregularly furrowed bark and whorled spreading branches, of regular pyramidal habit while young, in old age with a broad flat-topped head; winter-buds globose or ovoid, not resinous: leaves linear, not grooved above or with a conspicuous rib, with a ridge or rib underneath, pale green below, appearing 2-ranked by twist of the stalk-like base but spirally disposed, leaving a circular scar when detached: staminate flowers arranged in clusters; anthers 2-celled: cones upright and long, with persistent woody scales, maturing the first year, not shedding or falling apart, bracts about half as long as scales and not showing; seeds with wings as long as the scale and 2 to each one; cotyledons 2, remaining underground in germination (hypogœal). The genus (keteleè-ria) bears the name of Jean Baptiste Keteleer, nurseryman born in Belgium in 1813.—*Keteleeria*, Carrière in Rev. Hort., 449 (1866).

The keteleerias are presumably reliably hardy only in the middle or southern and Pacific states. Probably *K. Davidiana* is the hardier of the two here described.

A. Young branchlets orange-red, glabrous: cone-scales suborbicular, slightly
    inflexed at apex..1. *K. Fortunei*
AA. Young branchlets yellowish-gray, puberulous or sometimes glabrous: cone-
    scales ovate, recurved at apex......................................2. *K. Davidiana*

1. **Keteleeria Fortunei.** Attractive pyramidal tree with appearance of a fir, to 100 feet; branchlets glabrous, orange-red: leaves linear, rigid, mucronate or spiny-pointed, obtusish on old trees, flat, with the midrib prominent on both sides, glossy dark green above, paler below, 1–1¼ inches long: cones ovoid or cylindric-ovoid, 3–7 inches long; scales suborbicular, pur-ple while young, later reddish-brown. Southeastern China. It bears the name of Robert Fortune, 1812–1880, noted British collector in China.—*Keteleeria Fortunei,* Carrière in Rev. Hort. 449 (1866); *Abies Fortunei,* Murray in Proc. Hort. Soc. Lond. 421 (1862); *Abietia Fortunei,* Kent in Veitch, Manual of the Coniferæ, ed. 2, 485 (1900); *Pinus Fortunei,* Parlatore in DeCandolle, Prodromus, xvi, II, 430 (1868); *Pseudotsuga jezoensis,* Bertrand in Ann. Sci. Nat., ser. 5, xx, 86 (1874).

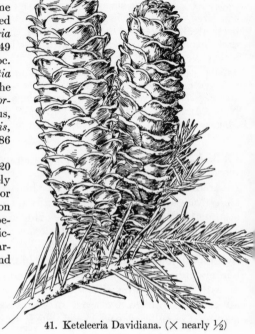

2. **K. Davidiana.** Fig. 41. To 120 feet; young branchlets puberulous, rarely glabrous: leaves linear, rounded or notched at the apex, midrib raised on both sides, glossy green above, paler below, 1–1½ inches long: cones cylindric-oblong, 6–8 inches long, with orbicular-ovate scales, erose at the margin and recurved at the apex. Western China and Formosa, sometimes making forests in rather dry climates. Dedi-cated to Père Armand David, who discovered it in 1869 (see *Pinus Armandi); K. Evelyniana* and *K. for-*

41. Keteleeria Davidiana. (× nearly ½)

mosana are probably synonyms or varieties of *K. Davidiana.*—*Keteleeria Davidiana,* Beissner, Handbuch der Nadelholzkunde, 424 (1891); *Abies sacra,* David, Journ. de Trois Voy. ii, 29 (1875), *nomen nudum; A. Davidiana,* Franchet in Nouv. Arch. Mus. Paris, ser. 2, vii, 98 (1884); *Pseudotsuga Davidiana,* Bertrand ex Carrière in Rev. Hort., 37 (1873). *Keteleeria Evelyniana,* Masters in Gard. Chron., ser. 3, xxxiii, 194 (1903). *Keteleeria formosana,* Hayata in Gard. Chron., ser. 3, xliii, 194 (1908).

4. **PSEUDOTSUGA.** HANGCONE-FIR. Monœcious evergreen trees of western North America and eastern Asia, fir-like in appearance and in foliage (once included in Abies) but differing in the hanging cones with lobed bracts that project beyond the scales, one of them much planted for ornament and interest: tall forest trees with irregularly whorled branches; winter-buds ovoid, acute, not resinous; branchlets nearly smooth, marked with

oval scars after the leaves have fallen: leaves more or less 2-ranked, linear, flattened, green and grooved above, with a stomatiferous white band on each side of the prominent midrib beneath, with only 1 vascular bundle in the center, and with 2 subepidermal resin-canals: staminate flowers axillary, cylindric; female flowers terminal on short branchlets: cones pendent, ovate-oblong, maturing the same season; scales rounded, rigid, persistent; bracts longer than the scales, 2-lobed at the apex with the midrib produced into a rigid awn; each scale with 2 nearly triangular seeds with a wing shorter than the scale (Fig. 42); cotyledons 6–12. Pseudotsuga (pseudotsù-ga) means *false tsuga*, from resemblance to that genus. Species six or seven; the species of China, Japan, and Formosa appear not to be planted in North America. — *Pseudotsuga*, Carrière, Traité Général des Conifères, ed. 2, 256 (1867).

42. Two seeds under the cone-scale of Pseudotsuga Douglasii. Somewhat enlarged.

Pseudotsuga Douglasii. DOUGLAS FIR. Plate XXI. The leading lumber tree of the western region in North America, and in cultivation yielding many forms, hardy and attractive in southern New England, central and western New York and southern Ontario: pyramidal tree attaining 200 feet in height and sometimes more, with a trunk becoming 12 feet in diameter, clothed with ridged dark red-brown bark; branches horizontal, with pendulous branchlets: leaves linear, straight or curved, obtuse, slender and flexible, dark green or bluish-green, $\frac{3}{4}$–$1\frac{1}{4}$ inches long: staminate catkins orange, the fertile ones reddish: cones pendulous, oval-ovoid, 2–$4\frac{1}{2}$ inches long, with broad rounded scales and much exserted bracts; seed $\frac{1}{3}$–$\frac{1}{2}$ inch long, with broad wing, light reddish-brown. British Columbia to California, Montana, Colorado, western Texas, and northern Mexico. Introduced to Great Britain more than a century ago by David Douglas. The hardiness of the Douglas fir depends somewhat on the source of the original seed. Propagated by seeds, and the special varieties by graftage.— *Pseudotsuga Douglasii*, Carrière, Traité Général des Conifères, ed. 2, 256 (1867); *P. Lindleyana*, Carrière in Rev. Hort., 152 (1868); *P. taxifolia*, Britton in Trans. N. Y. Acad. Sci. viii, 74 (1889); *P. mucronata*, Sudworth in Contrib. U. S. Nat. Herb. iii, 266 (1895); *Abies Douglasii*, Lindley in Penny Cyclopædia, i, 32 (1833); *Abietia Douglasii*, Kent in Veitch, Manual of the Coniferæ, ed. 2, 476 (1900); *Picea Douglasii*, Link in Linnaea, xv, 524 (1841); *Pinus taxifolia*, Lambert, A Description of the Genus Pinus, i, 51 (1803), not Salisbury.

Var. **glauca.** ROCKY MOUNTAIN DOUGLAS FIR. Sometimes considered to be a distinct species: of more compact habit; branches more ascending: leaves shorter, bluish-green: cones smaller, with often reflexed bracts. Hardier than the type. In northern Arizona and New Mexico a form of this variety occurs with gray, thick and corky bark (var. *suberosa*). There are other blue Douglas firs than this native form.— *Pseudotsuga Douglasii* var. *glauca*, Mayr, Die Waldungen von Nordamerika, 307 (1890); *P. glauca*, Mayr in Mitteil. Deutsch. Dendrol. Ges., 86 (1902); *P. taxifolia* var. *glauca*, Schneider in Silva-Tarouca, Unsere Freiland-Nadelhölzer, 269 (1913). The earliest incontestable name appears to be *Douglasii* (*Abies Douglasii*) of Lindley, 1833. *Abies mucronata* of Rafinesque in the autumn of 1832 has been supposed to be this tree but the name will remain dubious unless authentic specimens of Rafinesque are found; he describes the cone-scales as rounded and mucronate which they are not in Douglas fir; it is thought he might have confused scales and bracts but we have no warrant to make such assumption for the purpose of stabilizing the name; it may be difficult to apply his name to any other species, but this does not constitute identification; nor do we know what form of Douglas fir could have been intended by his var. *palustris*. Probably *Douglasii* cannot be dislodged from horticultural practice.

Var. **argentea.** Similar to var. *glauca*, with almost silvery-white foliage.—*Pseudotsuga Douglasii argentea*, Koster; *P. taxifolia* var. *argentea*, Sudworth.

Var. **brevibracteata.** Smaller tree: leaves longer and darker: bracts of cone shorter.—*Pseudotsuga Douglasii* var. *brevibracteata*, Hort.; *P. taxifolia* var. *brevibracteata*, Ascherson & Graebner.

Var. **cæsia.** Similar to the type except that the leaves are bluish-green; it seems to be somewhat hardier.—*Pseudotsuga Douglasii cæsia*, Schwerin; *P. taxifolia* var. *cæsia*, Ascherson & Graebner.

Var. **compacta.** A compact conical form with short and dense foliage.—*Pseudotsuga Douglasii compacta*, Carrière; *P. taxifolia* var. *compacta*, Sudworth.

Var. **densa.** Plate XXI. A dwarf flat-topped form with shorter dark green leaves. —*Pseudotsuga taxifolia* var. *densa*, Slavin; *P. taxifolia* forma *densa*, Slavin.

Var. **fastigiata.** Narrow pyramid with ascending branches and shorter leaves.— *Pseudotsuga Douglasii* var. *fastigiata*, Carrière; *P. taxifolia* var. *fastigiata*, Sudworth.

Var. **Fretsii.** Leaves short and broad, about ½ inch long, obtuse at apex. Originated in nurseries of Frets & Son, Holland.—*Pseudotsuga Douglasii Fretsii*, Beissner; *P. taxifolia* var. *Fretsii*, Rehder.

Var. **glauca pendula.** A form of var. *glauca* with pendulous branches and bluish-green or bluish-white foliage.—*Pseudotsuga Douglasii glauca pendula*, Rueppell; *P. taxifolia* var. *glauca pendula*, Schneider.

Var. **glauca pumila.** A bush form of var. *glauca.*—*Pseudotsuga Douglasii pumila*, Beissner; *P. taxifolia* var. *glauca pumila*, Hort.

Var. **globosa.** A dwarf globose form.—*Pseudotsuga Douglasii* var. *globosa*, Lutz; *P. taxifolia* var. *globosa*, Ascherson & Graebner.

Var. **pendula.** With pendulous branches and dark green foliage.—*Pseudotsuga Douglasii* var. *pendula*, Engelmann; *P. taxifolia* var. *pendula*, Sudworth.

Var. **pyramidata.** Of conical habit but partially dwarf, with shorter bright leaves. —*Pseudotsuga taxifolia* var. *pyramidata*, Slavin; *P. taxifolia* forma *pyramidata*, Slavin.

Var. **viridis.** The typical green-leaved form from the coast region; it is of rapid growth and more open habit than the Rocky Mountain form, but tenderer.—*Pseudotsuga Douglasii viridis*, Schwerin; *P. taxifolia* var. *viridis*, Ascherson & Graebner.

P. macrocarpa. BIGCONE SPRUCE. Closely related to *P. taxifolia*: a smaller tree with more remote and usually pendulous branches: leaves acutish, curved, bluish-green: cones 4–6½ inches long, with slightly exserted upright bracts. Southern California. Apparently not yet introduced to cultivation.—*Pseudotsuga macrocarpa*, Mayr, Die Waldungen von Nordamerika, 278 (1890); *P. Douglasii* var. *macrocarpa*, Engelmann in S. Watson, Botany of California, ii, 120 (1880).

P. japonica. Tree to 100 feet tall; branchlets glabrous, pale yellowish-gray: leaves more or less directed forward, often slightly curved, emarginate, ⅗-1 inch long, lustrous bright green above: cones ovoid, 1¾-2 inches long; bracts exserted and reflexed. Japan. At the Arnold Arboretum the species did not prove hardy. —*Pseudotsuga japonica,* Beissner in Mitteil. Deutsch. Dendrol. Ges. v, 62 (1896); *Tsuga japonica,* Shirasawa in Bot. Mag. Tokyo, ix, 86 (1895).

P. sinensis. Related to *P. japonica:* tall tree; branchlets brown, pubescent: leaves to 1¼ inches long, emarginate, more or less pectinately arranged: cones to 2½ inches long, with puberulous scales and upright or reflexed bracts. Western China. At the Arnold Arboretum it did not prove hardy.—*Pseudotsuga sinensis,* Dode in Bull. Soc. Dendr. France, 58 (1912).

43. Dotted lines on spruce leaf; enlarged.

5. PICEA. SPRUCE. Well-known pyramidal or conical monœcious evergreen trees of the habit and aspect of Abies (which see) but the leaves mostly strongly angled or even squared in cross-section and each borne on a little foot (sterigma, plural sterigmata, from Greek meaning a *support* or *prop*) which is a projection from a cushion (pulvinus) that makes an elevation lengthwise the branchlet, disarticulating from the sterigmata when they die leaving the twig rough from the projecting points (Fig. 36b) and shedding when a branch is cut and dried; cones deflexed or hanging (or at least not erect) and not shattering at maturity, about forty species around the earth in the northern hemisphere and most of them planted for ornament and some for forestation. Bark scaly: leaves usually 4-angled, with white lines formed by numerous stomata arranged in rows on all four sides, or compressed and stomatiferous (Fig. 43) only on the upper or ventral side which, on the lateral branchlets, by twisting of the leaf-stalk appears to be the lower one, sessile: flowers catkin-like, terminal or axillary; the staminate yellow or red, consisting of numerous spirally arranged anthers with the connective enlarged at the apex and scale-like; the fertile ones greenish or purple, consisting of spirally arranged scales each subtended at the base by a small bract and bearing 2 ovules at the inner side: cones pendulous or spreading, with persistent scales not separating from the axis after shedding the seeds, which are provided with a large and thin obovate or oblong wing; cotyledons 4-15. Picea is the ancient Latin name of the spruce, derived from *pix,* pitch. — *Picea* (pì-cea or píc-ea), Dietrich, Flora der Gegund um Berlin, 794 (1824).

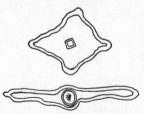

44. Cross-section of spruce leaves, showing the angular above and compressed beneath; enlarged. Diagrammatic.

The spruces occur from the arctic circle to high

mountains of warm-temperate regions. In cultivation they are much more adaptable and easily grown than the firs. They thrive in various kinds of soil and many or most of them withstand smoke and dust. The Norway spruce (*Picea Abies*) is probably the most widely planted of the conifers in North America although not the best species for general ornament.

Piceas are particularly difficult of identification, so closely do they resemble each other even though really distinct. Many of the species are also readily variable under cultivation and natural marks of separation may become obscure.

The spruces are propagated usually from seed, and special kinds or those not seeding are grafted, the stock commonly being the Norway. Good plants are obtainable from cuttings, often better than by grafting, although more time is required.

About a dozen species of Picea from the Far East have been introduced into cultivation in North America within the present century, through the Arnold Arboretum, by the late E. H. Wilson and therefore known as "the Wilson spruces." Mostly they are yet imperfectly known in cultivation and mature characters have not developed. There is confusion among planters in identification of these valuable trees; labels may have been lost or transferred in some cases. It is yet too early to attempt the identification of much of the stock; judgment must be withheld until plants are more mature. The descriptions of these spruces in this volume (from Rehder) are from original sources. The species are *Picea ascendens, asperata, aurantiaca, Balfouriana, heterolepis, Koyamai, montigena, morrisonicola, purpurea, retroflexa, Sargentiana, Watsoniana, Wilsoni.*

KEY to the species of Picea:

§1. The angular-leaved spruces. Leaves in cross-section 4-sided or at least strongly angled or rhombic (not distinctly flat), usually evident when taken between the fingers (Fig. 44); the white-dotted stomatiferous lines (apparent under a lens in bright light) running lengthwise the four sides. The angular character is particularly apparent in dried leaves.
  A. Leaf nearly equally stomatiferous on all four sides; cross-section usually as high as broad or even higher.
    B. Branchlets glabrous (sometimes exceptions in forms of *P. Abies* or Norway spruce, and in No. 4).
      c. Direction of leaves, at least of those of the upper ranks, more or less forward (pointing toward tip of shoot).
        D. Color of branchlets brown or yellowish-brown or reddish.
          E. Cone 4–6 inches long: leaves bright or dark green, often spiny-pointed, usually ½–¾ inch long.
            F. Winter-buds not resinous, the terminal one with a few acuminate, keeled and ciliate scales at base: cone-scales not or slightly emarginate.................. 1. *P. Abies*
          FF. Winter-buds resinous, their scales all obtuse, glabrous, revolute at apex: lower cone-scales deeply emarginate. 2 *P. heterolepis*

EE. Cone 1¼–2½ inches long: leaves usually more or less glaucous, acute or obtusish, usually ⅓–⅗ inches long: bud-scales round and more or less revolute at apex, often emarginate.

    F. Sterigmata erect or somewhat spreading: cone narrowly cylindrical, the scales sometimes minutely denticulate. 3. *P. glauca*

    FF. Sterigmata large and strongly diverging: cone ovate, nearly as broad as long at maturity, the scales entire.. 4. *P. albertiana*

DD. Color of branchlets gray or yellowish to orange.

    E. Disposition of leaves radial, ¾–1¾ inches long: branchlets pendulous: cones 3–6 inches long.

        F. Winter-buds pointed: leaves 1–1¾ inches long, slender, gradually pointed................................ 5. *P. Smithiana*

        FF. Winter-buds obtuse: leaves ¾–1¼ inches long, rather abruptly pointed............................... 6. *P. Schrenkiana*

    EE. Disposition of leaves pectinate below: branchlets not pendulous: winter-buds acute or acutish.

        F. Branchlets pale gray or yellowish.

            G. Length of leaves ½–¾ inch: pulvini (leaf-cushions) produced into a short petiole.................... 7. *P. Watsoniana*

            GG. Length of leaves ⅓–⅗ inch: pulvini scarcely produced into a petiole.......................... 8. *P. Wilsoni*

        FF. Branchlets bright yellow to orange: pulvini produced into a stalk $\frac{1}{24}$ inch long............................. 9. *P. aurantiaca*

CC. Direction of leaves radial or nearly so, spreading at nearly right angles.

    D. Winter-buds very resinous: leaves ⅓–¾ inch long..........10. *P. Maximowiczii*

    DD. Winter-buds slightly or not at all resinous.

        E. Bud-scales firmly appressed or flattened down, dark brown: leaves light green and higher than broad in cross-section.11. *P. polita*

        EE. Bud-scales more or less revolute at apex, light yellowish-brown; leaves usually bluish-green, in cross-section about as high as broad.................................12. *P. pungens*

BB. Branchlets pubescent (No. 4 may also be sought here).

    C. Terminal winter-buds with broad or at least not subulate (awl-like) scales.

        D. Color of branchlets yellowish to grayish.

            E. Length of leaves ¾–1 inch: foliage often glaucous: cone to 3 inches long, the rhombic scales flexible and erose or ragged..13. *P. Engelmanni*

            EE. Length of leaves ¾ inch or less: cone bearing stiff entire obovate scales.

                F. Cone 3–5 inches long: leaves slender, somewhat sharp, straight.......................................14. *P. asperata*

                FF. Cone 3 inches or less long: leaves stout, not sharp, usually curved...................................15. *P. Meyeri*

        DD. Color of branchlets brown: leaves dark green: cone-scales rounded and entire at apex, stiff: cones 2–3 inches long.

            E. The leaves pointed, ⅓–¾ inch long, spreading (see also No. 1, *P. Abies*).

                F. Leading shoot glabrous or nearly so: leaves with more numerous stomata above than beneath.............16. *P. Koyamai*

                FF. Leading shoot and other branchlets pubescent: leaves equally stomatiferous on all four sides..............17. *P. obovata*

            EE. The leaves obtuse, very lustrous, ¼–½ inch long, more or less appressed.......................................18. *P. orientalis* cc. Terminal winter-buds with a ring of conspicuous subulate scales at base: leaves often with fewer stomata beneath than above: cone 1¼–2¼ inches long.

D. Pubescence of branchlets non-glandular....................19. *P. Glehnii*

DD. Pubescence of branchlets glandular.

E. Cones green before maturity, falling soon after maturity, often exceeding 1½ inches long: leaves lustrous green..20. *P. rubens*

EE. Cones persisting for several years, purple before maturity, seldom reaching 1½ inches long: leaves glaucous or bluish-green..21. *P. mariana*

AA. Leaf more or less compressed, in cross-section broader than high, with at least twice as many stomata above as beneath (see also 19, *P. Glehnii*).

B. Stomata about twice as many above as beneath and leaves slightly compressed.

C. Branchlets at least partly glabrous: bud-scales not acuminate.

D. Length of leaves ½–⅗ inch: leading branchlets glabrous or nearly so, the lateral ones glandular-pubescent...........16. *P. Koyamai*

DD. Length of leaves ¾–1 inch: the leading branchlets pubescent, the lateral ones glabrous...............................22. *P. bicolor*

CC. Branchlets pubescent: lower bud-scales long-acuminate and keeled: cone with thin denticulate scales...................23. *P. montigena*

BB. Stomata of leaves of only 1 or 2 usually broken rows beneath: leaves distinctly compressed, with conspicuous bands above: cone with thin denticulate scales.

C. Apex of leaves acute or mucronate: cone brown or slightly purplish, with nearly rounded scales.......................24. *P. Balfouriana*

CC. Apex of leaves obtuse or bluntly mucronate: cone purple, the scales attenuate above the middle and wavy ....25. *P. purpurea*

§2. The flat-leaved spruces. Leaves in cross-section distinctly flattened (Fig. 44 bottom); the white-dotted lines of stomata showing only on upper surface, or at most occasionally only a broken or imperfect row underneath. (By twist of the stalk, the surfaces may be upside down).

A. Direction of leaves not radially spreading, more or less pectinate below: branchlets short, not or slightly pendent.

B. Branchlets glabrous: cone-scales thin, erose-denticulate.

C. Leaf not pungent, though often pointed, ½–¾ inch long.......26. *P. jezoensis*

CC. Leaf pungent, rigid, ⅗–1 inch long..........................27. *P. sitchensis*

BB. Branchlets pubescent or the leading shoots glabrescent: cone-scales stiff, appressed before maturity.

C. Color of branchlets yellow to orange-brown, the leading ones usually glabrous or becoming so with age: winter-buds without subulate scales at base: leaves usually without distinct green midrib above.

D. Leaf acutely pointed, often pungent, to ⅘ inch long........28. *P. complanata*

DD. Leaf obtusish or obtusely mucronulate.

E. Cone-scales broadly cuneate-obovate, rounded at apex: leaves ⅖–¾ inch long, and about 1/16 inch broad.......29. *P. Sargentiana*

EE. Cone-scales rhombic, narrowed toward the truncate and erose apex: leaves about ¾ inch long, and about 1/24 inch broad 30. *P. ascendens*

CC. Color of branchlets brown, all pubescent: terminal winter-buds with subulate scales at base: leaves with distinct green midrib above.31. *P. Omorika*

AA. Direction of leaves more or less radially spreading: branchlets long and pendulous.

B. Branchlets pubescent: leaves obtuse or obtusish, ¾–1 inch long, not keeled...32. *P. Breweriana*

BB. Branchlets glabrous: leaves pungent, 1–1½ inches long, slender, keeled on both sides..33. *P. spinulosa*

1. **Picea Abies.** NORWAY SPRUCE. COMMON SPRUCE of Europe. Plate XXIII. A cosmopolitan tree in cultivation, widely variable in the seed-row and many named kinds in the lists differing in stature, habit, color, and shape of leaves; to 150 feet and more tall, with spreading branches and usually pendulous branchlets; bark reddish-brown; young branches brown, glabrous or pubescent; winter-buds reddish or light brown, without resin, the terminal bud at base with a few acuminate keeled pubescent scales: leaves quadrangular, acute, dark green and usually shining, ½–¾, rarely to 1 inch long: staminate and fertile flowers bright purple: cones cylindric-oblong, 4–7 inches long, light brown; scales rhombic-ovate, emarginate or truncate at apex, with erose-denticulate margin. Middle and northern Europe, east to the Ural Mountains. Early introduced to this country where it is hardy as far north as Saskatchewan. It is extensively planted as an ornamental tree in the northern and eastern states; it is of rapid growth and a handsome tree when young, with its graceful habit and dark green dense foliage, but, like many spruces and firs, loses much of its beauty when it grows old, although particular trees in suitable locations may hold their lower linbs to 75 years or more. It is one of the best conifers to plant for shelters and windbreaks; employed abroad in forestation.

The Norway spruce is commonly known as *Picea excelsa* (Latin *excelsus*, elevated, tall), a name bestowed by Link in 1841. To Linnæus, as we have seen (page 7), all the spruces and firs were included in the genus Pinus and this plant he called *Pinus Abies*, 1753, taking over the name Abies from earlier authors. Under rules of nomenclature the oldest specific name (or species-name) follows a plant into whatever genus it may go; therefore *Picea Abies* regularly becomes the botanical title of this tree, displacing other names.—*Picea Abies*, Karsten, Deutsche Flora: Pharm. Med. Bot. 324 (1881); *P. rubra*, Dietrich, Flora der Gegund um Berlin, ii, 795 (1824); *P. excelsa*, Link in Linnaea, xv, 517 (1841); *Pinus Abies*, Linnæus, Species Plantarum, 1002 (1753); *P. Picea*, DuRoi, Observationes Botanicas, 37 (1771).

The legion forms of *Picea Abies* in cultivation in North America may be grouped into: (a) foliage variables, as *argentea, argenteo-spica, aurea, aurescens, cincinnata, finedonensis;* (b) cone variables, as *chlorocarpa, erythrocarpa;* (c) stature and habit variables. Group c may be further divided into: (1) columnar or tall pyramidal kinds, as *columnaris, cupressina, pyramidata;* (2) globose, depressed or low pyramidal kinds, as *capitata, Clanbrasiliana, compacta, conica, diffusa, dumosa, echinæformis, elegans, Ellwangeriana, Gregoryana, highlandia, humilis, Maxwellii, Merkii, microsperma, mucronata, nana, nidiformis, Ohlendorffii, Parsonsii, parviformis, procumbens, pseudo-Maxwelli pumila, pumila nigra, pygmœa, pyramidalis gracilis, Remontii, repens, tabuliformis, Veitchii;* (3) pendulous or little-branched kinds, as *inversa, monstrosa, pendula, viminalis, virgata;* (4) low irregular more or less monstrous kinds, as *Barryi.*

Var. **argentea.** Leaves variegated with white.—*Picea Abies* var. *argentea*, Rehder; *P. excelsa variegata*, Beissner.

Var. **argenteo-spica.** A form with the tips of young branchlets white.—*Picea Abies* var. *argenteo-spica*, Rehder; *P. excelsa argenteo-spica*, Hesse.

Var. **aurea.** Leaves golden-yellow on the exposed side; does best in partly shaded situation.—*Picea Abies* var. *aurea*, Nash; *P. excelsa aurea*, Carrière.

Var. **aurescens.** Young foliage golden-yellow becoming yellowish-green.—*Picea Abies* var. *aurescens*, Slavin; *P. Abies* forma *aurescens*, Slavin.

Var. **Barryi**. With vigorous thick branches and few short branchlets, dark green. Named for Patrick Barry, nurseryman, 1816–1890.—*Picea Abies* var. *Barryi*, Nash; *P. excelsa Barryi*, Beissner.

Var. **capitata**. Shoots close together at ends of branches, forming heads.—*Picea excelsa* var. *capitata*, Carrière.

Var. **chlorocarpa**. Young cones green: leaves obtusish, more or less appressed; leafing later than the type.—*Picea Abies* var. *chlorocarpa*, Th. Fries; *P. excelsa* var. *chlorocarpa*, Purkyne.

Var. **cincinnata**. Branchlets pendulous: leaves long and comparatively broad, curved upward and spirally twisted: a very peculiar form.—*Picea Abies* var. *cincinnata*, Rehder; *P. excelsa cincinnata*, Hesse.

Var. **Clanbrasiliana**. A compact roundish rather flat-topped bush rarely exceeding 6 to 7 feet, with very short and crowded thin whitish branchlets: leaves nearly radial and pointing forward or pectinate on under side of branchlets, thin, $\frac{1}{8}$–$\frac{3}{8}$ inch long, tapering to a very fine point, lustrous light green. Named for Lord Clanbrasil of Ireland who introduced the plant into cultivation.—*Picea Abies* var. *Clanbrasiliana*, Th. Fries; *P. excelsa Clanbrasiliana*, Carrière; *Abies excelsa Clanbrasiliana*, Loudon.

Var. **columnaris**. With very short horizontal or slightly pendent much ramified branches, forming a narrow column.—*Picea Abies* var. *columnaris*, Rehder; *P. excelsa columnaris*, Carrière.

Var. **compacta**. A subglobose dense form with slender branchlets and acute short leaves.—*Picea Abies* var. *compacta*, Nash; *P. excelsa compacta*, Beissner.

Var. **conica**. Plate XLVII. A dense conical pyramid with ascending branches and very crowded slender light brown branchlets: leaves radially arranged, thin and pointed, light green.—*Picea Abies* var. *conica*, Th. Fries; *P. excelsa conica*, Carrière.

Var. **cupressina**. Tree with ascending densely ramified branches forming a dense broad column.—*Picea Abies* var. *cupressina*, Rehder; *P. excelsa cupressina*, Thomas.

Var. **diffusa**. Dense wide-spreading form with light yellowish-green foliage.—*Picea excelsa* var. *diffusa*, Hornibrook.

Var. **dumosa**. A tufted form with horizontal spreading branches and short leaves far apart.—*Picea Abies* var. *dumosa*, Bailey; *P. excelsa* var. *dumosa*, Carrière.

Var. **echinæformis**. A very dwarf slow-growing form with long prickly leaves, resembling a hedgehog.—*Picea excelsa* var. *echinæformis*, Beissner.

Var. **elegans**. A dense conical form similar to var. *conica*, with short crowded branchlets densely covered with short radially arranged leaves.—*Picea Abies* var. *elegans*, Rehder; *P. excelsa elegans*, Beissner.

Var. **Ellwangeriana**. A pyramidal round bush of somewhat loose habit with stout bright orange branchlets and bright dark green stiff leaves $\frac{3}{4}$ inch long and gradually tapering. Likely to suffer in severe winters. Bears the name of George Ellwanger, nurseryman, 1816–1906.—*Picea Abies* var. *Ellwangeriana*, Rehder; *P. excelsa Ellwangeriana*, Beissner.

Var. **erythrocarpa**. Young cones violet-purple: leaves spreading; leafing early.—*Picea Abies* var. *erythrocarpa*, Rehder; *P. excelsa* var. *erythrocarpa*, Purkyne.

Var. **finedonensis**. Leaves pale yellow at first, becoming bronzy brown and finally green.—*Picea Abies* var. *finedonensis*, Nash; *P. excelsa finedonensis*, Beissner; *Abies excelsa finedonensis*, Gordon.

Var. **Gregoryana.** A very dwarf form, conical or subglobose, rarely exceeding 2 feet in height, with short crowded spreading branches and very crowded thin whitish to grayish-brown branchlets slightly pubescent in the grooves: leaves radially arranged, irregular in direction, ¼–½ inch long, pale gray-green.—*Picea Abies* var. *Gregoryana*, Nash; *P. excelsa Gregoryana*, Beissner; *Abies excelsa Gregoryana*, Gordon.

Var. **highlandia.** Low dome-like form with branches ascending at ends and lustrous dark green foliage.—*Picea Abies* var. *highlandia*, Slavin; *P. Abies* forma *highlandia*, Slavin.

Var. **humilis.** Very dwarf with small dark green leaves.—*Picea excelsa* var. *humilis*, Beissner.

Var. **inversa.** Similar to var. *pendula*, but branches more closely appressed to the stem, more densely branched, with thick lustrous leaves.—*Picea Abies* var. *inversa*, Nash; *P. excelsa inversa*, Beissner; *Abies excelsa inverta*, Gordon.

Var. **Maxwellii.** A low flat dense form, not exceeding 2 feet in height with very short and thick whitish to yellow-brown branchlets and light green radially arranged leaves tapering to a fine hair-like point. Raised at Maxwell Nurseries, Geneva, New York.—*Picea Abies* var. *Maxwellii*, Nash; *P. excelsa Maxwellii*, Beissner.

Var. **Merkii.** A low and dense broad round form growing finally into a broad pyramid; branchlets rather fine, yellowish-white, irregularly arranged: leaves very thin, ½ inch long, tapering to a fine hair-like point, lustrous grass-green, crowded above and pointing forward, pectinate below.—*Picea Abies* var. *Merkii*, Rehder; *P. excelsa* var. *Merkii*, Ohlendorff.

Var. **microsperma.** A dense compact conical or round bush with much-crowded and ascending branches and branchlets; branchlets gray-brown: leaves light bright green, close-set and pointing forward, thick, slightly curved and bluntly pointed, about ½ inch long.—*Picea Abies* var. *microsperma*, Rehder; *P. excelsa* var. *microsperma*, Hornibrook.

Var. **monstrosa.** An extreme form of var. *virgata* and destitute of all branches; it consists only of a single stem clothed with thick rigid leaves.—*Picea Abies* var. *monstrosa*, Rehder; *P. excelsa monstrosa*, Schroeter; *P. excelsa* var. *monocaulis*, Noerdl.; *Abies excelsa monstrosa*, Loudon.

Var. **mucronata.** Strong-growing pyramidal shrub with ascending or sometimes spreading branches and branchlets; branchlets very crowded, stout, bright red-yellow: leaves very crowded, stout, abruptly sharp-pointed, dark lustrous green.—*Picea Abies* var. *mucronata*, Rehder; *P. excelsa mucronata*, Carrière.

Var. **nana.** A depressed-globose or sometimes conical form with very crowded ascending branches and short orange-yellow branchlets, sometimes swollen and monstrous with larger and stouter leaves and large buds: leaves radially arranged, rather distant and nearly appressed, about ½ inch long, stiff, abruptly tapering to a sharp point.—*Picea Abies* var. *nana*, Nash; *P. excelsa nana*, Carrière.

Var. **nidiformis.** Very densely branched form with top like an inverted cone.—*Picea Abies* var. *nidiformis*, Bailey; *P. excelsa* var. *nidiformis*, Beissner.

Var. **nigra.** Densely branched pyramidal form with crowded falcate obtusish dark green leaves; occasionally found wild in central and northern Europe.—*Picea Abies* var. *nigra*, Th. Fries; *P. excelsa* var. *nigra*, Willkomm; *Abies excelsa* var. *nigra*, Loudon.

Var. **Ohlendorffii**. Compact globular form with very stiff branches and pale yellowish-green foliage.—*Picea excelsa* var. *Ohlendorffii*, Spaeth.

Var. **Parsonsii**. Similar to var. *Gregoryana*, but of loose more straggling habit, with spreading branches and pendulous branchlets: leaves thinner and flatter, more distant, pectinately arranged. Named for S. B. Parsons, nurseryman, 1819–1906.—*Picea Abies* var. *Parsonsii*, Rehder; *P. excelsa Gregoriana* forma *Parsonsii*, Hornibrook.

Var. **parviformis**. A broadly pyramidal form with thin regular branchlets and very short thin pungent leaves of bright green color.—*Picea Abies* var. *parviformis*, Rehder; *P. excelsa parviformis*, Beissner; *Abies excelsa parviformis*, Maxwell.

Var. **pendula**. With pendulous branches and branchlets: whorls of branches often irregular.—*Picea Abies* var. *pendula*, Nash; *P. excelsa* var. *pendula*, Jacques & Herincq; *P. excelsa reflexa*, Carrière.

Var. **procumbens**. A prostrate form with horizontal branches and numerous stiff bright yellow branchlets in flat layers: leaves pointing forward, yellow-green, thin and flat, ¼–½ inch long, pointed.—*Picea Abies* var. *procumbens*, Rehder; *P. excelsa procumbens*, Carrière; *P. excelsa* var. *prostrata*, Schneider.

Var. **pseudo-Maxwelli**. Cushion-like form with branches in horizontal layers.—*Picea excelsa* var. *pseudo-Maxwelli*, Hornibrook.

Var. **pumila**. A dwarf depressed-globose densely branched form with red-brown thick and stiff spreading branchlets: leaves thin, short, ⅜ inch long, tapering to a blunt point, lustrous dark green or bluish-green (var. *pumila glauca*).—*Picea Abies* var. *pumila*, Nash; *P. excelsa pumila*, Beissner; *Abies excelsa pumila*, Maxwell.

Var. **pumila nigra**. A form of the above with dark bluish-green leaves.—*Picea Abies* var. *pumila nigra*, Slavin; *P. excelsa pumila nigra*, Beissner.

Var. **pygmæa**. Plate XXVII. A very dense small conical form with crowded and irregular ascending short whitish branchlets and bright or dark green radially spreading short leaves.—*Picea Abies* var. *pygmœa*, Rehder; *P. excelsa pygmœa*, Carrière.

Var. **pyramidalis gracilis**. Dwarf compact nearly globose form with ascending branches and bright green leaves.—*Picea Abies* var. *pyramidalis gracilis*, Slavin; *P. excelsa* var. *pyramidalis gracilis*, Beissner.

Var. **pyramidata**. Branches ascending at a very acute angle, the lower ones very long, decreasing toward the apex, forming a narrow slender pyramid.—*Picea Abies* var. *pyramidata*, Rehder; *P. excelsa pyramidata*, Carrière; *P. excelsa pyramidalis*, Voss; *P. excelsa erecta*, Schroeter.

Var. **Remontii**. An ovoid to globose or conical form of slow growth with crowded light yellow thin branchlets and fine radially spreading light green leaves.—*Picea Abies* var. *Remontii*, Rehder; *P. excelsa Remontii*, Beissner.

Var. **repens**. Low with procumbent or arching branches and crowded leaves.—*Picea excelsa* var. *repens*, Simon-Louis.

Var. **tabuliformis**. A low flat form with horizontally spreading branches and rather distant thin yellow-brown branchlets: leaves pointing slightly up and forward, yellow-green, very thin, ¼–⅓ inch long, blunt.—*Picea Abies* var. *tabuliformis*, Th. Fries; *P. excelsa tabuliformis*, Carrière.

Var. **Veitchii**. Similar to var. *Gregoryana*, but less compact and more conical, with more vigorous branchlets to 1½ inches long and inclined to droop: leaves radial and stiff on the leading shoots, thinner and flatter and more pectinately arranged on the lateral branchlets. Bears the name of Veitch, British nurserymen.—*Picea Abies* var. *Veitchii*, Rehder; *P. excelsa Gregoriana* forma *Veitchii*, Hornibrook.

Var. **viminalis**. Branches in remote whorls, almost horizontal, with very long and slender branchlets without or with very few lateral branchlets.—*Picea Abies* var. *viminalis*, Th. Fries; *P. excelsa* var. *viminalis*, Caspary.

Var. **virgata**. Sparingly branched, with long and slender branches destitute of branchlets, spreading, usually the lower ones pendulous and the upper ones ascending. —*Picea Abies* var. *virgata*, Th. Fries; *P. excelsa* var. *virgata*, Caspary; *P. excelsa Cranstoni*, Carrière.

Forms of doubtful or unknown botanical identity are *acrocompona, brevifolia, erimata, filicoides, micraforma, parviflora, robusta, Sieboldii, Smithii, stricta, tenuifolia*.

2. P. heterolepis. Large spruce distinguished by the emarginate or notched scales toward the base of the cone, tree tending to cone when young; tree to 80 feet tall; branchlets reddish or yellowish-brown, glabrous, with spreading prominent petioles; winter-buds large, ovoid, resinous, light brown, with obtuse scales revolute at apex: leaves quadrangular, stout, often slightly curved, abruptly spiny-pointed, ½–¾ inch long, bluish-green, often glaucescent: cones cylindric, 4–6 inches long, with rigid rhombic-ovate scales, the lower ones deeply emarginate at the apex. Mountains of western China.—*Picea heterolepis*, Rehder & Wilson in Sargent, Plantæ Wilsonianæ, ii, 24 (1914).

3. P. glauca. WHITE SPRUCE. Plate XXIV. Fig. 45, left. A very hardy and frequently planted native spruce usually with bluish-green and sometimes glaucous foliage. open habit of growth with age and main branches then horizontal, branchlets more or less drooping; tree to 60 or 70, rarely to 120 feet tall, with ascending branches and usually pendent branchlets; bark grayish, scaly; branchlets glabrous, grayish- or pale-brown; winter-buds ovoid, obtuse, with glabrous usually loosely imbricated scales, rounded and bifid at the apex: leaves quadrangular, acute or acutish, slightly curved, ⅓–¾ inch long, more or less bluish-green, of strong disagreeable odor when bruised: cones cylindric-oblong, 1½–2 inches long, pale brown and lustrous, green before maturity; scales suborbicular, with rounded entire margin. Labrador to Alaska, south to Montana, Minnesota, and New York. Introduced about 1700 to Europe. Hardy as far north as Labrador and Saskatchewan. An ornamental species of dense habit when young and with rather light

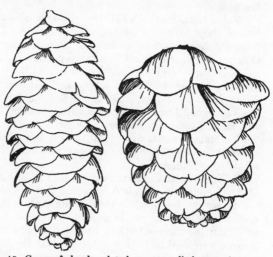

45. Cones of closely related spruces, a little over-size. Picea glauca at left; P. albertiana at right.

bluish-green foliage; it often endures heat and drought better than *P. mariana* and *P. rubens.—Picea glauca*, Voss in Mitteil. Deutsch. Dendrol. Ges. 93 (1907); *P. alba*, Link, Handbuch zur Erkennung der . . . . Gewachse, ii, 478 (1831); *P. laxa*, Sargent in Garden and Forest, ii, 496 (1888); *P. canadensis*, Britton, Sterns & Poggenburg, Preliminary Catalogue. . . of New York City, 71 (1888), not *Abies canadensis*, Miller (*nomen confusum*); *Pinus glauca*, Moench, Verzeichniss ausländischer Bäume and Stauden, 73 (1785); *P. alba*, Aiton, Hortus Kewensis, iii, 371 (1789); *Abies alba*, Michaux, Histoire des Arbres Forestiers de l'Amérique Septentrionale, i, 136 (1810).

Var. **densata**. BLACK HILLS SPRUCE. A very hardy slow-growing tree of compact close habit, making a dense symmetrical or rounded body, the foliage varying from fresh green to bluish-green with 4 glaucous lines, the lower limbs retained even in old subjects: cones cylindrical, 1½– about 2 inches long, like those of *P. glauca*, scales entire. One of the most desirable spruces for severe climates and when compact growth and attractive foliage are desired; grown extensively for many years in nurseries from seeds obtained in the Black Hills of South Dakota. The var. *densata* is here first described, to designate the plant in cultivation.

A very dwarf native form of *P. glauca*, probably not in cultivation, is forma *parva*, Fernald & Weatherby, of Quebec, with a trunk 7 feet or less long and often prostrate, the head very broad, of numerous branches making a close matted top. (Rhodora, xxxiv, 187, 1932).

Var. **aurea**. Foliage golden-yellow.—*Picea glauca* var. *aurea*, Rehder; *P. alba aurea*, Beissner.

Var. **cærulea**. Of dense habit, with light bluish-green or almost silvery-white leaves.—*Picea glauca* var. *cærulea*, Rehder; *P. canadensis cærulea*, Schneider; *P. alba cærulea*, Carrière; *P. alba argentea*, Hort.; *P. alba glauca*, Hort.; *Abies rubra violacea*, Loudon.

Var. **conica**. Plate XXVII. Dwarf very compact hardy form, multiplied by cuttings from a single little tree discovered in Alberta by J. G. Jack in 1904 and sent to the Arnold Arboretum, now to be seen in collections; plant densely narrow-pyramidal, closely foliaged with small thin sharp-pointed radially spreading leaves; an odd distinct-looking subject that has not coned and the botanical position undetermined; it may be a form of the Alberta spruce, and it is sometimes known as *Picea albertiana.—Picea glauca* var. *conica*, Rehder.

Var. **nana**. Dwarf dense form with spreading less crowded leaves.—*Picea glauca* var. *nana*, Rehder; *P. alba nana*, Carrière.

Var. **tabuliformis**. Dwarf flat-topped form with horizontal layered branches and crowded bluish-green foliage.—*Picea glauca* var. *tabuliformis*, Slavin; *P. glauca* forma *tabuliformis*, Slavin.

4. **P. albertiana**. ALBERTA SPRUCE. Fig. 45, right. A slender broad-coned spruce of the Canadian Rockies in Alberta and British Columbia, said to occur also in northern Wyoming, described by the late Stewardson Brown of Philadelphia, not yet well understood; probably not in general cultivation unless *P. glauca* var. *conica* belongs to it, but the name *albertiana* has been applied to the Black Hills spruce which at present is referred to *P. glauca* var. *densata:* the Alberta spruce differs from the white spruce (*glauca*) particularly in the prominent widely spreading sterigmata which sometimes stand at nearly right angles to the shoot, in the shorter broader and darker

colored cones that have rounded scales and minute sharply angled bracts; from the black spruce (*mariana*) in the lighter colored and smooth twigs and longer sterigmata, in the light blue or blue-green leaves, and in broader entire cone-scales and angular-tipped bracts: *P. albertiana* is a tree reaching 50 feet and more; twigs never glaucous, smooth and shining or sometimes slightly glandular, yellowish-brown when young but becoming darker with age; sterigmata prominent and strongly reflexed: leaves pale blue or blue-green, 4-sided, surrounding the stem but crowded toward upper side, incurved, 1 inch or less long, ending in a rigid sharp often very short tip: cones ovate, 1– nearly 1½ inches long and nearly as broad when expanded, falling early; scales rounded and entire.—*Picea albertiana*, S. Brown in Torreya, vii, 126 (1907); *P. canadensis* var. *albertiana*, Rehder in Mitteil. Deutsch. Dendrol. Ges. xxiv, 213 (1915); *P. glauca* var. *albertiana*, Sargent in Bot. Gaz. lxvii, 208 (1919).

5. **P. Smithiana.** HIMALAYAN SPRUCE. Plate XXV. Noble tree with very long incurved dark colored leaves and drooping spray; to 150 feet tall, with wide-spreading branches and slender pendulous branchlets; dark brownish-gray, shallowly fissured; branchlets gray, glabrous and lustrous; winter-buds ovoid, acute, up to ¼ inch long: leaves radially disposed, pointing forward, slender, usually higher than broad, acute, bright or dark green, ¾–2 inches long: fertile flowers purple: cones 5–7 inches long, dark brown and glossy; scales suborbicular, with entire margin, firm. Himalayas: Bhutan to Afghanistan. Dedicated to Sir James E. Smith, 1759–1828, British botanist. Hardy as far as southern Connecticut. A very handsome spruce; young trees are of broad-pyramidal habit with gracefully pendulous branchlets. The young growth starts very early and is sometimes injured by frost in spring, especially when planted in warm and damp situations; hardy in southern Connecticut.—*Picea Smithiana*, Boissier, Flora Orientalis, v, 700 (1884); *Pinus Smithiana*, Wallich, Plantæ Asiaticæ Rariores, iii, 24 (1832); *P. Morinda*, Link in Linnaea, xv, 522 (1841).

6. **P. Schrenkiana.** ASIAN SPRUCE. Large tree much like *P. Smithiana* in habit but with shorter leaves and branchlets less drooping; to 100 feet or more, with pendulous glabrous gray branchlets; winter-buds subglobose, the terminal one with acuminate keeled and pubescent scales at base: leaves radially disposed, equally 4-sided, acute, dull dark green, ¾–1½ inches long, on young plants often slightly shorter: cones cylindric-ovate, 3–4 inches long; scales with entire margin. Central Asia; discovered in Siberia about 1841 by Schrenk. Hardy as far north as Massachusetts. Similar in habit to the preceding species but branchlets little pendulous on younger plants and leaves shorter. A very desirable and hardy spruce.—*Picea Schrenkiana*, Fischer & Meyer in Bull. Acad. Sci. St. Petersb. x, 253 (1842); *P. obovata* var. *Schrenkiana*, Carrière, Traité Général des Conifères, ed. 2, 338 (1867); *P. tianschanica*, Ruprecht in Mem. Acad. Sci. St. Petersb., ser. 7, xiv, 72 (1869).

Var. *glauca* is mentioned.

7. **P. Watsoniana.** WATSON CHINESE SPRUCE. Narrow-pyramidal tree to 60 feet tall, with slender short branches; winter-buds brown, not resinous, with obtuse closely appressed scales; branchlets glabrous, yellow or yellowish-gray, lustrous: leaves pointing forward, quadrangular, slender, ½–¾ inch long and scarcely $\frac{1}{24}$ inch wide, straight, acuminate or acute, dark green: cones cylindric-oblong, 1½–2 inches long, falling soon after maturity; scales obovate, entire, rounded or slightly and abruptly produced into a short point. Mountains of central and western China. Hardy as far

north as Massachusetts and growing well. Remarkable for its very thin and slender leaves. Named in compliment to C. Haines Watson of the Chinese Maritime Customs Service.—*Picea Watsoniana*, Masters in Journ. Linn. Soc., Bot. xxxvii, 419 (1906).

A closely related species is **P. morrisonicola**. Tree to 140 feet tall, with brown scaly bark; winter-buds conic-ovoid, brown, slightly resinous; branchlets dull yellow to reddish, with prominent leaf-stalks: leaves slender, ⅓–¾ inch long, acuminate: cones ovoid-oblong, 2–2½ inches long; scales orbicular-obovate. Mt. Morrison, Formosa. Probably tender.—*Picea morrisonicola*, Hayata in Journ. Coll. Sci. Tokyo, xxv, art. 19, 220 (1908).

8. **P. Wilsoni.** Wilson Chinese Spruce. Pyramidal tree to 80 feet tall, with short spreading branches; branchlets glabrous, pale gray, with scarcely produced petioles; winter-buds ovoid, dark brown and lustrous: leaves quadrangular, stout, straight or curved, pungent, about ½ inch long, dark green: cones cylindric-oblong, 1¾–2½ inches long, persistent for about a year after maturity; scales suborbicular, entire, finally recurved at margin. Mountains of central China. Introduced by the late E. H. Wilson to the Arnold Arboretum and named for him. A handsome spruce of dense habit with short pungent dark green leaves.—*Picea Wilsoni*, Masters in Gard. Chron., ser. 3, xxxiii, 133 (1903).

9. **P. aurantiaca.** Golden Chinese Spruce, from the orange-colored branchlets. Tree to 80 feet tall, spire-like, with short horizontal branches; bark pale gray to nearly white, exfoliating in thin plates; buds conical, resinous, with obtuse scales becoming more or less revolute at apex; branchlets glabrous, orange, often slightly bloomy, with prominent spreading petioles: leaves quadrangular, often curved, sharply pointed, ½–¾ inch long: cones cylindric, 4–5 inches long, with broad rounded slightly erose scales. Western China, in high mountains; hardy in Conn.—*Picea aurantiaca*, Masters in Journ. Linn. Soc., Bot. xxxvii, 420 (1906).

A related species is **P. retroflexa.** A taller tree differing chiefly in the darker bark, brighter yellow lustrous branchlets, longer leaves less sharply pointed, and in the more lustrous sometimes slightly pointed cone-scales. Western China.—*Picea retroflexa*, Masters in Journ. Linn. Soc., Bot. xxxvii, 420 (1906).

10. **P. Maximowiczii.** Japanese

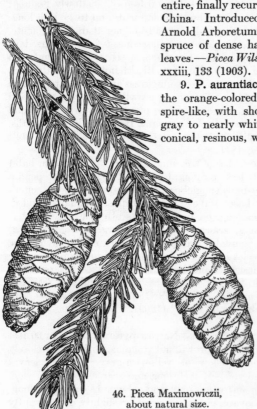

46. Picea Maximowiczii, about natural size.

Bush Spruce. Fig. 46. Known in cultivation as a small or bushy compact tree, of indifferent ornamental value; to 80 feet or occasionally to 120 feet tall, with horizontal branches ascending at the ends; branchlets glabrous, yellowish or reddish-brown; winter-buds small, resinous, with firmly appressed scales: leaves radially spreading, quadrangular, rigid and pungent, ⅓–⅗ inch long, dark green: cones oblong, 1½–2½ inches long, lustrous brown, green before maturity, with rounded entire scales. Japan. It bears the name of C. J. Maximowicz, 1827–1891, distinguished Russian botanist. Hardy as far north as Massachusetts and usually seen in cultivation as a small compact bushy tree. — *Picea Maximowiczii*, Regel, Index Seminum quæ Hortus Botanicus Imperialis Petropolitanus, 33 (1865), *nomen;* Masters in Gard. Chron. xiii, 363 (1880); *P. Tschonoskii*, Mayr, Fremdländische Wald- und Parkbäume für Europa, 339 (1906); *P. excelsa* var. *obovata japonica*, Beissner, Handbuch der Nadelholzkunde, ed. 2, 220 (1909).

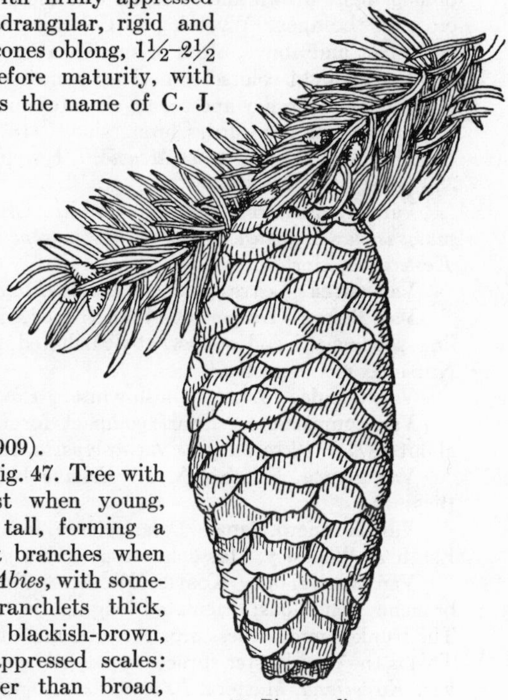

11. **P. polita.** Tigertail Spruce. Fig. 47. Tree with stiff stout brown branchlets, at least when young, starting late in spring; to 90 feet tall, forming a dense broad pyramid, with rigid stout branches when young, older trees with the habit of *P. Abies*, with somewhat pendulous branches; young branchlets thick, glabrous, yellowish-brown; winter-buds blackish-brown, acute, ¼–⅖ inch long, with closely appressed scales: leaves radially spreading, rigid, higher than broad, often falcate, shining dark green, ½–1 inch long: fertile flowers green, staminate yellowish: cones oblong, 4–5 inches long, brown, glossy; scales broad, with finely

47. Picea polita.
(× about ⅖)

denticulate margin. Japan; hardy to southern Ontario and New England. It is one of the most distinct spruces; of very striking appearance with its rigid spiny leaves spreading in all directions from the stout branches, but usually of rather irregular habit; also the conspicuous dark winter-buds are a feature of this species.—*Picea polita*, Carrière, Traité Général des Conifères, 256 (1855); *P. Torano*, Koehne, Deutsche Dendrologie, 22 (1893); *P. Thunbergii*, Ascherson & Graebner, Synopsis der Mitteleuropaischen Flora, ed. 2, i, 300 (1912); *P. bicolor*, Hort.

12. **P. pungens.** Colorado Spruce. Plates I, XX. A well-known large hardy adaptable tree, commonly planted particularly in the blue-leaved variations as Colorado blue spruce which are much prized as small and medium-sized subjects; the typical greener-leaved kind is planted as var. *viridis:* the Colorado spruce is a tree 80–100, or sometimes to 150 feet, with horizontal stout branches in rather remote whorls, forming a broad regular pyramid; winter-buds with brownish-yellow usually reflexed

scales; branchlets glabrous, bright yellowish-brown: leaves more or less radially spreading, quadrangular, rigid, incurved, spiny-acuminate, bluish-green to silvery-white or rarely dull green, $\frac{3}{4}$–1$\frac{1}{5}$ inches long, with 2 resin-ducts: cones cylindric-oblong, light brown and glossy, 2$\frac{1}{2}$–4 inches long; scales rhomboidal, narrowed and erose at the apex. Wyoming to Colorado, Utah, and New Mexico at elevations of 6,500 feet and above, often of small stature. A very handsome tree of symmetrical habit, with light colored sometimes almost silvery-white foliage. Very popular as a lawn tree and for dry and severe climates one of the best of the spruces.—*Picea pungens*, Engelmann in Gard. Chron., xi, 334 (1879); *P. Parryana*, Sargent in Garden and Forest, x, 481 (1897); *Abies Menziesii*, Engelmann in Amer. Journ. Sci., ser. 2, xxxiv, 330 (1862), not Lindley.

Var. **argentea.** Foliage silvery-white. Often known as Koster blue spruce.—*Picea pungens* var. *argentea*, Beissner; *P. pungens* var. *Kosteri*, Beissner; *P. pungens* var. *Kosteriana*, Hort.

Var. **aurea.** Leaves golden-yellow.—*Picea pungens* var. *aurea*, Niemetz.

Var. **Bakeri.** Deeper blue than var. *argentea* and has rather longer needles. Seedling propagated and somewhat distributed, by Ellery Baker, then manager of Hiti Nurseries in Connecticut.

Var. **cærulea.** Leaves bluish-white.—*Picea pungens* var. *cœrulea*, Beissner.

Var. **compacta.** A dwarf compact form, originated at the Arnold Arboretum about 1877.—*Picea pungens* var. *compacta*, Rehder.

Var. **glauca.** Plate XXVI. Foliage bluish-green.—*Picea pungens* var. *glauca*, Beissner.

Var. **Hunnewelliana.** Dwarf dense form. Bears the name of the Hunnewell Estate at Wellesley, Massachusetts.—*Picea pungens* var. *Hunnewelliana*, Hornibrook.

Var. **Kosteriana.** KOSTER WEEPING BLUE SPRUCE. Foliage bluish-white and branches pendulous; originated long ago in the Koster Nurseries, Boskoop, Holland. The trunk is more or less prostrate and must be tied up if a tree-like subject is desired. This is the true Koster spruce, apparently not regularly in the trade.—*Picea pungens* var. *Kosteriana*, Masters; *P. pungens* var. *glauca pendula*, Beissner.

Var. **Moerheimii.** Compact form with blue foliage.—*Picea pungens* var. *Moerheimii*, Rujis.

Var. **viridis.** Leaves green.—*Picea pungens* var. *viridis*, Regel.

13. **P. Engelmanni.** ENGELMANN BLUE SPRUCE. Plate XLIV. Fig. 48. A tall spruce of western North America, known from *P. pungens* by its pubescent branchlets, less spreading and less pungent-pointed leaves, and smaller cones: tree to 150 feet tall, with slender spreading branches in closely arranged whorls, forming a dense and narrow pyramid in young trees; winter-buds with brownish-yellow usually appressed or little spreading scales; branchlets pale brownish-yellow, pubescent: leaves more or less directed forward, slender, straight or slightly incurved, acute, bluish-green to steel-blue, $\frac{1}{2}$–1 inch long, without resin-canals, of a strong aromatic odor when bruised: flowers purple: cones oval- to cylindric-oblong, light brown, 1$\frac{1}{2}$–3 inches long; scales thin and flexible, rhomboidal, narrowed and truncate or rarely acute at the erose-denticulate apex. British Columbia and Alberta to Oregon, Arizona and New Mexico. It bears the name of the distinguished German-American botanist of St. Louis, George Engelmann, 1809–1884. Hardy as far north as Saskatchewan. A

very ornamental tree varying in the color of its foliage.—*Picea Engelmanni*, Engelmann in Trans. St. Louis Acad. Sci. ii, 212 (1863); *P. columbiana*, Lemmon in Garden and Forest, x, 183 (1897); *Abies Engelmanni*, Parry, Trans. St. Louis Acad. Sci. ii, 122 (1863).

Var. **argentea.** Foliage silvery-gray.—*Picea Engelmanni* var. *argentea*, Beissner.

Var. **Fendleri** has pendulous branchlets and longer and slenderer leaves often slightly exceeding 1 inch in length, with 4 rows of stomata on each side above and half as many beneath. Supposed to have come from New Mexico. Named for Augustus Fendler, German-American botanical collector.—*Picea Engelmanni* var. *Fendleri*, Henry.

Var. **glauca.** Foliage bluish or steel-blue. — *Picea Engelmanni* var. *glauca*, Beissner.

14. **P. asperata.** Rapid-growing Chinese spruce with relatively few spreading branches; tree to 100 feet tall, with grayish-brown bark peeling off in thin flakes; branchlets pale yellowish-gray, pubescent, with often spreading or recurved petioles; winter-

48. Picea Engelmanni. ($\times$ ½)

buds conical-ovoid, yellowish-brown: leaves quadrangular, often curved, ⅖–⅗ inch long, acute or acutish and beveled at the apex, dark green: cones cylindric-oblong, 3¼–4 inches long, fawn-gray when ripe, finally changing to chestnut-brown; cone-scales usually rounded and entire at the apex. Mountains of western China; hardy S. Conn.—*Picea asperata*, Masters in Journ. Linn. Soc., Bot. xxxvii, 419 (1906).

Var. **notabilis.** Leaves ½–¾ inch long: cones 3½–5 inches long; scales rhombic-ovate, narrowed toward the apex.—*Picea asperata* var. *notabilis*, Rehder & Wilson in Sargent, Plantæ Wilsonianæ, ii, 23 (1914).

Var. **ponderosa.** Bark thicker, brownish-gray; branchlets nearly glabrous, yellowish: cones 5–6 inches long.—*Picea asperata* var. *ponderosa*, Rehder & Wilson in Sargent, Plantæ Wilsonianæ, ii, 23 (1914).

15. **P. Meyeri.** MEYER CHINESE SPRUCE. Medium-sized tree; branchlets yellowish or light brown, densely pubescent or rarely nearly glabrous, often densely pubescent one year and the continuation of the same branch glabrescent the following year; winter-buds conical, light brown, resinous, the scales at the base of the terminal bud acute and pubescent: leaves quadrangular, obtusish, often curved, ⅓–¾ inch long, bluish-green: cones cylindric-oblong, 2½–3 inches long, lustrous brown, with obovate rounded scales. Northern China, in high altitudes.—*Picea Meyeri*, Rehder & Wilson in Sargent, Plantæ Wilsonianæ, ii, 28 (1914), named by them in compliment to the late F. N. Meyer, agricultural explorer.

16. **P. Koyamai.** KOYAMA SPRUCE. Narrow-pyramidal tree to 60 feet tall; bark grayish-brown, scaly, peeling off in thin flakes; branchlets reddish-brown and slightly

bloomy, the lateral ones glandular-pubescent, the leading shoots nearly glabrous; winter-buds conical, brown, resinous: leaves quadrangular, slightly compressed, straight or curved, acute or obtuse, ⅓–½ inch long, the white bands above each with 5–8 rows of stomata, those beneath with 2–4 rows each and inconspicuous: cones cylindric-oblong, 2–4 inches long, pale brown, pale green before maturity; scales broad, rounded, denticulate, very firm. Japan, "known to grow only on the slopes of Yatsuga-dake, on the borders of Kai and Shinano provinces" (Wilson), where it was discovered in 1911 by Mitsua Koyama; hardy in Conn.—*Picea Koyamai*, Shirasawa in Bot. Mag. Tokyo, xxvii, 127 (1913); *P. koraiensis*, Nakai in Bot. Mag. Tokyo, xxxiii, 195 (1919); *P. Moramomi*, Hort.

17. **P. obovata.** SIBERIAN SPRUCE. Fig. 49. Much like Norway spruce, but slow-growing and more graceful, the branchlets drooping, cones much smaller, known in different forms in Europe but little planted in North America: tree to 100 feet, similar in habit to the following species, with somewhat pendulous branchlets brown when young and minutely pubescent; winter-buds conical with closely appressed scales, the terminal bud at base with acuminate keeled ciliate scales: leaves quadrangular, slightly higher than broad, acute, ½–¾ inch long, dull or bluish-green: female flowers purple: cones oblong-ovoid, 2½–3 inches long, light brown; scales broad and rounded at apex, entire. Northern Europe and northern Asia to Kamchatka and Manchuria; hardy as far north as Canada and probably to Saskatchewan. A smaller tree than the Norway spruce, with which it has been united; grows best in colder and mountainous regions, but is little known in cultivation.—*Picea obovata*, Ledebour, Flora Altaica, iv, 201 (1833); *P. excelsa* var. *obovata*, Blytt, Norges Flora, ii, 391 (1874); *P. Abies* var. *obovata*, Voss in Mitteil. Deutsch. Dendrol. Ges. xvi, 93 (1907).

49. Picea obovata.
Slightly enlarged.

Var. **alpestris.** Slow-growing compact tree; young branchlets densely short-pubescent: leaves obtuse or acutish, ½–⅔ inch long, bluish- or grayish-green: cones 3–5 inches long. Resembles in habit and foliage somewhat *P. glauca*. European Alps at high altitudes.—*Picea obovata* var. *alpestris*, Henry in Elwes & Henry, Trees of Great Britain and Ireland, vi, 1360 (1912); *P. excelsa* var. *alpestris*, Bruegger in Jahresbericht, xvii, 154, fide Beissner, Handbuch der Nadelholzkunde, 357 (1891).

Var. **fennica.** Leaves dark green: cone-scales rounded, finely denticulate. Northern Europe.—*Picea obovata* var. *fennica*, Henry in Elwes & Henry, Trees of Great Britain and Ireland, vi, 1360 (1912); *P. excelsa* var. *medioxima*, Willkomm, Forstliche Flora, ed. 2, 75 (1887); *P. excelsa* var. *fennica*, Schroeter in Vierteljahrsschr. Naturf. Ges. Zurich, xliii, 139 (1898).

18. **P. orientalis.** ORIENTAL SPRUCE. Plate XLVII. Fig. 50. A beautiful tree with dense dark green foliage and compact growth, holding its lower limbs well; to 100 or even to 150 feet tall, with ascending and spreading branches and somewhat pendulous branchlets; bark brown, scaly; branchlets brown, pubescent; winter-buds acute, brown, the terminal bud at base with a few acuminate keeled scales: leaves thick, obtuse, ¼–⅜ inch long, dark green and shining, crowded and more or less appressed to the branches: flowers carmine: cones cylindric-ovate, 2½–3½ inches long, less that 1 inch thick; scales orbicular, entire at the margin. Caucasus, Asia Minor; long in cultivation. Hardy as far north as southern Ontario and New England. A very graceful spruce with dark glossy foliage; of rather slow growth and therefore valuable for smaller gardens. It has a dense closely branched habit.—*Picea orientalis*, Carrière, Traité Général des Conifères, 244 (1855).

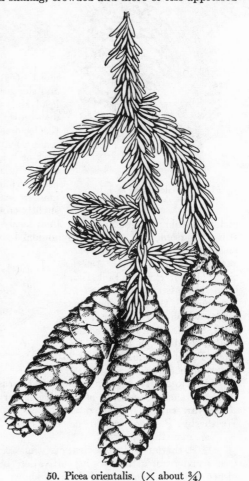

Var. **aurea.** Leaves bronzy-golden. —*Picea orientalis* var. *aurea*, Hesse.

Var. **aureo-spicata.** Young leaves yellow, changing later to green.—*Picea orientalis* var. *aureo-spicata*, Beissner.

Var. **nana.** Low form of broadly pyramidal habit, with wide-spreading branches.—*Picea orientalis* var. *nana*, Carrière; *P. orientalis* var. *compacta*, Hort.

19. **P. Glehnii.** SAGHALIN SPRUCE. Fig. 51. Desirable hardy narrow-pyramidal tree of pleasing aspect; to 120 feet tall, with slender, short and spreading branches; bark red-brown, fissured into thin flakes; branchlets reddish-brown, densely short-pubescent; winter-buds conic-ovoid, chestnut-brown, resinous, the terminal bud at base with subulate scales: leaves quadrangular, slightly compressed, obtuse or on young plants pointed, ¼–½ inch long, deep green, with 2

50. Picea orientalis. (× about ¾)

rows of stomata on each side above and with 1 row on each side beneath: cones cylindric-oblong, 2–3 inches long, lustrous brown, violet before maturity; scales sub-orbicular, rounded or slightly produced in the middle, entire or slightly erose. Japan and Saghalin; named for Glehn, who collected it in 1861. Probably hardy as far north as Canada.—*Picea Glehnii*, Masters in Gard. Chron., ser. 2, xiii, 300 (1880); *Abies Glehnii*, Fr. Schmidt in Reise in Amurlande, etc., 176 (1868) (Mem. Acad. Imp. Sci. St. Petersb., ser. 7, no. 2, 1866).

20. **P. rubens.** RED SPRUCE. Plate XXIV. Attractive native spruce but does not take well to cultivation except in cool and moist situations: tree to 100 feet tall, with short and slender branches forming a narrow pyramidal head and with red-brown bark; branchlets reddish-brown, pubescent; winter-buds ovoid, acute, the terminal bud at base with subulate pubescent scales: leaves quadrangular, acute or mucronate, dark or bright green, shining, about ½ inch long: flowers purple: cones oblong, 1¼–2 inches long, green while young, later light reddish-brown, glossy; scales obovate, rounded and entire or slightly erose at the margin. From Canada to the high mountain peaks of North Carolina; hardy probably as far north as Saskatchewan. It is a handsome tree of narrow-pyramidal habit, but it is less drought-enduring than

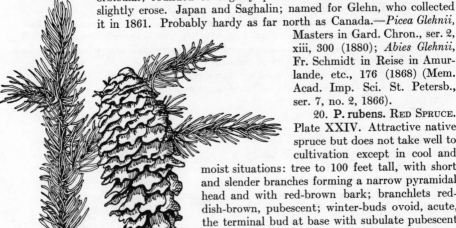

51. Picea Glehnii. (× ⅔)

most other species.—*Picea rubens*, Sargent, Silva of North America, xii, 33 (1898); *P. rubra*, Link, Handbuch zur Erkennung der . . . . Gewächse, ii, 478 (1831), not Dietr. (1824) which is *P. Abies*; *P. australis*, Small, Flora of Southeastern United States, 30 (1903); *Abies rubra*, Poiret in Lamarck, Encyclopédie Méthodique, vi, 520 (1804).

Var. **virgata** is a sparingly branched form with long and slender branches destitute of branchlets, very similar to *P. Abies* var. *virgata*.—*Picea rubens* forma *virgata*, Fernald & Weatherby; *P. rubra* var. *virgata*, Rehder.

Var. **monstrosa** is listed.

21. **P. mariana.** BLACK SPRUCE. Fig. 52. Mostly a small tree, usually not attractive in cultivation being poorly furnished with branchlets and foliage, known from *P. rubens*

52. Picea mariana. (× 1)

by the glaucous or bluish-green leaves and shorter cones; usually to 20–30 or occasionally to 100 feet tall, with slender often pendulous branches forming a narrow irregular head; bark gray-brown; branchlets brown or yellowish-brown, pubescent: leaves quadrangular, often slightly compressed from above, obtusish, dull dark or bluish-green, glaucous especially on the upper side, ¼–¾ inch long, stomatic bands above usually somewhat broader than those beneath: flowers purple: cones oval-oblong, globose-ovoid when open, dark purple while young, later dull grayish-brown, ½–1½ inches long; scales rounded and finely denticulate at the margin. From Labrador to Alaska and south to Wisconsin and Michigan and in the mountains to West Virginia; hardy as far north as Labrador and Saskatchewan. Very variable in habit; when growing in swamps, plants only a few feet high may bear cones; often makes a desirable tree when well cared for.—*Picea mariana*, Britton, Sterns & Poggenburg, Preliminary Catalogue... of New York City, 71 (1888); *P. nigra*, Link, Handbuch zur Erkennung der... Gewächse, ii, 478 (1831); *P. brevifolia*, Peck, Spruces of the Adirondacks, 13 (1897); *Abies mariana*, Miller, Gardeners Dictionary, ed. 8, no. 5 (1768).

53. Picea bicolor. (× 1)

Var. **Beissneriana.** Similar to var. *Doumetii* but somewhat broader at the base with lighter bluish-green foliage. Named for Ludwig Beissner.—*Picea mariana* var. *Beissneriana*, Rehder; *P. nigra mariana*, Beissner.

Var. **Doumetii.** The most ornamental garden form, with ascending crowded branches forming a dense conical pyramid.—*Picea mariana* var. *Doumetii*, Schneider; *P. nigra Doumetii*, Carrière.

Var. **ericoides.** A pyramidal loosely branched bush of slow growth with short finely pointed bluish-green leaves; the leading shoots glabrescent towards the apex.—*Picea mariana* var. *ericoides*, Rehder; *P. ericoides*, Masters.

Var. **fastigiata.** A columnar form with ascending branches and short acute leaves.—*Picea mariana* var. *fastigiata*, Rehder; *P. nigra fastigiata*, Carrière; *Abies nigra pumila*, Knight.

22. **P. bicolor.** IRAMOMI or ALCOCK SPRUCE. Plate XXV. Fig. 53. Pyramidal spruce, the leaves marked by 2 light colored bands on upper side; tree 80–150 feet tall, with rather stiff spreading or ascending branches; bark grayish-brown, fissured into thin plates; young branches dull yellowish-brown, glabrous, usually only leading shoots pubescent; winter-buds conic-ovoid, brown, slightly resinous: leaves quadrangular, slightly compressed from above, somewhat curved, with 2 bluish-white bands above, dark green beneath and with only 2–4 rows of stomata on each side, sharply acuminate, ½–¾ inch long: cones oblong, brown, purple before ripening, 3–4 inches long; scales

obovate, finely denticulate and slightly wavy at the often recurved margin. Japan; hardy as far north as southern Ontario and New England. A handsome tree growing well in the eastern states.—*Picea bicolor*, Mayr, Monographie der Abietineen des Japanischen Reiches, 49 (1890); *P. Alcockiana*, Carrière, Traité Général des Conifères, ed. 2, 343 (1867); *P. Alcockiana nova*, Hort.; *Abies bicolor*, Maximowicz in Bull. Acad. Sci. St. Petersb. x, 488 (1866).

Var. **acicularis**. Leaves curved: cone-scales entire.—*Picea bicolor* var. *acicularis*, Shirasawa.

Var. **reflexa**. Leaves curved: cone-scales nearly entire, recurved at apex.—*Picea bicolor* var. *reflexa*, Shirasawa.

23. **P. montigena**. CANDELABRA CHINESE SPRUCE. Handsomely furnished spruce with branches ascending or upturned at the end; tree to 100 feet tall, with rather long horizontally spreading branches ascending at the ends; branchlets yellow or pale brown, hairy; winter-buds ovoid, acute, resinous, the lower scales of the terminal bud acuminate and keeled: leaves quadrangular, slightly compressed, rhombic in section, obtuse or acutish, curved, obtusely keeled above, ⅓–½ inch long, with 2 white bands above, each with about 5 rows of stomata, those beneath inconspicuous, with 2–3 rows each: cones cylindric-oblong, 3–4 inches long, cinnamon-brown, with rhombic-ovate, thin, erose scales. Western China, in high mountains; hardy in southern Connecticut. —*Picea montigena*, Masters in Gard. Chron., ser. 3, xxxix, 146 (1906).

24. **P. Balfouriana**. BALFOUR CHINESE SPRUCE. Tree to 120 feet tall, with short horizontal branches; bark gray, deeply furrowed into thick irregular plates; branchlets densely villous, yellowish or yellowish-gray, with spreading villous petioles $\frac{1}{24}$ inch long; winter-buds broadly ovoid or conical, brown, slightly resinous, with appressed scales: leaves quadrangular, compressed, straight or slightly curved, acutish or obtuse, ⅓–⅜ inch long, with 2 white bands above, those beneath inconspicuous and with only 1–4 rows of stomata: cones ovoid-oblong, 2½–3½ inches long, violet-purple; scales brownish on back, striate toward the apex, flexible, rhombic-ovate, often contracted below the apex and produced into a point, erose above the middle and usually laciniate and wavy. Western China, at high elevations.—*Picea Balfouriana*, Rehder & Wilson in Sargent, Plantæ Wilsonianæ, ii, 30 (1914), who named this spruce in compliment to F. R. S. Balfour of Scotland, "a lover and enthusiastic planter of trees."

25. **P. purpurea**. PURPLE-CONE CHINESE SPRUCE. Tree to 60 feet tall, with wide-spreading branches; bark dark gray, fissured and separating in thin scales; branchlets orange-yellow, densely pubescent, with short spreading petioles; winter-buds broadly ovoid, resinous, with appressed scales: leaves quadrangular, more or less compressed, curved, obtuse or acutish, with 2 white bands above, green beneath, usually with 2 incomplete rows of stomata, ⅓–½ inch long: cones cylindric-oblong, 2–2½ inches long, purple, more or less so even at maturity; scales rhombic-oblong, contracted, narrowed from about the middle, erose-denticulate, acutish or truncate at the apex. Mountains of western China. The fruiting tree is ornamental with its numerous purple cones.—*Picea purpurea*, Masters in Journ. Linn. Soc., Bot. xxxvii, 418 (1906); *P. likiangensis* var. *purpurea*, Dallimore & Jackson, Handbook of Coniferæ, 334 (1923).

A related species is **P. likiangensis**. Tree to 100 feet tall; branchlets pale yellow, pubescent, with spreading petioles about $\frac{1}{24}$ inch long: leaves acute or mucronate, beneath with 1 or 2 often incomplete rows of stomata on each side: cones cylindric-oblong, about 3½ inches long, with rhombic-ovate thin scales denticulate and nearly rounded at apex. Western China. The related *P. hirtella* is not in cultivation.—*Picea likiangensis*, Pritzel ex Diels in Engler Bot. Jahrb. xxix, 217 (1900).

26. **P. jezoensis.** YEZO SPRUCE. Fig. 54.
Flat-leaved tree of narrow-pyramidal habit and slender branches, 100–150 feet tall or occasionally higher; bark dark gray, scaly, deeply fissured in old trees; branchlets glabrous, shining, yellowish-brown or yellowish-green, the leaf-cushions slightly swollen, with usually recurved petioles; winter-buds conical, resinous, lustrous: leaves compressed, slightly curved, acute, slender, slightly ridged on both sides, dark green and shining below, silvery-white above, ½–¾ inch long: flowers carmine: cones oblong, light brown, 1½–3½ inches long; scales thin and flexible, oval-oblong, erose. Northeastern Asia to northern Japan; named for the island of Yezo (or Yeso), Japan.—*Picea jezoensis*, Carrière, Traité Général des Conifères, 255 (1855); *P. ajanensis*, Fischer ex Trautvetter & C. A. Meyer in Middendorff, Reise in den äussersten Norden und Osten Sibiriens, i, pt. ii, 87 (1856); *Abies jezoensis*, Siebold & Zuccarini, Flora Japonica, ii, 19 (1842).

Var. **hondoensis.** HONDO SPRUCE. To 100 feet; branchlets light reddish-brown with

54. Picea jezoensis. About natural size. Scale margins likely to look more erose at dehiscence.

much swollen leaf-cushions: leaves shorter, more obtuse, dull green below. Central Japan (island of Hondo). It is hardy as far north as Massachusetts and is a handsome ornamental tree of broad-pyramidal habit and bright green dense foliage. The typical form is rarely cultivated and is not doing well in the eastern states; it is of thinner habit and is liable to suffer from late frosts on account of its early leafing.—*Picea jezoensis* var. *hondoensis*, Rehder in Mitteil. Deutsch. Dendrol. Ges. xxiv, 214 (1915); *P. hondoensis*, Mayr, Monographie der Abietineen des Japanischen Reiches, 51 (1890);

P. ajanensis var. *microsperma*, Beissner, Handbuch der Nadelholzkunde, ed. 2, 291 (1909).

A hybrid between *P. jezoensis* and *P. mariana* is **P. Moseri**. Branchlets smooth, olive-brown: leaves quadrangular, acute, ½-¾ inch long, slightly compressed, glaucous above, green beneath. Originated in France some time before 1900 and bears the name of M. Moser of Versailles.—*Picea Moseri*, Masters in Journ. Roy. Hort. Soc. xxvi, 110 (1901).

27. **P. sitchensis.** SITKA or TIDELAND SPRUCE. Very large timber tree, in southern Connecticut doing well if watered in dry times; usually 100, occasionally 200 feet high, with slender horizontal branches, forming a broad pyramid in young trees; in old trees the upper branches short and ascending, the lower ones slender and spreading, clothed with slender branchlets; bark bright or dark red-brown; branchlets rigid, light brownish-yellow, glabrous; winter-buds conical, acutish, light brown, resinous, the terminal bud at base with a few acuminate scales: leaves bright green, shining and rounded on the lower side, flat, slightly ridged and silvery-white on the upper side, sharply acute or acuminate, ½-1 inch long: staminate flowers red: cones cylindric-oval, pale yellowish- or reddish-brown, 2½-4 inches long; scales rounded at the apex and erose; bracts visible between the scales. Alaska to California. In the eastern states it is not generally thriving, as it cannot stand the hot and dry summer. Where it grows well, it is a highly ornamental tree, especially attractive on account of the contrasting colors of its leaves.—*Picea sitchensis*, Carrière, Traité Général des Conifères, 260 (1855); *P. sitkaensis*, Mayr ex Beissner, Handbuch der Nadelholzkunde, 390 (1891); *Abies Menziesii*, Lindley in Penny Cyclopædia, i, 32 (1833); *Pinus sitchensis*, Bongard, Observations .... Végétation .... Sitcha, 46 (1832).

Var. **speciosa** is of slower growth and more compact habit, with more ascending branches and shorter more rigid leaves.—*Picea sitchensis* var. *speciosa*, Beissner.

28. **P. complanata.** Tree to 80 feet tall, with horizontal branches and short pendulous branchlets; bark pale gray, comparatively smooth, on older trees darker and fissured; branchlets orange-brown, pubescent or the leading shoots glabrescent, with swollen pulvini and very short petioles; winter-buds dark brown, ovoid, acutish: leaves compressed, abruptly acuminate and often pungent, ½-⅘ inch long, with broad white bands above, green and keeled beneath: cones cylindric-oblong, 5-6½ inches long, with broad, rounded or truncate scales; bracts long-acuminate. Mountains of western China.—*Picea complanata*, Masters in Gard. Chron., ser. 3, xxxix, 146 (1906).

29. **P. Sargentiana.** SARGENT CHINESE SPRUCE. Tree to 75 feet tall, with spreading slightly pendent branches; bark grayish-brown, fissured into irregular plates; branchlets at maturity orange to pale yellow, the weaker ones more or less stipitate-glandular, the stronger shoot usually glabrous, with short slightly recurved petioles; winter-buds conspicuous, dark brown, conic-ovoid, acutish to obtusish: leaves compressed, curved, acutish or obtuse, ⅖-⅗ inch long and about ¹⁄₁₆ inch broad, with 2 broad white bands above, green and lustrous beneath, keeled on both sides: cones oblong-cylindric, 2½-5 inches long, often persisting one year after maturity; scales firm, broadly cuneate-obovate, rounded or truncate at apex, spreading at maturity; bracts minute, rounded at apex. Western China, in mountains.—*Picea Sargentiana*, Rehder & Wilson in Sargent, Plantæ Wilsonianæ, ii, 35 (1914); bears the name of Charles Sprague Sargent, 1841-1927, Director of the Arnold Arboretum.

30. **P. ascendens.** Pyramidal tree to 80 feet tall, with horizontally spreading branches upturned at the ends and with slender pendent branchlets; branchlets pale brown, setosely hairy or the stronger shoots glabrous or glabrescent; winter-buds dark brown, ovoid or obtusish: leaves compressed, acutish or obtusely mucronulate, ½–¾ inch long, with 2 broad white bands above, green and keeled beneath: cones cylindric-oblong, 3–4 inches long; scales rhombic, narrowed toward the truncate or emarginate erose apex; bracts linear-oblong, obtuse, 4–5 times shorter than scale. Mountains of western China.—*Picea ascendens*, Patschke in Engler Bot. Jahrb. xlviii, 632 (1913); *P. brachytyla* f. *rhombisquama*, Stapf in Bot. Mag. t. 8969 (1922).

A closely related species is **P. brachytyla.** Tree to 80 feet tall; bark dark brown, deeply fissured; branchlets nearly glabrous, with prominent pulvini: leaves about ½ inch long: cones 3–4 inches long, with obovate scales entire at the margin. Central China.—*Picea brachytyla*, Pritzel ex Diels in Engler Bot. Jahrb. xxix, 216 (1900); *P. pachyclada*, Patschke in Engler Bot. Jahrb. xlviii, 630 (1913).

31. **P. Omorika.** SERBIAN SPRUCE. One of the best of the large hardy spruces for ornament: to 100 feet or higher, with rather short spreading and ascending branches and short pendent branchlets forming a narrow pyramidal head; bark brown, separating into thin plates; branchlets brown, pubescent; winter-buds dark brown, not resinous: leaves compressed, obtuse and mucronulate, dark green and shining below, with whitish bands above, ⅓–½ inch long, keeled on both sides: flowers purple: cones ovoid-oblong, cinnamon-brown, glossy, 1½–2½ inches long; scales almost orbicular, very convex, with finely denticulate margin. Southeastern Europe; Omorika is the vernacular. If protected in windy places hardy as far north as southern Ontario and New England and possibly farther north. A desirable ornamental tree of dense narrow-pyramidal habit when young; one of the best spruces for the northeastern states.—*Picea Omorika*, Purkyne in Oester. Monatschr. Forstwesen, xxvii, 446 (1877); *Pinus Omorika*, Pancic, Eine Neue Conifere in den Östlichen Alpen, 4 (1876); *Abies Omorika*, Nyman, Conspectus Floræ Europæa, 673 (1881).

Var. *pendula* is listed.

32. **P. Breweriana.** WEEPING or BREWER SPRUCE. Handsome and striking tree in its native places but indifferently adapted to cultivation in the East, 80–120 feet high, with the branches at the top slightly ascending, the lower ones horizontal or pendulous, with whip-like pendulous branchlets often 7 to 8 feet long, furnished with similar slender lateral branchlets; branchlets reddish-brown, pubescent; winter-buds conical, chestnut-brown: leaves radially spreading, straight or slightly curved, obtuse, rounded and dark green at the lower surface, almost flat and with white bands above, ¾–1 inch long: staminate flowers purple: cones oblong, 2½–5 inches long, light orange-brown; scales obovate, with entire margin. Siskiyou Mountains of southern Oregon and northern California. Named in compliment to Professor W. H. Brewer, 1828–1910, collector in California, professor at Yale. Hardy in sheltered positions as far north as Massachusetts; it does not seem to take kindly to cultivation and only a few rather small trees are known to exist in Europe and in the eastern states. In its native habitat it is a handsome tree remarkable for its pendulous whip-like branches. —*Picea Breweriana*, S. Watson in Proc. Amer. Acad. xx, 378 (1885). Probably *Picea pendula* is the oldest binomial for this spruce: Watson, Botany of California, ii, 122 (1880); see also Sargent, Silva, xii, 52, note.

33. **P. spinulosa.** SIKKIM SPRUCE. Tree to 150 feet tall, with spreading branches and slender pendulous branchlets; branchlets glabrous, yellowish-gray; winter-buds ovoid, obtuse, scarcely resinous: leaves imperfectly radially arranged, slightly compressed, slender, straight or slightly curved, acute and pungent, ¾–1½ inches long, with 2 glaucous bands above, green beneath, keeled on both sides: cones cylindric-oblong, 2½–4 inches long, with suborbicular scales, entire or slightly denticulate and undulate at the margin. Himalayas: Bhutan and Sikkim. Little known in this country and probably not hardy north of the Middle Atlantic states; at the Arnold Arboretum young plants did not survive the first winter. A distinct and graceful spruce somewhat similar in habit to *P. Smithiana*, but slenderer and thinner.—*Picea spinulosa*, Henry in Gard. Chron., ser. 3, xxxix, 219 (1906); *P. morindoides*, Rehder in Sargent, Trees and Shrubs, i, 95 (1903); *Abies spinulosa*, Griffith, Journals, 259 (1847).

6. **TSUGA.** HEMLOCK. HEMLOCK SPRUCE. Attractive evergreen monœcious trees, yielding timber and prized also as ornamentals, fourteen species now recognized and many horticultural varieties, native in temperate regions of North America, and the eastern Himalayas to Japan; trees with slender horizontal branches and cinnamon-red furrowed bark; winter-buds minute, not resinous: leaves usually 2-ranked, short-petioled, linear, flat or angular, falling away in drying: staminate flowers axillary, subglobose; ovule-bearing flowers terminal, the scales about as long as the bracts, each with 2 ovules at the base: cones small, ovate or oblong with thin flexible persistent scales, much longer than the bracts; seeds winged; cotyledons 3–6. Tsuga (tsù-ga) is the Japanese name of the genus.—*Tsuga*, Carrière, Traité Général des Conifères, 185 (1855).

The genus is closely allied to Abies and Picea and differs little in the structure of the flowers; the cones are very similar to those of the larch, but the leaves, which are much like those of Abies in their outward appearance, though smaller, are very different in their internal structure from all allied genera, having a solitary resin-duct situated in the middle of the leaf below the fibro-vascular bundle. The hemlocks have a graceful slender spray and small mostly 2-ranked leaves very unlike the firs and spruces in appearance; the small hanging cones are neat and attractive. At first the hemlocks were included in Pinus and then in Abies and Picea; it was not until 1855 that they were separated as a genus by themselves. Only a few of the species are in general cultivation, but others known only infrequently are here included. The hemlocks are raised from seeds, and the horticultural varieties are grafted on *T. canadensis*.

KEY to the species of Tsuga:

I. The true hemlocks: leaves 2-ranked and each bearing 2 white lines underneath, flattened and with a groove above: cones less than 2 inches long.
   A. Margins of leaves with small teeth, at least toward apex (well seen toward the light with hand-lens, on young leaves particularly), the apex either obtuse or acutish.

   B. Leaves tapering gradually from base to apex, the bands underneath
     well defined.
     c. Cones peduncled, with glabrous almost orbicular scales: leaves
       ⅔ inch or less long......................................1. *T. canadensis*
     cc. Cones sessile, with nearly or quite glabrous scales: leaves often
       longer, 1 inch or more.................................3. *T. dumosa*
  BB. Leaves uniform in width from base to near the apex, the bands not
     clearly defined and much broader than green margin............4. *T. heterophylla*
 AA. Margins of leaves entire, the apex usually emarginate or distinctly obtuse.
   B. Branchlets glabrous, grayish- or yellowish-brown.................5. *T. Sieboldii*
  BB. Branchlets pubescent or hairy, often reddish.
     c. Apex of leaf distinctly emarginate (some leaves perhaps different
      in No. 6); white bands mostly indistinct underneath or not con-
      spicuous or narrow.
       D. Pubescence on all sides of branchlets......................6. *T. diversifolia*
       DD. Pubescence chiefly in the grooves of branchlets: leaves to 1 inch
        long..7. *T. chinensis*
     cc. Apex of leaf obtuse, not emarginate or only indistinctly so: under
      surface with conspicuous white bands......................2. *T. caroliniana*
II. The Hesperpeuce section: leaves spirally arranged, rather stiff, entire, with
  white or stomatiferous lines on both surfaces, flat or convex above: cones
  2 inches or more long...8. *T. Mertensiana*

1. **Tsuga canadensis.** COMMON or CANADA HEMLOCK. Fig. 55. Large timber and
tanbark tree, often attaining great size and originally making extensive forests in
northeastern America; sometimes 100 feet in height and 4 feet in diameter, but commonly smaller; winter-buds obtuse, slightly puberulous; young branchlets yellowish-

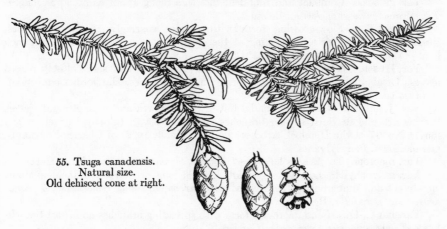

55. Tsuga canadensis.
Natural size.
Old dehisced cone at right.

brown, pubescent: leaves linear, obtuse or acutish, dark green and obscurely grooved
above, with 2 whitish bands beneath, ¼–⅔ inch long: cones ovoid, ½–¾ inch long,
peduncled; scales orbicular-obovate, almost as wide as long. Nova Scotia to Minnesota
and south along the mountains to Alabama; for the most part now seen in isolated
groves or mixed with other trees in woods, and in rocky neglected areas, and about old
pastures and fields.—*Tsuga canadensis*, Carrière, Traité Général des Conifères, 189

(1855); *T. americana*, Farwell in Bull. Torr. Bot. Club, xli, 629 (1915); *Abies canadensis*, Michaux, Flora Boreali-Americana, ii, 206 (1803).

No botanical varieties of *Tsuga canadensis* are recognized in nature. Trees are various, however, particularly when young, and many of the forms have been collected and transferred to gardens under names; seedlings in the nursery-row may be diverse. Any number of varieties may thus be added to the lists, being multiplied by graftage, since the hemlock is prized in cultivation for its color, form and gracefulness. Sometimes planted for hedges.

Var. **albo-spica.** Tips of the young branchlets creamy-white.—*Tsuga canadensis* var. *albo-spica*, Beissner; *T. canadensis* var. *argentea*, Hort.

Var. **atrovirens.** Foliage very dark green.—*Tsuga canadensis* var. *atrovirens*, Hort.

Var. **aurea.** Foliage tinged yellow.—*Tsuga canadensis* var. *aurea*, Hort.

Var. **compacta.** Dwarf conical pyramid with numerous short branchlets clothed with small leaves.—*Tsuga canadensis* var. *compacta*, Sénéclauze; *T. canadensis* var. *compacta nana*, Beissner.

Var. **Dawsoniana.** Slow-growing compact form with dark green foliage. Originated at the Hunnewell Estate in Wellesley and named for the late Jackson Dawson by the late T. D. Hatfield ("*Dawsoniana-Hunnewelliana*").

Var. **fastigiata.** Narrow or columnar.—*Tsuga canadensis* var. *fastigiata*, Hort.

Var. **Fremdii.** Of pyramidal habit, slow-growing, with dark green foliage.—*Tsuga canadensis* var. *Fremdii*, Koster. It was found at Rye, New York, in 1887 by Mr. Fremd, and propagated in Holland.

Var. **globosa.** Compact and rounded, the head being about as broad as long.—*Tsuga canadensis* var. *globosa*, Beissner.

Var. **gracilis.** Slow-growing form with slender sparingly ramified branches, spreading and more or less drooping at the ends: leaves very small, about ¼ inch long.—*Tsuga canadensis* var. *gracilis*, Carrière.

Var. **Hussii.** Very dwarf with short twiggy branches and short closely placed leaves. Originated with Mr. Huss, Superintendent of Parks, Hartford, Connecticut. —*Tsuga canadensis* var. *Hussii*, Hort.

Var. **Jenkinsii.** Narrow-pyramidal but of open growth and with straight leader, bearing graceful declined slender branches and short leaves (mostly ⅜ inch or less long). No. 17 of the Hemlock Arboretum (Bull. No. 1, 1932) of Charles F. Jenkins, Germantown, Pennsylvania.

Var. **macrophylla.** Leaves larger.—*Tsuga canadensis* var. *macrophylla*, Hort.

Var. **microphylla.** Leaves very small, ¼ inch long or shorter: branchlets stout, closely set and numerous.—*Tsuga canadensis* var. *microphylla*, Sénéclauze; *T. canadensis* var. *parvifolia*, Beissner.

Var. **nana.** Dwarf and depressed form with spreading branches and short branchlets.—*Tsuga canadensis* var. *nana*, Carrière.

Var. **parvifolia.** Bushy with short branches: leaves small, about ¼ inch long: English variety.—*Tsuga canadensis* var. *parvifolia*, Smith.

Var. **pendula.** WEEPING or SARGENT WEEPING HEMLOCK. Plates XXIX, XLI. Low more or less flat-topped form with spreading framework and drooping branchlets. —*Tsuga canadensis* var. *pendula*, Beissner; *T. canadensis* var. *Sargentiana*, Kent; *T. canadensis* var. *Sargenti pendula*, Hort. There may be more than one weeping hemlock to which the name *pendula* may apply. The cited plates show a relatively young and old plant known as Sargent weeping: tall specimens may be natural developments with age or the result of top-grafting; see Charles S. Sargent in Garden & Forest, x, 490 (1897) where it is said that the plant then usually called Sargent's hemlock "was found about forty years ago on the Fishkill Mountains, in New York, and was first cultivated and made known by Mr. H. W. Sargent," who was a well-known lover and planter of trees.

2. **T. caroliniana.** CAROLINA HEMLOCK. Fig. 56. Attractive tree, not attaining as great size as *T. canadensis*, of more compact habit and darker foliage, entire leaves and longer cones, much prized as an ornamental, being hardy North; to 70 feet; winter-buds obtuse, pubescent; young branchlets light reddish-brown, finely pubescent or almost glabrous: leaves linear, obtuse or slightly emarginate, dark green and glossy above, with white bands beneath, ⅓–¾ inch long: cones oblong, 1–1½ inches long, peduncled; scales oblong. Mountains of southwestern Virginia to northern Georgia. Generally hardy in New England and a very desirable tree. —*Tsuga caroliniana*, Engelmann in Coult. Bot. Gaz. vi, 223 (1881); *Abies caroliniana*, Chapman, Flora of the Southern United States, ed. 2, 650 (1883).

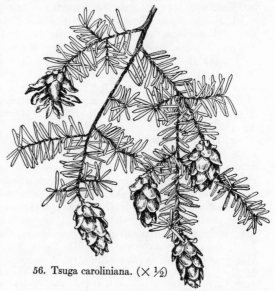

56. Tsuga caroliniana. (× ½)

Var. **compacta** is a denser round-topped form.—*Tsuga caroliniana* var. *compacta*, Hornibrook.

3. **T. dumosa.** HIMALAYAN HEMLOCK. Great tree to 120 feet and diameter of 8–9 feet, introduced in this country but perhaps not now surviving; branchlets light brown and pubescent, of drooping habit; winter-buds globose and flattened at top, pubescent: leaves to 1¼ inches long, narrow, tapering to an acute and somewhat recurved apex, the bands underneath broad and leaving little green margin: cones ovoid, to 1 inch long, with rounded glossy scales. Himalayas, at high elevations.— *Tsuga dumosa*, Sargent, Silva of North America, xii, 60 (1898); *T. Brunoniana*, Carrière, Traité Général des Conifères, 188 (1855); *Pinus dumosa*, D. Don, Prodromus Floræ Nepalensis, 55 (1825).

4. **T. heterophylla.** WESTERN HEMLOCK. Tree attaining 200 feet in height, with short slender usually pendulous branches forming a rather narrow pyramidal head in older, but rather broad in young trees; winter-buds ovoid, obtuse; young branchlets pale yellowish-brown, pubescent for five or six years and with long pale hairs while young: leaves linear, obtuse or acutish, distinctly grooved and dark green above, with

white bands below, ½–¾ inch long: cones oblong-ovoid, sessile, ¾–1 inch long; scales oval, slightly puberulous outside. Alaska to Idaho and California. Introduced to Great Britain in 1851. A handsome tree of rapid growth in rich humid soil, but not doing well in the dry climate of the eastern states and not hardy north of New York. —*Tsuga heterophylla*, Sargent, Silva of North America, xii, 73 (1898); *T. Mertensiana*, Carrière, Traité Général des Conifères, ed. 2, 250 (1867); *T. albertiana*, Sénéclauze, Conif. 18 (1867); *Abies heterophylla*, Rafinesque, Atlant. Journ. i, 119 (1832).

5. **T. Sieboldii.** SOUTHERN JAPANESE or SIEBOLD HEMLOCK. Tree attaining 100 feet, with spreading slender branches; winter-buds ovoid, acutish, with glabrous ciliate scales; branchlets pale yellowish-brown, somewhat glossy, glabrous, with reddish leaf-cushions: leaves linear, usually broadest at the apex, emarginate, grooved and glossy dark green above, with narrow white bands beneath, ¼–¾ inch long: cones ovoid, 1–1¼ inches long, the peduncle exceeding the bud-scales; scales orbicular; bracts bifid. Japan. Hardy as far north as Massachusetts in sheltered positions. This tree bears the name of the German botanist, Philipp Franz von Siebold, 1796–1866, well-known early authority on Japanese plants.—*Tsuga Sieboldii*, Carrière, Traité Général des Conifères, 186 (1855); *T. Araragi*, Koehne, Deutsche Dendrologie, 10 (1893).

6. **T. diversifolia.** NORTHERN JAPANESE HEMLOCK. Plate XXVIII. Much like *T. Sieboldii* but differing according to Wilson (Conifers and Taxads of Japan) in the branching, especially in young trees, more dense and intricate, leaves shorter and crowded on twigs and less lustrous, cone smaller and its peduncle less apparent; old trees sometimes difficult to distinguish; winter-buds obovoid, flattened, minutely pubescent and ciliate: leaves linear, emarginate or obtuse, shorter and narrower, broadest at the middle or toward the base, ⅕–⅗ inch long: cones smaller, ½–¾ inch long; peduncle not exceeding the bud-scales; bracts truncate, crenulate, not or slightly bifid; cone-scales orbicular-ovate, lustrous, with slightly beveled margin. Japan. Hardy as far north as Massachusetts. A graceful and handsome species growing well in the eastern states.—*Tsuga diversifolia*, Masters in Journ. Linn. Soc. xviii, 514 (1881); *T. Sieboldii* var. *nana*, Carrière, Traité Général des Conifères, 186 (1855); *Abies diversifolia*, Maximowicz in Bull. Acad. Sci. St. Petersb. xii, 229 (1868).

7. **T. chinensis.** CHINESE HEMLOCK. Handsome hemlock yet little known in North America but promising well, being hardy in sheltered places as far north as Massachusetts; tree to 150 feet tall; winter-buds ovoid, obtuse, glabrous; branchlets yellowish, later pale yellowish-gray, hairy only in the grooves: leaves linear, emarginate, ½–1 inch long, lustrous dark green above, beneath with broad whitish bands becoming inconspicuous: cones ovoid, ⅗–1 inch long; scales suborbicular, lustrous, yellowish-brown, with slightly beveled margin. Western China.—*Tsuga chinensis*, Pritzel in Engler Bot. Jahrb. xxix, 217 (1900).

The closely related **T. yunnanensis,** YUNNAN HEMLOCK, differs in the more densely pubescent branchlets, shorter and narrower, obtuse, not emarginate leaves always very white beneath and in the dull cones with fewer scales slightly recurved at the apex. Western China. Tenderer than the preceding species.—*Tsuga yunnanensis*, Masters in Gard. Chron., ser. 3, xxxix, 236 (1906).

8. **T. Mertensiana.** MOUNTAIN HEMLOCK. Unlike the other hemlocks in foliage and cones; the name has been applied to *T. heterophylla* and the two species may there-

fore be confused in gardens although very distinct: tree attaining 100 and occasionally 150 feet, with slender pendent branches usually forming an open pyramid; winter-buds ovoid, acute; young branchlets light reddish-brown, pubescent, usually short and upright: leaves spirally arranged around the branches, linear, usually curved, acutish, mostly rounded or keeled, rarely slightly grooved above, light bluish-green or pale bluish-white, with whitish lines on both sides, ½–1 inch long: cones cylindric-oblong, usually violet-purple before maturity, brown when ripe, 2–3 inches long; scales obovate, puberulous outside. Southern Alaska to northern Montana, Idaho, and California. Hardy in sheltered positions as far north as Massachusetts, rarely culti-vated in the eastern states. Named for Karl Heinrich Mertens (1795–1830), physician and naturalist.—*Tsuga Mertensiana*, Sargent, Silva of North America, xii, 77 (1898); *T. Hookeriana*, Carrière, Traité Général des Conifères, ed. 2, 252 (1867); *T. Pattoniana*, Sénéclauze, Conif. 21 (1867); *T. Roezlii*, Carrière in Rev. Hort. 217 (1870); *Abies Williamsii*, Newberry in Pacific Railroad Rept. vi, 53 (1857); *Hesperopeuce Pattoni-ana*, Lemmon in Rept. Calif. State Bd. For. iii, 126 (1890); *Pinus Mertensiana*, Bongard, Flora Sitcha, 54 (1832).

Var. **argentea** has bluish-white foliage.—*Tsuga Mertensiana* var. *argentea*, Sud-worth.

Var. *glauca* is listed.

A supposed hybrid of this and the preceding species is **T. Jeffreyi**. Buds ovoid, acute: leaves radially spreading and directed outward, green and grooved above with a few broken lines of stomata near apex, finely serrulate. Originated from seed of *T. Mertensiana* introduced in 1851 by Jeffrey.—*Tsuga Jeffreyi*, Henry in Henry & Flood in Proc. Irish Acad. xxxv, B 55 (1919); *T. Mertensiana* var. *Jeffreyi*, Schneider in Silva-Tarouca, Unsere Freiland-Nadelhölzer, 294 (1913).

CHAPTER V

THE TRUE CONE-BEARERS—CEDARS, LARCHES, CYPRESSES, AND OTHERS

STILL to be treated are about two dozen genera of various relationships, and many of them of minor importance in horticulture and of few species, keyed in this book for easy recognition. The botanical relationships of these groups run as follows in their subfamilies: Cedrus, Larix, Pseudolarix, remainders of the Abietineæ; then Taxodineæ with Taxodium, Glyptostrobus, Sequoia, Cryptomeria, Cunninghamia, Athrotaxis, Taiwania, Sciadopitys; Araucarineæ comprising Araucaria and Agathis; and Cupressineæ with Cupressus, Chamæcyparis, Thuja, Thujopsis, Libocedrus, Callitris, Actinostrobus, Widdringtonia, Tetraclinis, Fitzroya. See key on pages 38 and 39.

Number of genus, and page:

7. CEDRUS. CEDAR. Four very similar evergreen monœcious or diœcious trees in the Mediterranean region and western Himalayas, perhaps to be regarded as geographical forms of a single species: trees of striking appearance in age, with branches horizontally spreading and irregular and massive trunks; bark smooth on young stems and gray, but becoming thick and fissured: leaves angular and stiffish, single and alternate on young shoots but clustered or fascicled on spurs on the older shoots something as in larches (to which the genus is related), mostly falling when the twig is dried: flowers appearing in middle or late summer; staminate flowers terminal on spurs forming stiff upright cylindrical catkins about 2 inches long; pistillate flowers making greenish or purplish catkins about ½ inch long composed of many nearly orbicular 2-ovuled scales subtended by little bracts: cones erect, ovoid to ovoid-oblong and blunt or rounded or even concave at apex, 3–5 inches long, closely packed with very broad thin imbricate scales that usually fall apart soon after maturity, ripening second or third year, resinous; seeds angular, with large thin wings; cotyledons 8–10. Cedrus (ced′-rus or cè-drus), Latinized from *kedros*, a name employed in ancient Greek for resinous trees, chiefly juniper.—*Cedrus*, Link, Handbuch zur Erkennung der. . . . Gewächse, ii, 479 (1831).

The cedars are not permanently reliably hardy in the northeastern states as far north as New York and New England, although there are isolated examples of trees that have reached maturity in favored locations, and young trees may stand several years in sheltered places; probably the source of the seed from which the trees are grown may be an important factor in hardiness. In the southern states and on the Pacific side the cedars are valuable, either as single specimens or on broad avenues. They are ornamental in their young and middle stages, and picturesque in age. Propagation is by seeds, and named forms are grafted on available stocks of the species.

A. Main or leading shoot stout, upright or at most only nodding or curved or bent, and the side branchlets only exceptionally pendulous; axis of new growth glabrous or short-pubescent: cone truncate (flat) to concave on top.
  B. Branchlets glabrous or slightly pubescent: leaves usually 1–1¼ inches long, broader than high in cross-section.................................1. *C. libanitica*
  BB. Branchlets closely short-pubescent: leaves mostly less than 1 inch long, the breadth in cross-section not equaling or not exceeding the height.......2. *C. atlantica*
AA. Main or leading tip and also the branchlets mostly pendulous and densely pubescent: cones rounded at top when mature........................3. *C. Deodara*

1. **Cedrus libanitica.** CEDAR OF LEBANON. Fig. 57. Great tree, sometimes reaching 100 feet in height and with a wide spread of top and massive trunk that may divide into several, at maturity making a majestic object with long horizontal arms and irregular crown; young trees usually with erect or ascending branches and the leading shoot bent or inclined near tip; branchlets many: developed leaves commonly 1 inch or a little more long, broader than thick in the cross-section, curved, pointed, green or glaucous: cones keg-shaped, 3–4 inches or perhaps more long and 2 inches or more broad at middle, tightly furrowed crosswise, brown, often resinous; seeds brown, with a thin sidewise wing ½–¾ inch across, the wings of the two seeds closely pressed against the large thin horizontal scale which is about 2 inches wide. Asia Minor on the Taurus and Antitaurus Mountains, and the Lebanon Mountains of Syria where it is said to be now rare. Hardy as far north as southern New York, but a hardier race was introduced in 1904 through the Arnold Arboretum from high altitudes of the Cilician Taurus; this race has proved hardy at the Arnold Arboretum, only in unusually severe winters the trees have been slightly injured, but they have always fully recovered

the following summer. The cedar of Lebanon usually grows well under cultivation and thrives in any fairly good soil. It is a beautiful tree of distinct and characteristic appearance which even in cultivation attains considerable dimensions, as many stately old trees in European gardens bear witness.

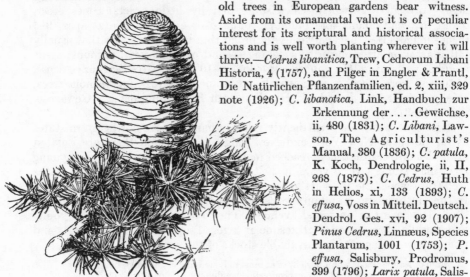

Aside from its ornamental value it is of peculiar interest for its scriptural and historical associations and is well worth planting wherever it will thrive.—*Cedrus libanitica*, Trew, Cedrorum Libani Historia, 4 (1757), and Pilger in Engler & Prantl, Die Natürlichen Pflanzenfamilien, ed. 2, xiii, 329 note (1926); *C. libanotica*, Link, Handbuch zur Erkennung der....Gewächse, ii, 480 (1831); *C. Libani*, Lawson, The Agriculturist's Manual, 380 (1836); *C. patula*, K. Koch, Dendrologie, ii, II, 268 (1873); *C. Cedrus*, Huth in Helios, xi, 133 (1893); *C. effusa*, Voss in Mitteil. Deutsch. Dendrol. Ges. xvi, 92 (1907); *Pinus Cedrus*, Linnæus, Species Plantarum, 1001 (1753); *P. effusa*, Salisbury, Prodromus, 399 (1796); *Larix patula*, Salisbury in Trans. Linn. Soc. viii, 314 (1808).

57. Cone of Cedrus libanitica, not fully mature. (× ⅖)

Several horticultural forms are recorded, but few of them are known in North America.

Var. **aurea**. Foliage yellowish-green.—*Cedrus Libani* var. *aurea*, Hort.

Var. **glauca**. Foliage of blue or nearly silvery-white hue.—*Cedrus libanotica* var. *glauca*, Rehder; *C. Libani* var. *argentea*, Gordon.

Var. **nana**. Dwarf and compact with shorter thinner leaves.—*Cedrus libanotica* var. *nana*, Rehder; *C. Libani* var. *nana*, Loudon.

Var. **pendula**. Branches drooping.—*Cedrus libanotica* var. *pendula*, Rehder; *C. Libani* var. *Sargenti pendula*, Hornibrook.

A closely related species, or perhaps a regional variety of *C. libanitica*, is **C. brevifolia** of the island of Cyprus: a plant of stunted habit or appearance, much shorter glaucous leaves and smaller cones: probably not introduced in North America.—*Cedrus brevifolia*, Henry in Elwes & Henry, Trees of Great Britain and Ireland, iii, 467 (1908); *C. Libani* var. *brevifolia*, Hooker f. in Journ. Bot. xviii, 31 (1880); *C. libanotica* subsp. *brevifolia*, Holmboe, Studies on the Vegetation of Cyprus, 29 (1910).

2. **C. atlantica**. ATLAS CEDAR. In age much like *C. libanitica* but when young at least with erect leading shoot, branchlets usually densely short-pubescent, leaves shorter being mostly less than 1 inch long and as high as broad or higher in cross-section, pale or bluish-green: cones 2–3 inches long and more cylindrical, light brown;

scales about ½ inch wide. Atlas Mountains of Algeria and Morocco.—*Cedrus atlantica*, Manetti, Catalogus Plantarum Cæsarei Regii Horti prope Modiciam, Suppl. 8 (1844 ?).

Var. **argentea**. Leaves silvery-white.—*Cedrus atlantica* var. *argentea*, Murray.

Var. **aurea**. Foliage yellowish.—*Cedrus atlantica* var. *aurea*, Hort.

Var. **fastigiata**. Of narrow-pyramidal habit.—*Cedrus atlantica* var. *fastigiata*, Carrière.

Var. **glauca**. Foliage glaucous, with silvery hue; a very desirable and vigorous form. This form is hardier than the type and will survive in sheltered positions as far north as Massachusetts.—*Cedrus atlantica* var. *glauca*, Carrière.

Var. **pendula**. Branches and branchlets drooping.—*Cedrus atlantica* var. *pendula*, Carrière.

3. **C. Deodara.** Deodar Cedar. Plate XXX. Known by drooping or strongly declined branches and graceful regular appearance: tree to 200 feet or more high, of pyramidal habit, the leading shoot (at least in young trees) and the branches pendulous, the young axes densely pubescent: leaves 1–2 inches long, dark bluish-green, rather rigid, as broad as high in cross-section: cones large, 3–5 inches long, 2–3½ inches in diameter, reddish-brown; scales 2 or more inches wide. Western Himalaya at 4,000 feet and above. Deodar is a name in India for certain trees associated with temples. —*Cedrus Deodara*, ·Loudon, Arboretum et Fruticetum Britannicum, iv, 2428 (1838); *C. Libani* var. *Deodara*, Hooker f., Flora of British India, v, 653 (1888).

Var. **argentea**. Foliage silvery-white.—*Cedrus Deodara* var. *argentea*, Nelson.

Var. **aurea**. Foliage yellow.—*Cedrus Deodara* var. *aurea*, Nelson.

Var. **crassifolia**. A stiff stunted tree with shorter and thicker leaves than the type.—*Cedrus Deodara* var. *crassifolia*, Hort.

Var. **pendula**. Branches long and drooping.—*Cedrus Deodara* var. *pendula*, Beissner.

Var. **robusta**. With stouter branches and more rigid leaves about 2 inches long.— *Cedrus Deodara* var. *robusta*, Carrière.

Var. **verticillata**. A compact form with bluish-white foliage.—*Cedrus Deodara* var. *verticillata*, Hort.

Var. **viridis**. A form with the foliage of deeper green.—*Cedrus Deodara* var. *viridis*, Carrière.

The varietal names *compacta* and *repandens* are also listed.

8. **LARIX.** Larch. Annually deciduous monœcious conifers of the cooler and higher parts of the northern hemisphere, ten species, a few of them fairly well known in cultivation, cones persistent or not shattering: resinous trees with irregularly whorled spreading branches and thick furrowed and scaly bark: leaves linear, in crowded clusters on short spurs except on the leading shoots where they are spirally arranged: staminate flowers in small globose to oblong solitary catkins consisting of numerous short-stalked spirally arranged anthers; fertile catkins larger, consisting of several or numerous scales, each scale with 2 ovules at the base and borne in the axil of a much longer bract: cones with woody 2-seeded scales; seeds with large thin wings, ripening the first year; cotyledons 6–8, usually 6. Larix (là-rix) is the ancient

Latin name of the larch tree.—*Larix*, Miller, Gardeners Dictionary, ed. 7 (1759).

Neither in nature nor in cultivation do the larches exhibit much marked variation, and the named varieties are few. They are notable among the conifers, with Pseudolarix and some of the Taxodiums, in having a complete leaf-fall in autumn and a vivid revival in spring. Although they sometimes inhabit wet grounds or even swamps, they thrive in the drier lands of parks and estates. They are employed mostly as single or specimen trees, but sometimes as groves in the remoter or less-planted parts of the property. They are mostly hardy. *L. decidua* is the species commonly planted. Propagation is by seeds, and named or singular forms by grafting on stocks of the available species.

KEY to the species of Larix:

A. Leaves flat or rounded above.
  B. Bracts shorter than the scales.
    c. Under surface of leaves without conspicuous white bands, shape very narrow: cone-scales not reflexed at apex.
      D. Cone-scales pubescent or puberulous on back, 40–50 in each cone: branchlets usually glabrous.
        E. Scales of cone not incurved at apex, straight; bracts about half as long as scale: leaves up to 1½ inches long.............1. *L. decidua*
        EE. Scales of cone slightly incurved at apex, longitudinally convex; bracts about one-third as long as scale: leaves up to 2 inches long...2. *L. sibirica*
      DD. Cone-scales glabrous, striate, lustrous.
        E. Branchlets usually pubescent: leaves exceeding 1¼ inches in length: cone with 20–40 scales..........................3. *L. Gmelini*
        EE. Branchlets glabrous, brown: leaves 1¼ inches long or less: cone with 12–15 scales......................................4. *L. laricina*
    cc. Under surface of leaves with 2 white bands: cone-scales reflexed at apex.5. *L. Kaempferi*
  BB. Bracts exceeding the scales..6. *L. occidentalis*
AA. Leaves keeled on both sides: bracts of the cones exceeding the scales......7. *L. Potaninii*

1. **Larix decidua.** EUROPEAN LARCH. Fig. 58. Great tree at its best, 100–150 feet high and 4 feet or more in diameter, known in cultivation mostly as a tree of medium size although becoming very tall, hardy in the United States, with pyramidal, later often irregular, head; bark dark grayish-brown; branchlets slender, glabrous, yellowish: leaves compressed, triangular, soft and obtuse, bright green, ¾–1½ inches long: fertile flowers purplish: cones ¾–1½ inches long, with 40–50 almost orbicular scales, usually puberulous or glabrous on the back, loosely appressed at maturity; seed-wings extending to the upper margin of the scale. Mountains of northern and central Europe and Siberia.—*Larix decidua*, Miller, Gardeners Dictionary, ed. 8, no. 1 (1768); *L. europœa*, DeCandolle, Flore Française, iii, 277 (1805); *L. Larix*, Karsten, Deutsche Flora: Pharm. Med. Bot. 326 (1880–83); *Pinus Larix*, Linnæus, Species Plantarum, 1001 (1753).

Var. **pendula.** A form with pendulous branches.—*Larix decidua* var. *pendula*, Henkel & Hochstetter; *L. decidua* var. *pendulina*, Regel; *L. europœa* var. *pendula*, Lawson.

Var. **pyramidalis.** Of narrow pyramidal habit with ascending branches.—*Larix decidua* var. *pyramidalis*, Slavin; *L. decidua* forma *pyramidalis*, Slavin.

2. **L. sibirica.** SIBERIAN LARCH. Very hardy tree differing from the European larch in its slender longer leaves that appear earlier in spring and by the incurved cone-scales and shorter cone-bracts; to 120 feet, with straight slender stem and rather short ascending branches; branchlets yellow; winter-buds grayish-brown and dark brown or nearly black at the base: leaves linear, 1–2 inches long: fertile flowers usually green, sometimes whitish or brownish: cones ovate-oblong, usually 1½ inches long; scales about 30, larger than in the preceding species, finely tomentose on the back, truncate or rounded at the margin, half-spreading at maturity; seed-wings not extending to the upper margin of the scales. Northeastern Russia to Siberia. Hardy as far north as Saskatchewan.— *Larix sibirica*, Ledebour, Flora Altaica, iv, 204 (1833); *L. decidua* var. *rossica*, Henkel & Hochstetter, Synopsis der Nadelhölzer, 132 (1865); *L. decidua* var. *sibirica*, Regel in Gartenflora, xx, 101 (1871).

3. **L. Gmelini.** DAHURIAN LARCH. Little known in cultivation and of inferior importance for ornament: tree to 70 feet, of fairly regular habit while young, old trees usually irregular with wide-spreading branches; branchlets bloomy; winter-buds yellowish-brown, darker or nearly black at the base: leaves bright green, linear, about 1½ inches long: cones small, ¾–1 inch long; scales orbicular or ovate, rounded or emarginate at

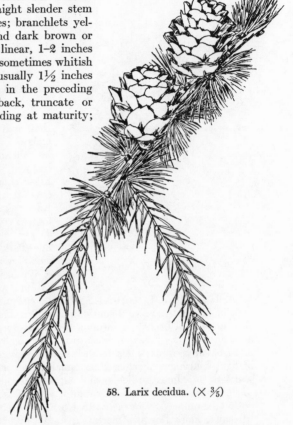

58. Larix decidua. (× ⅗)

the apex, lustrous, about 20 or more. Northeastern Asia; hardy probably as far north as Saskatchewan. The Latin name of this larch commemorates Samuel Gottlieb Gmelin, 1743–1774, botanist and traveler in Russia. The English name (from *Larix dahurica*, once used) refers to a region in Asia.—*Larix Gmelini*, Litvinov, Schedæ ad Herbarium Floræ Rossicæ, viii, 77 (1922); *L. dahurica*, Trautvetter in Plant. Imag. er Descript. fasc. 7, t. 32 (1846); *L. Cajanderi*, Mayr, Fremdländische Wald- und Parkbäume für Europa, 297 (1906); *Pinus dahurica*, Fischer in Turczaninow in Bull. Soc. Nat. Mosc. 101 (1838), *nomen nudum; Abies Gmelini*, Ruprecht, Beitr. Pflanzenk. Russ. Reich. ii, 56 (1845).

Var. **japonica.** KURILE LARCH. Young branchlets reddish and often bloomy, pubescent. Saghalin, Kurile Islands. Introduced in 1888 to Europe by Dr. H. Mayr and in 1894 to the Arnold Arboretum where it has proved perfectly hardy and is growing well.—*Larix Gmelini* var. *japonica,* Pilger in Engler & Prantl, Die Natürlichen Pflanzenfamilien, ed. 2, xiii, 327 (1926); *L. kamtchatica,* Carrière, Traité Général des Conifères, 279 (1855); *L. dahurica* var. *japonica,* Regel in Gartenflora, xx, 105 (1871); *L. kurilensis,* Mayr, Fremdländische Wald- und Parkbäume für Europa, 300 (1906).

59. Larix Kaempferi. Somewhat over-size.

Var. **Principis Rupprechtii.** PRINCE RUP-PRECHT LARCH. Cones larger, to 1½ inches long; scales 30–40, truncate at the apex; bracts at least on the lower part of the cone more than half as long as the scales. Northern China. Introduced to Europe by Dr. H. Mayr in 1903 and to the Arnold Arboretum in 1909 by Wm. Purdom. It is perfectly hardy in Massachusetts and is growing well.—*Larix Gmelini* var. *Principis Rupprechtii,* Pilger in Engler & Prantl, Die Natürlichen Pflanzenfa-milien, ed. 2, xiii, 327 (1926); *L. Principis Rupprechtii,* Mayr, Fremdländische Wald- und Parkbäume für Europa, 309 (1906); *L. dahurica* var. *Principis Rupprechtii,* Rehder & Wilson in Sargent, Plantæ Wilsonianæ, ii, 21 (1914).

4. **L. laricina.** TAMARACK. AMERICAN LARCH. Well-known tree across the continent in high latitudes and south to West Virginia, often in swamps; to 60 feet tall, with horizontal branches, forming a narrow pyramidal head, sometimes broad and open on older trees; bark reddish-brown; branchlets slender, glabrous, reddish-yellow, often bloomy; winter-buds reddish-brown: leaves linear, obtuse, 1–1½ inches long, of light bluish-green color: cones small, oval or almost globular, ½–¾ inch long; scales 12–15, almost orbicular and entire, glabrous. From Labrador to Alaska, south to Pennsylvania, Indiana, Minnesota, and British Columbia. Hardy as far north as Saskatchewan.—*Larix laricina,* K. Koch, Dendrologie, ii, II, 263 (1873); *L. americana,* Michaux, Flora Boreali-Americana, ii, 203 (1803); *Pinus laricina,* DuRoi, Observationes Botanicas, 49 (1771).

L. pendula, the WEEPING LARCH, is a supposed hybrid between *L. laricina* and *L. decidua:* it differs from *L. laricina* chiefly in its larger cones, with 20–30 scales pubescent below the middle; from *L. decidua* in its smaller cones with the scales glabrous above the middle and in its shorter bracts. Originated in England before 1800.—*Larix pendula,* Salisbury in Trans. Linn. Soc. viii, 313 (1808); *L. americana* var. *pendula,* Loudon, Encyclopædia of Trees and Shrubs, 1057 (1842).

5. **L. Kaempferi.** JAPANESE LARCH. Fig 59. Probably the best of the larches for ornament, of spreading habit and rapid growth, hardy in New York and as far as

Massachusetts: tree to 90 feet tall, with short horizontal branches; bark gray, peeling off in narrow strips leaving red scars; branchlets yellowish- or reddish-brown, glabrous, usually bloomy the first year; spurs short and globular: leaves rather broad, obtuse, soft, ½–1¾ inches long, light or bluish-green: cones ovoid-oblong, ½–1½ inches long, with emarginate roundish ovate scales. Japan. The dwarf form of the high mountains of Japan, var. **minor**, reverts under cultivation to the normal form. The name is in memory of Engelbert Kaempfer, born 1631, early traveler in Japan. The *Larix Kaempferi* of some authors is *Pseudolarix amabilis.*—*Larix Kaempferi*, Sargent, Silva of North America, xii, 2 (1898); *L. japonica*, Carrière, Traité Général des Conifères, 272 (1855); *L. leptolepis*, Murray in Proc. Roy. Hort. Soc. Lond. ii, 633 (1862); *Pinus Kaempferi*, Lambert, A Description of the Genus Pinus, ed. 2, preface vi (1828).

L. eurolepis, the DUNKELD LARCH, from the place in Scotland where it first appeared, is a hybrid between *L. Kaempferi* and *L. decidua:* tree of vigorous growth, intermediate between the parents: from *L. Kaempferi* it differs chiefly in the less bloomy young branchlets, yellow or grayish-yellow the second year, in the shorter and narrower leaves with fewer rows of stomata; from *L. decidua* in the slightly bloomy branchlets and in the larger leaves, those of the shoots with the stomatic bands above composed of 2–4 and the bands beneath composed of 5–7 rows of stomata, those of the spurs with 1 or 2 rows on each side above and with 3–5 rows on each side beneath.—*Larix eurolepis*, Henry in Proc. Irish Acad. xxxv B, 60 (1919); *L. hybrida*, Farquhar, Catalogue of New Rare Plants 7 (1916), *nomen; L. Henryana*, Rehder in Journ. Arnold Arb. i, 52 (1919).

6. **L. occidentalis**. WESTERN TAMARACK. WEST AMERICAN LARCH. Fig. 60. Tall tree to 150 feet high, with dark colored bark, becoming bright cinnamon-red on older trunks, and with short horizontal branches, forming a narrow pyramidal head; branchlets orange-brown, pubescent when young, soon glabrous; winter-buds dark chestnut-brown: leaves rigid, sharply pointed, triangular, keeled beneath, 1–1¾ inches long, pale green: cones oblong, 1–1½ inches long; scales orbicular, almost entire, tomentose beneath. British Columbia to Montana and Oregon. Hardy as far north as Massachusetts and perhaps farther north. — *Larix occidentalis*, Nuttall, North American Sylva, iii, 143 (1849).

L. Griffithiana is related to *L. occidentalis*. It is a tree to 60 feet tall, with pendulous branches; branchlets dull reddish-brown: leaves obtuse: cones oblong, 3–4 inches long; scales truncate or slightly emarginate at apex; bracts lanceolate, reflexed. Southwestern China and Himalaya. Introduced first in 1848 and later repeatedly, but it never succeeded in cultivation. Bears the name of W. Griffith, discoverer of the plant.—*Larix Griffithiana*, Carrière, Traité Général des Conifères, 278 (1855); *L. Griffithii*, Hooker f. & Thomson in Hooker f., Illustrations of Himalayan Plants, t. 21 (1855).

7. **L. Potaninii**. CHINA LARCH. Tree to 100 feet tall, with rather short horizontal branches

60. Larix occidentalis.
Natural size.

and gray or grayish-brown bark; branchlets pendulous, glabrous, lustrous, orange-brown to reddish-brown, the winter-buds of the same color but darker: leaves linear, slender, acute, ¾–1¼ inches long, grayish-green, with bands of stomata on both sides each consisting of 1 or 2 rows: cones ovoid-oblong, 1¼–1¾ inches long, at maturity violet-purple changing to grayish-brown; scales suborbicular, with rounded entire slightly incurved margin; bracts long-acuminate, exceeding the scales, upright, purple. Western China. This larch bears the name of Gregory Potanin, Russian botanist, died 1920.—*Larix Potaninii*, Batalin in Act. Hort. Petrop. xiii, 385 (1893); *L. chinensis*, Beissner in Mitteil. Deutsch. Dendrol. Ges. v, 68 (1896); *L. thibetica*, Franchet in Journ. de Bot. xiii, 262 (1899).

A closely related species is **L. Mastersiana**. Tree to 60 feet tall; branchlets pale yellowish-brown, slightly pubescent when young: leaves compressed: cones brown, with long-acuminate purple bracts exceeding the scales and reflexed. Western China. Introduced in 1908 by E. H. Wilson to the Arnold Arboretum, but the young plant did not do well. Bears the name of M. T. Masters, 1833–1907, English botanist.— *Larix Mastersiana*, Rehder & Wilson in Sargent, Plantæ Wilsonianæ, ii, 19 (1914).

Another related species is **L. Lyallii**, LYALL LARCH. Tree to 80 feet tall, with remote long branches; branchlets stout, brown-tomentose: leaves 4-angled, rigid, acute, 1–1½ inches long: cones 1½–2 inches long, with pubescent scales spreading at maturity and finally reflexed; bracts long-acuminate, exserted, upright. High mountains of British Columbia and Alberta to Washington and Montana. Introduced several times into cultivation but it never succeeded. Discovered by David Lyall, 1817–1895, surgeon and naturalist to the British Boundary Commission.—*Larix Lyallii*, Parlatore, Enumeratio Seminum in Horto Botanico Regii Musæi Florentini, 259 (1863).

9. **PSEUDOLARIX.** GOLDEN-LARCH. Fig. 61. One remarkable deciduous monœcious tree in eastern China, valuable in cultivation and hardy in New York and Massachusetts, distinguished from the true larches by the pendulous stalked cones, the acuminate-pointed spreading cone-scales that often fall or shatter after maturity, as well as by the very different staminate flowers, broad long leaves, and odd ringed short flowering spurs: leaves linear, in dense clusters on short spurs, those of the young shoots spirally arranged: staminate flowers catkin-like, slender-stalked and clustered at the end of short spurs: cones short-stalked, pendent, with ovate-lanceolate deciduous scales and with bracts about half as long as the scales; each scale with 2 seeds with the wings nearly as long as the scale; cotyledons 5–6. The name (pseudolà-rix) means *false larix*, from its resemblance to the larches.—*Pseudolarix*, Gordon, Pinetum, 292 (1858).

Pseudolarix amabilis. Fig. 61. Resinous tree with wide-spreading branches and light graceful foliage that becomes golden-yellow in autumn, attaining 130 feet in height; bark reddish-brown, fissured into small narrow scales: leaves linear, acuminate, soft, light green, bluish-green beneath, 1½–3 inches long and 1–1½ lines broad: staminate flowers yellow, about ¼ inch long, slender-stalked; fertile flowers about

¾ inch long: cones ovate, reddish-brown, 2½–3 inches long, 1⅔–2 inches broad; scales triangular, ovate-lanceolate, cordate at the base, emarginate at the apex, woody; bracts ovate-lanceolate, much smaller than the scales; seeds about ⅓ inch long. Eastern China, in Kiangsi and Chekiang provinces at 3,000–4,000 feet.—*Pseudolarix amabilis*, Rehder in Journ. Arnold Arb. i, 53 (1919); *P. Kaempferi*, Gordon, Pinetum, 292 (1858); *P. Fortunei*, Mayr, Monographie der Abietineen des Japanischen Reiches, 99 (1890); *Larix Kaempferi*, Carrière in Flore des Serres, xi, 97 (1856); *L. amabilis*, Nelson, Pinaceæ, 84 (1866); *Laricopsis Kaempferi*, Kent in Veitch, Manual of the Coniferæ, ed. 2, 404 (1900); *Pinus Kaempferi*, Parlatore in DeCandolle, Prodromus, xvi, II, 412 (1868); *Abies Kaempferi*, Lindley in Gard. Chron. 255, 455 (1854), not Lindley in Penny Cyclopædia, i, 34 (1833).

61. Pseudolarix amabilis. (× about ½)

Var. **nana.** A dwarf form.—*Pseudolarix amabilis* var. *nana*, Hort.

10. **TAXODIUM.** YEW-CYPRESS. Three species of resinous monœcious deciduous or variously evergreen trees of the western hemisphere, considerably planted for ornament and interest usually as single specimens: leaves alternate, linear, usually 2-ranked, falling in autumn or the second year together with the short lateral branchlets: flowers small; staminate flowers in catkin-like or bud-like clusters, consisting of spirally arranged anthers with 4–9 anther-cells and forming terminal panicles; fertile flowers solitary or in pairs at the ends of branchlets of the previous year, composed of imbricated scales bearing 2 ovules inside at the base: cones globose or nearly so, maturing the first year, consisting of spirally arranged woody thick more or less peltate scales enlarged at the apex into an irregularly 4-sided disk with a mucro in the middle and narrowed toward the base into a slender stalk; 2 triangular winged seeds under each scale; cotyledons 4–9. The name (taxò-dium) refers to the similarity of the foliage to that of *Taxus.*—*Taxodium*, Richard in Ann. Mus. Par. xvi, 298 (1810).

A. Leaves spreading or standing away from the twig and distinctly 2-ranked
 (distichous), straight, abruptly pointed to obtuse.
  B. Tree clearly deciduous...1. *T. distichum*
  BB. Tree evergreen (leaves holding about two years), or perhaps partially
   deciduous when planted north of its range......................2. *T. mucronatum*
AA. Leaves appressed to the twig on all sides and therefore more or less parallel
 with it, usually incurved, very narrow and long awl-pointed (perhaps
 somewhat spreading on shoots just starting) ....3. *T. ascendens*

1. **Taxodium distichum.** COMMON BALD-CYPRESS. Fig. 62. Forest tree prized for its timber, forming erect projections or "knees" from the roots when growing in water, becoming 150 feet high, with a buttressed trunk usually 4–5, but sometimes attaining 12 feet or more in diameter, often hollow in old age; bark light cinnamon-brown, shallowly fissured into broad flat ridges covered with long fibrous scales; branches erect or spreading, distichously ramified, forming a pyramidal head, becoming at maturity broad and rounded, with slightly pendulous branches: leaves narrowly linear, acute, thin, light green, ½–¾ inch long: panicles of the purplish staminate flowers 4–5 inches long: cones almost globose, rugose, about 1 inch across and destitute of mucros at maturity, seed ¼ inch long. Flowering in spring. Delaware to Florida, west to southern Illinois, Oklahoma and Texas. Notwithstanding its range and habitat, this tree thrives in western New York and similar climates on well-drained upland. A handsome pyramidal tree with a feathery head of light green foliage.—*Taxodium distichum*, Richard in Ann. Mus. Par. xvi, 298 (1810); *Cupressus disticha*, Linnæus, Species Plantarum, 1003 (1753); *Schubertia disticha*, Mirbel in Mem. Mus. Par. xiii, 75 (1825).

62. Taxodium distichum. (× ⅘) Twig of Taxodium ascendens above.

Var. **fastigiatum.** A slender erect form.—*Taxodium distichum* var. *fastigiatum*, Hort.

Var. **nanum.** Dwarf and shrubby.—*Taxodium distichum* var. *nanum*, Hort.

Var. **pendulum.** Branchlets drooping: cones more oval and larger, 1½ inches long.—*Taxodium distichum* var. *pendulum*, Slavin.

Var. **pyramidalis.** Narrow pyramidal form with short ascending branches.—*Taxodium distichum* var. *pyramidalis*, Carrière.

2. **T. mucronatum.** MONTEZUMA YEW-CYPRESS. Similar to the preceding species: taller evergreen tree, occasionally 170 feet high with a trunk 20 feet or more in diameter: leaves shorter, obtusish and mucronulate, falling with the branchlet the second year: staminate panicles and cones larger. Flowering in autumn. Occasionally cultivated in California.—*Taxodium mucronatum*, Tenore in Ann. Sci. Nat., ser. 3, xix, 355 (1853); *T. mexicanum*, Carrière, Traité Général des Conifères, 147 (1855); *T. distichum* var. *mexicanum*, Gordon, Pinetum, 307 (1858); *T. distichum* var. *mucronatum*, Henry in Elwes & Henry, Trees of Great Britain and Ireland, i, 175 (1906).

3. **T. ascendens.** Pond-Cypress. Plate XXXI. Fig. 62, top. Smaller tree than *T. distichum* with spreading arms and upright or ascending branchlets, mostly in pineland ponds from Virginia to Florida and Alabama, and also hardy North but a less handsome subject; bark thick and furrowed: leaves close to the twig and pointing the same way, making the branchlets look narrow and rush-like, very narrow and prominently sharp-pointed.—*Taxodium ascendens*, Brongniart in Ann. Sci. Nat., ser. 1, xxx, 182 (1833); *T. distichum* var. *imbricarium*, Croom, Catalogue of Plants. . . of New Bern, N. C. 30 (1837); *T. imbricarium*, Harper in Bull. Torr. Bot. Club, 383 (1902).

Var. **nutans.** Branchlets drooping.—*Taxodium ascendens* var. *nutans*, Rehder; *T. ascendens* var. *pendulum*, Schneider; *Glyptostrobus pendulus*, Endlicher, Synopsis Coniferarum, 71 (1847).

11. GLYPTOSTROBUS.

Genus separated from Taxodium, differing in the lengthened obovate and not peltate cone-scales, as well as in the peduncled pyriform cones, different seeds with small wings, and dimorphic leaves: one monœcious deciduous tree in wet places in southeastern China. The name (glyptós-trobus) means *carved cone*, alluding to the configuration of the scales.—*Glyptostrobus*, Endlicher, Synopsis Coniferarum, 69 (1847).

Glyptostrobus pensilis. Chinese Water-Pine or Bald-Cypress. Small tree with broad base, bearing two kinds of leaves, those on sterile branches linear and 3-ranked and to ½ inch long, those on bearing branches scale-like and imbricate: staminate catkins like those in Taxodium: cones about ¾ inch long, with obovate not thick scales. Little known in North America, although introduced, and probably adapted only to warmer parts of the country; the statement that this tree has stood in the North is due to confusion with a form of *Taxodium ascendens*.—*Glyptostrobus pensilis*, K. Koch, Dendrologie, ii, II, 191 (1873); *G. heterophyllus*, Endlicher, Synopsis Coniferarum, 70 (1847); *G. sinensis*, Loder in Gard. Chron., ser. 3, lxvi, 259 (1919); *Taxodium heterophyllum*, Brongniart in Ann. Sci. Nat., ser. 1, xxx, 184 (1833); *Thuya pensilis*, Staunton, Embassy to China, ii, 436 (1798).

12. SEQUOIA.

Two titanic monœcious evergreen trees in the Pacific region of North America of much public interest, prized for ornament in regions in which they thrive, with thick red fibrous and deeply grooved bark; heartwood dark red soft durable straight-grained; sapwood thin and nearly white: leaves persistent, alternate, linear or awl-shaped or scale-like, often dimorphic: staminate catkins axillary and terminal, each of the numerous spirally arranged stamens bearing 2–5 pollen-sacs; fertile catkins terminal, composed of many spirally arranged scales, each with 4–7 ovules at base: cones woody, persistent, the divergent scales widened at summit which is rhomboidal, wrinkled, and with a depressed center; seeds flattened, winged; cotyledons 4–6. Named for Sequoyah (sequò-ia), a Cherokee half-breed of Georgia, originator of the Cherokee alphabet; about 1770–1843.—*Sequoia*,

Endlicher, Synopsis Coniferarum, 197 (1847); *Wellingtonia*, Lindley in Gard. Chron., 819 (1853).

A. Leaves mostly spreading in 2 ranks: buds scaly: cone less than 2 inches long. 1. *S. sempervirens*
AA. Leaves appressed or slightly spreading, not 2-ranked: buds naked: cone
2 inches or more long.. 2. *S. gigantea*

63. Sequoia sempervirens.
(× ½)

1. **Sequoia sempervirens.** REDWOOD. Fig. 63. Very tall, to 300 and more feet, trunk 10–25 feet in diameter and often clear of limbs for 100 feet in mature specimens, the narrow crown with horizontal or downward-sweeping branches; bark dark brown, 6–12 inches thick, divided into rounded ridges covered with long and narrow fibrous scales, in falling disclosing the light cinnamon-red inner bark: leaves linear, mostly ½–1 inch long, 1–1¼ lines wide, spreading in flat sprays, or the upper leaves and those on main stems of the branches often only 1–5 lines long and awl-shaped: cones oval, ¾–1⅛ inches long, ½–¾ inch broad, maturing the first autumn; scales 14–26; seeds elliptic, narrowly margined, 2 lines long. Confined to northern and central coast ranges of southern Oregon and northern California, rarely more than thirty miles from the coast, forming extensive forests; a major timber tree. In the East it is probably not hardy north of Virginia. It is a handsome tree with spreading branches and yew-like dark green foliage. It holds the record as the tallest tree in the world, at least so far as actual measurements have been made, one specimen in Humboldt County, California, measuring 340 feet, according to Sargent. Greater heights assigned to species of Eucalyptus were erroneous. It reproduces by seeds and by stump-sprouts, the latter numerous and remarkably persistent, often producing merchantable lumber.—*Sequoia sempervirens*, Endlicher, Synopsis Coniferarum, 198 (1847).

Var. **adpressa.** Smaller tree with shorter branches: leaves shorter and broader, slightly appressed; young leaves and tips of branchlets creamy-white, glaucescent when older.—*Sequoia sempervirens* var. *adpressa*, Carrière; *S. sempervirens* var. *albo-spica*, Hort.

Var. **glauca.** BLUE REDWOOD. Foliage with a decidedly bluish cast.—*Sequoia sempervirens* var. *glauca*, R. Smith.

Var. **pendula.** Branches drooping.—*Sequoia sempervirens* var. *pendula*, Rovelli.

2. **S. gigantea.** BIG TREE. Plate XXXII. Fig. 64. Prodigious tree, 150–275, rarely to 325 feet high, with trunk 10–30 feet in diameter; crown pyramidal on young trees, rounded at summit or much broken in age; bark cinnamon-red, 1–2 feet thick, divided into rounded ridges 4–5 feet wide, corresponding to the lobes of the buttressed base and separating into loose fibrous scales; branches pendulous, cord-like: leaves scale-

like, 1/8–1/2 inch long, sharp-pointed, adherent to the stem which they thickly clothe, the tip free: cones ovoid, 2–3¾ inches long, 1½–2 inches broad, opening only slightly, maturing the second summer, persistent; scales 25–45; seeds oblong or somewhat ovate, wing-margined, 2½–3 lines long. Western slopes of Sierra Nevada, California, in several natural groves. In the East it is not reliably hardy north of Philadelphia, although in southern and western New York trees have occasionally reached a fair size and in the neighborhood of Boston have survived ordinary winters for a number of years. Trees more than sixty years old in western New York perished in 1919 as a result of severe winters, but one of them still persists at Aurora on Cayuga Lake and bears cones, with a girth of 10 feet, although having lost its lower limbs from the winter of 1919. A tree of similar size stands at the old Painters' Arboretum near Philadelphia. Trees now and then found in grounds in the Northeast are usually small frost-bitten specimens. As usually seen in cultivation where it thrives, it is a handsome narrow-pyramidal tree clothed to the ground with short and slender upcurved branches, but in mature specimens the trunk is clear of limbs up to 80 to 200 feet. It is the most massive of all trees, although exceeded in girth by a few others, notably the African baobab. In nature it reproduces only by seeds and does not make stump-sprouts as the preceding species.—*Sequoia gigantea*, Decaisne in Bull. Soc. Bot. Fr. i, 70 (1854); *S. Wellingtonia*, Seeman in Bonplandia, iii, 27 (1855); *S. Washingtoniana*, Sudworth in Bull. U. S. Div. For. xiv, 61 (1897); *Wellingtonia gigantea*, Lindley in Gard. Chron., 823 (1853).

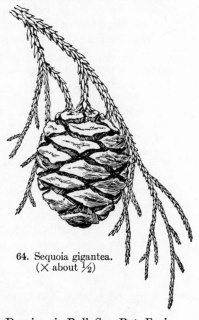

64. Sequoia gigantea.
(× about ½)

Var. **aurea**. Foliage yellow.—*Sequoia gigantea* var. *aurea*, Nicholson.

Var. **glauca**. Foliage bluish.—*Sequoia gigantea* var. *glauca*, Otto. There are other color forms.

Var. **pendula**. A form in which the branches are strongly recurved, closely covering the stem and producing a narrow cylindric effect similar to that of Italian cypress. —*Sequoia gigantea* var. *pendula*, Lav.

13. **CRYPTOMERIA.** CRYPTOMERIA. One great monœcious evergreen tree of Japan, known in cultivation for its ornamental and picturesque qualities, in general of pyramidal shape and straight slender trunk covered with reddish-brown bark, and irregularly whorled spreading branches ascending at the extremities: leaves spirally arranged, linear-subulate, acute, slightly curved, decurrent at the base: staminate flowers axillary, oblong, yellow, forming short racemes at the end of the branches; pistillate globular,

solitary at the end of short branchlets: cones globular, with thick wedge-shaped scales, furnished with the recurved point of the adnate bract on the back and with pointed processes at the apex, each scale with 3–5 narrow-winged erect seeds; cotyledons usually 3, rarely 2. Name (cryptomè-ria) derived from Greek meaning *hidden part;* application doubtful.—*Cryptomeria,* D. Don in Trans. Linn. Soc. xviii, 166 (1841).

Cryptomeria japonica. Fig. 65. Tree attaining 125 feet; bark cinnamon-brown peeling off in long ribbon-like shreds: leaves linear-subulate, compressed and slightly 4- or 3-angled, bluntly keeled on the dorsal and sharply keeled on the ventral side, bluish-green, ½–1 inch long: cones brownish-red, ¾–1 inch across, the scales with long-acuminate projections that give it a spiny look. In central and southern Japan and doubtfully native to China. It is much planted in Japan and China as an ornamental and as timber trees in the former country where the light and easily worked but durable wood is much used. Travelers in Japan remember the great avenue at Nikko, and other picturesque examples. It was first introduced in its Chinese form (var. *sinensis*) to Great Britain in 1842 and perhaps a few years earlier to Petrograd. It has proved hardy as far north as New York and in sheltered positions in the neighborhood of Boston and western New York in some of its forms.—*Cryptomeria japonica,* D. Don in Trans. Linn. Soc. xviii, 167 (1841).

The main varieties are *sinensis, Lobbii* and *elegans,* but the forms are many, arising from seeds.

Var. Lobbii. Similar to the preceding, of more compact habit, with more appressed dark green leaves and the cones with the processes and the bracts even longer. Introduced in 1845 by Wm. Lobb from Buitenzorg, Java.—*Cryptomeria japonica* var. *Lobbii,* Carrière.

Var. sinensis. Tree of more diffuse habit, with slenderer branches, deflexed branchlets and longer and slenderer leaves: cones with fewer scales which have shorter processes and shorter tips of scales. This was the first of the forms introduced into cultivation, as stated under the species. It is somewhat tenderer than the Japanese type.—*Cryptomeria japonica* var. *sinensis,* Siebold; *C. japonica* var. *Fortunei,* Henry; *C. Fortunei,* Hooibrenk.

Var. elegans. Low dense tree, with horizontal branches and pendulous branchlets: leaves linear, flattened, soft, spreading, longer than in the type, bright green, changing to bronzy red in fall and winter. Handsome when young.—*Cryptomeria japonica* var. *elegans,* Masters; *C. elegans,* Veitch.

Var. araucarioides. Branches deflexed with long distantly placed pendulous branchlets: leaves small, stout and stiff, incurved at apex, bright green.—*Cryptomeria japonica* var. *araucarioides,* Henkel & Hochstetter.

65. Cryptomeria japonica. Nearly natural size.

Var. compacta. Of very compact habit, with bluish-green foliage.—*Cryptomeria japonica* var. *compacta,* Beissner.

Var. **cristata.** Monstrous form with fasciated cockscomb-like branches, with occasional normal branches.—*Cryptomeria japonica* var. *cristata*, Beissner; *C. japonica* var. *Lobbii cristata*, Hort.

Var. **dacrydioides.** With long distant branches, close somewhat pendent branchlets, and short very closely set leaves of brownish color. —*Cryptomeria japonica* var. *dacrydioides*, Carrière.

Var. **nana.** Dwarf and procumbent densely branched form; adapted for rockeries. —*Cryptomeria japonica* var. *nana*, Carrière.

Var. **pungens.** PRICKLY CRYPTOMERIA. Compact form with spreading rigid and sharply pointed much-compressed leaves of bluish-green color. —*Cryptomeria japonica* var. *pungens*, Carrière.

Var. **selaginoides.** Branches long and slender, with short tufted branchlets near the tips. —*Cryptomeria japonica* var. *selaginoides*, Hort.

Var. **spiralis.** Slender shrub with strongly falcate leaves twisted spirally around the branchlets.—*Cryptomeria japonica* var. *spiralis*, Siebold & Zuccarini.

66. Cunninghamia sinensis. (× ½)

14. **CUNNINGHAMIA.** CUNNINGHAMIA. Two monœcious evergreen trees of farther Asia with large stiff very sharp-pointed leaves and prickly globular cones, planted in mild and warm regions; branches whorled, the branchlets opposite and 2-ranked, without distinct winter-buds: leaves linear-lanceolate, rigid, densely spirally arranged and 2-rowed in direction: staminate catkins oblong, fertile globose, both sexes in small clusters at the end of the branches: cones roundish-ovate, 1–2 inches long, with roundish-ovate, serrate and pointed scales with 3 narrow-winged seeds at the base; cotyledons 2. Named (cunninghà-mia) in honor of Dr. James Cunningham who discovered it in China in 1702.—*Cunninghamia*, R. Brown in Richard, De Coniferis, 149 (1826).

A. Leaves of fertile branches spiny-pointed, 1–2 inches long: cones about 1½ inches long...1. *C. lanceolata*
AA. Leaves of fertile branches obtusish, ½–¾ inch long: cones about ¾ inch long.2. *C. Konishii*

144 THE CULTIVATED CONIFERS IN NORTH AMERICA

1. Cunninghamia lanceolata. CHINA-FIR. SHA-SHU. Fig. 66. Tree attaining 80 feet and more in height: leaves linear-lanceolate, with broad decurrent base, sharply pointed, finely serrulate, light green and shining above and with 2 broad whitish bands beneath, 1½–2½ inches long: cones 1–2 inches long. Southern, central,

and western China where it is an indispensable timber tree. Hardy as far north as Pennsylvania in sheltered positions but injured in very severe winters. Handsome tree with horizontally spreading branches pendulous at the extremities. If cut down or killed back by frost, it sprouts from the stump and forms bushy specimens.—*Cunninghamia lanceolata*, Hooker in Bot. Mag. t. 2743 (1827); *C. sinensis*, R. Brown in Richard, De Coniferis, 80 (1826); *Pinus lanceolata*, Lambert, A Description of the Genus Pinus, 52 (1803).

2. C. Konishii. FORMOSA-FIR. Tree to 100 feet, with longitudinally furrowed cinnamon-brown bark becoming grayish-white with age: leaves on fertile shoots lanceolate, falcate, obtusish, ½–1 inch long, grayish-green with 2 broad white bands beneath and 2 narrow stomatic bands above, on young plants linear-lanceolate, to 1½ inches long, spiny-pointed and without stomatic lines above: cones ovoid, ¾–1 inch long; scales rounded with a sharp mucro at the apex. Formosa, where it was discovered on Mt. Randai by N. Konishi. It grows well in California and Florida. Young plants differ little from those of the preceding species.—*Cunninghamia Konishii*, Hayata in Gard. Chron., ser. 3, xliii, 194 (1908), and in Journ. Linn. Soc., Bot. xxxv, 299 (1908).

15. ATHROTAXIS. ATHROTAXIS. Three evergreen monœcious trees of western Tasmanian mountains, to be expected in California and perhaps in the southern states, also introduced under glass in the Northeast, somewhat like Cryptomeria; densely branched; bark peeling off in longitudinal shreds: leaves homomorphic, small, alternate or indistinctly decussate, either short, blunt, scale-like and appressed, or lanceolate and somewhat loosely disposed: staminate flowers in imbricated spiral aments, the anthers 2-celled; fertile flowers in spirally imbricated aments, 3–6 ovules under each scale, these aments becoming small globular cones with woody scales contracted at base and at apex dilated or pointed; seeds 3–6, winged; cotyledons 2. Name (athrotáx-is) from Greek, alluding to crowded cone-scales and leaves.—*Athrotaxis*, D. Don in Trans. Linn. Soc. xviii, 171 (1839).

67. Athrotaxis selaginoides.
(× about ½)

A. Leaves lanceolate or ovate-lanceolate.
  B. Cone-scales without process on back: leaves spiny-pointed............1. *A. selaginoides*
  BB. Cone-scales with large acute process on back: leaves obtuse or acute...2. *A. laxifolia*
AA. Leaves rhombic-ovate, obtuse.......................................3. *A. cupressoides*

1. **Athrotaxis selaginoides.** Fig. 67. Tree to 100 feet tall, with fibrous slightly furrowed bark: leaves spreading, lanceolate, incurved, acute, rigid and spiny pointed, ⅓–½ inch long, with 2 glaucous bands on the ventral side, keeled on back and with 2 small glaucous depressions; those of young seedlings narrower: cones ¾–1 inch diameter, the scales numerous, broad-ovate, acuminate.—*Athrotaxis selaginoides*, D. Don in Trans. Linn. Soc. xviii, 172 (1839); *A. alpina*, Van Houtte in Gordon, Pinetum, 31 (1858); *Cunninghamia selaginoides*, Zuccarini in Siebold & Zuccarini, Flora Japonica, ii, 9 (1842).

2. **A. laxifolia.** Tree to 40 feet tall: leaves slightly spreading, ovate-lanceolate, obtuse or acute, about ¼ inch long, with translucent entire margin, on the ventral side with glaucous stomatic bands, on the back with whitish depressions near the base: cones ¾ inch across, the scales thickened, with a large acute process on back.— *Athrotaxis laxifolia*, Hooker, Icones Plantarum, t. 573 (1843); *A. Doniana*, Henkel & Hochstetter, Synopsis der Nadelhölzer, 221 (1865).

3. **A. cupressoides.** Tree reaching 40 feet, with ascending branches: leaves rhombic-ovate, broad and obtuse, with translucent denticulate margin, ⅛–⅙ inch long, thick and keeled, closely appressed to the branches: cones ⅖–½ inch across, the scales rounded at top and bearing a triangular recurved process in the middle.— *Athrotaxis cupressoides*, D. Don in Trans. Linn. Soc. xviii, 173 (1839); *A. imbricata*, Maule in Gordon, Pinetum, Suppl. 16 (1862); *Cunninghamia cupressoides*, Zuccarini in Siebold & Zuccarini, Flora Japonica, ii, 9 (1842).

16. TAIWANIA. Taiwania.

One great evergreen of high mountains of Formosa and southwestern China, adapted only to California and other milder parts of the country, although raised elsewhere under glass: leaves dimorphic (of two forms), alternate, subulate, falcate, 4-angled, or on fruiting branches scale-like, imbricate, incurved: scales of pistillate flowers with 2 reversed ovules: cones terminal, subglobose, with many spirally arranged imbricate scales subtended by minute bracts; scales obovate, cuneate at base, mucronate, thin, each with 2 narrowly winged seeds; cotyledons 2. Name (taiwà-nia) from Taiwan, the Chinese name of Formosa. —*Taiwania*, Hayata in Journ. Linn. Soc., Bot. xxxvii, 330 (1906).

68. Taiwania cryptomerioides. Fruiting branch with adult foliage and branchlet with juvenile foliage. (× 1)

Taiwania cryptomerioides. Fig. 68. Tree to 200 feet high with a tall clean trunk sometimes 30 feet in girth and clean to the height of 100 or 150 feet, with short branches forming a small crown like Cryptomeria, as its name indicates; young plants with ascending branches and pendulous branchlets: leaves of sterile branches linear-subulate, pungent, incurved ·falcate, keeled on the ventral and dorsal side, ½–¾ inch long, those of fertile branches triangular, imbricate, obtusish or acutish, about ⅛–⅙ inch long: cones about ½ inch long with about 15 leathery scales; seeds oblong, with the wing about ¼ inch long. Plants are growing in California and Florida. When young it is a very handsome tree of broad-pyramidal outline.—*Taiwania cryptomerioides*, Hayata in Journ. Linn. Soc., Bot. xxxvii, 330 (1906).

17. SCIADOPITYS. Umbrella-Pine. A single interesting very large monœcious tree in certain areas in central Japan, well known in North America as far north as western New York and Massachusetts, in its juvenile state as a slow-growing compact handsome evergreen: leaves of two kinds; small and scale-like leaves scattered on the shoot, but crowded at its end and bearing in their axils a whorl of 20–30 long linear flat leaves furrowed on each side, more deeply beneath; these leaves really consist each of 2 connate leaves borne on undeveloped spurs like those of Pinus; they have been sometimes called cladodes, but are not true cladodes: staminate catkins oval, consisting of spirally disposed 2 - celled anthers and appearing in dense clusters at the ends of the shoots; the fertile ones are solitary at the ends of the shoots and consist of numerous spirally· arranged scales subtended by a small bract and bearing 7–9 ovules: cones oblong-ovate, woody, ripening the second season; bracts adnate to the broadly orbicular thick scales spreading at the margin; seeds oval, compressed, with narrow wing, marginate at the apex; cotyledons 2. Name (sciadop'-itys) derived from Greek, *umbrella*,

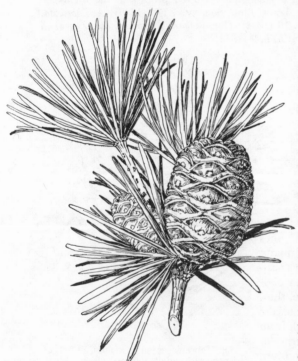

69. Sciadopitys verticillata. (× ⅓)

pine, alluding to the position of the leaves.—*Sciadopitys*, Siebold & Zuccarini, Flora Japonica, ii, 3 (1842).

Sciadopitys verticillata. Fig. 69. Tree attaining 120 feet, with short and slender horizontally spreading branches forming a narrow pyramidal compact head, in old age loose, wood straight-grained and nearly white; bark nearly smooth, separating in long thin shreds, gray to grayish-brown, red-brown below: scale-like leaves dark brown, ⅙ inch long; the large connate leaves 15–35 in each whorl, linear, stiff, obtuse and emarginate, deeply furrowed on both sides, dark green and glossy above, with 2 white bands beneath, 3–6 inches long: cones 3–5 inches long, ovate-oblong; seed ½ inch long.—*Sciadopitys verticillata*, Siebold & Zuccarini, Flora Japonica, ii, 3 (1842).

18. **ARAUCARIA.** ARAUCARIA. Southern hemisphere stately evergreens, mostly diœcious, prized in warm and tropical regions as specimen trees and some of them in cold countries in the juvenile state as tub and pot specimens; tall trees with regularly whorled branches, without distinct winter-buds: leaves spirally arranged, flat, subulate or scale-like and stiff, clothing all the branches uniformly and usually closely imbricated, dimorphic in some species: staminate catkins terminal and solitary or disposed in fascicles; anthers 6–8-celled; fertile flowers in ovoid or globose heads that become large woody cones with only 1 seed underneath each scale; scales numerous, elongated, cuneate, 2-edged or 2-winged; seeds wingless, adnate to the scale at the base, sometimes edible; cotyledons 2–4. Name (araucà-ria) from Arauco, a province of southern Chile where one of the species grows. About twelve species in South America, Australia, and the Pacific Islands to New Guinea.—*Araucaria*, Jussieu, Genera Plantarum, 413 (1789); *Dombeya*, Lamarck, Encyclopédie Méthodique, ii, 301 (1786), not Cavanilles.

KEY to the species of Araucaria:

I. The large-leaved araucarias: all the leaves alike (except in mere size), flattened, ¾–2 inches long and sometimes to ¼ or ¾ inch broad, sharp-pointed: cone-scales not winged: cotyledons 2 and hypogeal (remaining under ground in germination).
   A. Leaves imbricated or overlapping on all sides of the branch.
      B. Shape of leaves ovate-lanceolate, mostly ⅓–¾ inch broad near base, densely imbricated, green on both surfaces............1. *A. araucana*
      BB. Shape of leaves narrow-lanceolate, usually ⅓ inch or less broad, loosely placed, more or less glaucous-green...................2. *A. angustifolia*
   AA. Leaves in two rows or ranks, so that the branch looks flat..........3. *A. Bidwillii*
II. The small-leaved araucarias: leaves not exceeding ½ inch long, often awl-like, more or less of two kinds being much shorter on the fruit-bearing branches and more densely imbricate: cone-scales winged: cotyledons 4 and epigeal (rising above ground in germination).
   A. Leaves on sterile branches flattened, oblong-lanceolate or elliptic, obtusish, densely imbricated, at least $\frac{1}{12}$ inch broad.............4. *A. Rulei*
   AA. Leaves on sterile branches awl-like or linear and not distinctly flattened, about $\frac{1}{24}$ inch thick.

B. Leaf mucronate, not spiny, slightly or not keeled on the ventral
   side, triangular, falcate.
   c. Position of leaves loosely appressed and imbricate, broad at base
      and slightly decurrent, about ¼ inch long..................5. *A. columnaris*
   cc. Position of leaves spreading, laterally compressed, decurrent,
       ⅓–½ inch long...6. *A. excelsa*
BB. Leaf spiny-pointed, rigid, much flattened, strongly keeled on both
    sides, quadrangular, scarcely falcate........................7. *A. Cunninghamii*

1. **Araucaria araucana.** Monkey-Puzzle Tree. Fig. 70. An odd and striking
tree of pyramidal habit, to 100 feet tall; branches generally in whorls of 5, at first
horizontal, with upward-curving (sometimes downward-curving) tips, but finally
becoming much deflexed; branchlets in opposite pairs, curved upward when young,
and continuing to grow until several feet long when adult: leaves imbricated and
persisting, even on the trunk, ovate-lanceolate, very stiff, leathery, and sharp-pointed,
2 inches long on the primary stem and branches, 1 inch long on the branchlets, slightly
concave at the base, bright green on both sides: staminate flowers 3–5 inches long:
cones globose-ovoid, 5–8 inches in diameter; scales with lanceolate acuminate appen-
dage about 1 inch long at apex; seeds about 1 inch long, obscurely 4-angled. Western
slope of the Andes in Chile. A few plants were taken to England in 1795 by A. Menzies,
but remained very rare until in 1844 Wm. Lobb sent a large supply of seeds. This is
the hardiest species and can probably be grown as far north as the Middle Atlantic
states in sheltered locations. It thrives well in mild climates in a heavy loamy soil in a
moist valley or position sheltered from rough winds. The branches are heavy and rather
brittle and the beauty and symmetry are soon destroyed if planted in an exposed position. One of the most distinct conifers, of singular and impressive appearance when
clothed to the ground with its whorls of regularly branched stout and heavy branches
covered throughout with dark green spiny leaves. Sometimes seen under glass as an
oddity.—*Araucaria araucana*, K. Koch, Dendrologie, ii, II, 206 (1873); *A. imbricata*,
Pavon in Mem. Acad. Med. Madr. i, 199 (1797); *Pinus araucana*, Molina, Saggio
Sulla Storia Naturale del Chile, 182 (1782).

2. **A. angustifolia.** Brazilian Araucaria or Candelabra-Tree. Plate XXXIII.
Tree to 100 feet tall, with spreading and slightly pendent branches raised and tufted at
the end, in whorls of 5–7, with the branchlets and leaves tufted at the ends, tending to
disappear below as the plant grows: leaves oblong-lanceolate, 1–2 inches long, somewhat decurrent, much attenuated and very sharp-pointed, deep glaucous green,
loosely imbricated: staminate flowers 4–5 inches long: cones globose, 5–6 inches
across; scales with a recurved spine at apex. Southern Brazil.—*Araucaria angustifolia*, O. Kuntze, Revisio Generum Plantarum, iii, 375 (1893); *A. brasiliana*, A.
Richard in Dict. Class. Hist. Nat. i, 512 (1822); *A. brasiliensis* of authors; *Colymbea
angustifolia*, Bertoloni, Piante del Brasile, 7 (1820).

Var. **elegans.** A form with more numerous and slenderer branches and more
crowded, narrower, and often glaucous leaves.—*Araucaria brasiliana* var. *elegans*,
Lawson; *A. brasiliana* var. *gracilis*, Carrière.

Var. **Ridolfiana.** A more robust form with longer and larger leaves. Named for
Count Ridolf.—*Araucaria brasiliana* var. *Ridolfiana*, Gordon.

3. **A. Bidwillii.** Bunya-bunya. Tree attaining 150 feet in height, the trunk free
of branches for about half its height; branches in whorls of 10–15, sparingly ramified:

leaves in two rows, lance-ovate and very sharp-pointed, ¾–1½ inches long, thick, firm and shining: staminate flowers 2–3 inches long: cones globose-ovoid, about 9 inches long and 7 inches through; scales terminating in an acute edge. Australia. A handsome and graceful species, one of the commonest in parks and grounds in warm countries and also frequently seen under glass. It bears the name of the botanical explorer, J. C. Bidwill, 1815–1853.—*Araucaria Bidwillii,* Hooker in Lond. Journ. Bot. ii, 503 (1843).

70. Araucaria araucana. (× ¼)

4. **A. Rulei.** Tree to 60 feet tall, with the branches in whorls of 5–7; branchlets elongated, horizontal to slightly pendent or slightly ascending at the ends; leafy branchlets very long: leaves oblong-lanceolate to elliptic, imbricated, concave, arched toward the branch, nearly or quite obtuse, ½–¾ inch long, with a prominent dorsal nerve, silvery-gray on the upper and rich glossy green on the lower side. It is stated by Dallimore and Jackson (Handbook of Coniferæ) that "this species was discovered by Mr. W. Duncan, botanical collector to Mr. John Rule of Melbourne, near the summit of a lofty volcano on an island near New Caledonia where it is exposed to the violent hurricanes which sweep over that country." A very handsome plant of regular habit with stout branchlets and dark green foliage. Variable at different ages. When young, the branches are often drooping and the leaves compressed and obscurely 4-angled and nearly or quite subulate: var. **polymorpha.**—*Araucaria Rulei,* F. Mueller ex Lindley in Gard. Chron. 868 (1861).

Var. **Goldieana.** A form with more sparingly ramified erect or ascending branches and narrower leaves.—*Araucaria Rulei* var. *Goldieana,* Masters.

A. Balansæ is a related species rarely grown. It is a slow-growing plant with usually 5 slender branches in a tier: leaves imbricate, short, ovate, ⅛ inch long, stiff, falcate, obtuse, dark olive-green: cones subglobose, 4 inches long. New Caledonia, where it was collected by M. Balansa.—*Araucaria Balansæ,* Brongniart & Gris in Ann. Sci. Nat., ser. 5, xiii, 351 (1870–71).

5. **A. columnaris.** A slender columnar tree attaining 200 feet in height, much narrower in shape than *A. excelsa* which it closely resembles when young; branches disposed as in *A. excelsa,* but tree tending to shed the lower ones; branchlets crowded on the branches and turning upward in a boat-like form: young leaves rather closely arranged on the branchlet and ¼–⅓ inch long, broad and slightly decurrent at base, slightly curved, mucronate; adult leaves densely imbricated, short and ovate, obtuse: staminate flowers 1½ inches long: cones globose-ovoid, 4–5 inches high and 3–4 inches in diameter; scales terminating in a long subulate mucro. New Caledonia and New Hebrides; discovered by Captain Cook, circumnavigator.—*Araucaria columnaris,*

Hooker in Bot. Mag. t. 4635 (1852); *A. Cookii*, R. Brown ex D. Don in Trans. Linn. Soc. xviii, 164 (1841); *Cupressus columnaris*, Forster, Florulæ Insularum Australium Prodromus, 67 (1786).

6. A. excelsa. NORFOLK-ISLAND-PINE. Tree attaining 200 feet in height; branches frondose, in whorls of 4–7: leaves curved and sharp-pointed, rather soft, ⅓–½ inch long, and densely placed on the horizontal or drooping branchlets: cones subglobose, broadest at base, 4–6 inches across; scales terminating in an incurved spine. Norfolk Islands. This is the most commonly cultivated species, being much grown as small pot-specimens. It is an excellent house plant, and keeps well in a cool room near a window. In summer it may be used on the veranda, but should be shaded.—*Araucaria excelsa*, R. Brown in Aiton, Hortus Kewensis, ed. 2, v, 412 (1813).

Var. **albo-spica.** SILVER STAR ARAUCARIA. Tips of young branchlets white.— *Araucaria excelsa* var. *albo-spica*, Masters.

Var. **glauca.** With bluish-green foliage.—*Araucaria excelsa* var. *glauca*, Carrière.

Var. **robusta.** A strong-growing form with deep green foliage.—*Araucaria excelsa* var. *robusta*, Kent.

Var. **virgata.** The primary branches without or with very short secondary branchlets.—*Araucaria excelsa* var. *virgata*, Schwerin.

7. A. Cunninghamii. HOOP-PINE. MORETON-BAY-PINE. Tree attaining 200 feet in height, with spreading branches in whorls of 4–7, the upper ascending, the lower in older plants somewhat depressed: leaves acicular, straight or nearly so, stiff and pungent, ¼–½ inch long, laterally strongly compressed, with the dorsal midrib decurrent: staminate flowers 2–3 inches long: cones ovoid-globose, about 3 inches long; scales terminating in a lanceolate recurved mucro. Northern New South Wales and Queensland, Australia; the most widely distributed of the Australian araucarias and a valuable timber tree. Named for Allan Cunningham, 1791–1839, botanist and traveler. It is a less formal and symmetrical plant than *A. excelsa* and not much cultivated.— *Araucaria Cunninghamii*, Sweet, Hortus Britannicus, 475 (1827).

Var. **glauca** has silvery glaucous foliage.—*Araucaria Cunninghamii* var. *glauca*, Endlicher.

19. AGATHIS. DAMMAR-PINE. Great evergreen monœcious or diœcious trees of warm and tropical parts of the eastern hemisphere (species 20 or less) with broad flat leaves unlike those of common conifers, bearing whorled branches and lacking distinct winter-buds: leaves opposite or alternate, usually more or less 2-ranked, flat and broad, not needle-like, coriaceous: staminate flowers axillary, cylindric; fertile flowers terminal or axillary: cones usually on short lateral branchlets, globose-ovoid, usually depressed, composed of numerous broadly obovate scales without bracts; each scale with a solitary reversed winged seed; cotyledons 2. Name (ag'-athis) from Greek referring to the shape of cone.—*Agathis*, Salisbury in Trans. Linn. Soc. viii, 311 (1807).

A. Leaves sessile, oblong to narrow-lanceolate, ⅓–¾ inch broad..............1. *A. australis*
AA. Leaves short-petioled, generally oblong, ¾–1½ inches broad.
   B. Staminate flowers ¾ inch long: leaves obtuse, usually opposite..........2. *A. alba*
   BB. Staminate flowers about 1½ inches long: leaves short-acuminate to obtuse,
      often alternate...3. *A. Brownii*

1. **Agathis australis.** KAURI-PINE. Fig. 71. Immense massive tree to 100 or extremely to 200 feet tall and with a trunk diameter of 20 feet; bark glaucous gray, falling off in large flakes: leaves opposite, rarely alternate, sessile, oblong or obovate-oblong, ¾–1½ inches long, obtuse, on young trees oblong to narrow-lanceolate and 2–4 inches long: staminate flowers ¾–1½ inches long, solitary: cones terminal on short branchlets, erect, subglobose, 2–3 inches across; scales terminating in a short mucro. New Zealand. Cultivated out-of-doors in California, but not very successfully. Kauri gum, much used in the manufacture of varnish, is the partly fossilized resin of *A. australis.* It is found 5–6 feet below the surface of the ground in the northern part of New Zealand where there were vast forests of this tree in ages past.—*Agathis australis,* Steudel, Nomenclator Botanicus, ed. 2, i, 34 (1841); *Dammara australis,* Lambert, A Description of the Genus Pinus, ii, 14 (1824).

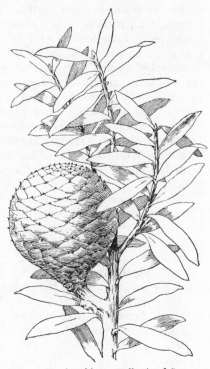

2. **A. alba.** Tree to 100 feet tall: leaves usually opposite, oblong to oblong-lanceolate, obtuse, 2–4 inches long, thickish, striated, dull green: staminate flowers about ¾ inch long: cones globose-ovoid, about 3½ inches long and 2–2½ inches in diameter. Malayan Archipelago. Introduced to Great Britain in 1804. Cultivated out-of-doors in California and in greenhouses elsewhere.—*Agathis alba,* Foxworthy in Philipp. Journ. Sci. vA, 173 (1910); *A. loranthifolia,* Salisbury in Trans. Linn. Soc. viii, 312 (1807); *A. Dam-mara,* A. Richard, De Coniferis, 83 (1826); *A. orientalis,* Rehder in Bradley Bibliography, ii, 25 (1912); *Dammara alba,* Lamarck, Encyclopédie Méthodique, ii, 259 (1786); *D. orientalis,* Lambert, A Description of the Genus Pinus, ed. 2, 70 (1832).

71. Agathis australis. (× ½)

3. **A. Brownii.** Tree to 150 feet tall, with nearly whorled branches: leaves ovate-lanceolate to oblong-lanceolate, obtuse to short-acuminate, 2–3, rarely to 4 inches long, striated: staminate flowers about 1½ inches long: cones globose-ovoid to obovoid, 3–4 inches long; seeds nearly ½ inch long, with an upright wing as long as the seed. Australia. Cultivated in California.—*Agathis Brownii,* new comb.; *A. robusta,* F. Mueller in Trans. Pharm. Soc. Vict. ii, 174 (1860); *Dammara robusta,* C. Moore ex F. Mueller, l. c.; *D. Brownii,* Lemaire, in Ill. Hort. ii, Misc. 60 (1855).

A. obtusa, from the New Hebrides, is closely related. It is but rarely cultivated in greenhouses in Europe.—*Agathis obtusa,* Morrison in Gard. Chron., ser. 3, xxi, 300 (1897); *Dammara obtusa,* Lindley in Journ. Hort. Soc. vi, 270 (1851).

20. CUPRESSUS. CYPRESS.　Monœcious evergreen trees, or sometimes shrubby, with shredding bark and aromatic foliage, about a dozen species, as the genus is now defined, in Pacific North America and Mexico, and in the eastern hemisphere from southeastern Europe to China, some of them well known in cultivation in the warmer parts of the United States and in tropics; branchlets quadrangular or terete, rarely compressed: leaves opposite, small, scale-like, appressed, minutely denticulate-ciliate, on young seedling plants linear-subulate and spreading: flowers minute, solitary on short branchlets, the two sexes on separate branches; staminate ovate or oblong, yellow, composed of 6–12 decussate stamens; fertile flowers subglobose: cones globular or nearly so, consisting of 3–7 pairs of ligneous peltate scales (Fig. 72), with a mucro or boss on the flattened apex, each bearing many or numerous seeds, but the lower scales usually sterile and smaller; they ripen the second year. *Cupressus* (cupress'-us) is the ancient Latin name of the cypress-tree, derived from the Greek *kuparissos.*—*Cupressus*, Linnæus, Species Plantarum, 1002 (1753).

Formerly, and at present by some authors, the species now separated as Chamæcyparis were included in Cupressus; that genus is distinguished by the few rather than many seeds under each cone-scale, cone annual, leaf-margins entire, and branchlets flattened. From Juniperus the genus Cupressus is separated at once by bearing regular cones instead of berry-like bodies; the awl-shaped leaves on seedlings of Cupressus are distinguished by bearing whitish lines or marks on the under rather than upper surface.

The cypresses yield close-grained and durable timber. The cypress lumber in North American markets, however, is Taxodium. Many of the cypresses become picturesque with age, and they abound in interesting horticultural varieties. Literary references are numerous. Propagation is by seeds when available, and the varieties by cuttings and by grafts on related stocks. While certain cypresses may survive in the milder parts of New England and New York, or with protection, they are not recommended for the North.

KEY to the species of Cupressus:

A. Branchlets irregularly ramified, the ultimate branchlets not in one plane.
　B. Apex of leaves obtuse or obtusish, dark green.
　　c. Leaves not at all or not conspicuously glandular: cones 1–1½ inches across.
　　　D. Length of leaves $\frac{1}{25}$ inch: staminate flowers with 10–12 stamens......................................1. *C. sempervirens*
　　　DD. Length of leaves $\frac{1}{16}$ inch: staminate flowers with 6–8 stamens..2. *C. macrocarpa*
　　cc. Leaves conspicuously resinous-glandular: cones ¾–1 inch long...3. *C. Macnabiana*
　B. Apex of leaves acute.
　　c. Leaves dark green: usually small tree or shrub with ascending or spreading branches: cones ⅓–1 inch across......4. *C. Goveniana*

cc. Leaves pale bluish-green or glaucescent: cones ¾-1¼ inches across.
  D. Branches upright or spreading; branchlets terete.
    E. Color of branchlets bright red, slender: leaves with small gland-pits.............................5. *C. guadalupensis*
    EE. Color of branchlets gray, stout: leaves glandless or conspicuously resinous-glandular.................6. *C. arizonica*
  DD. Branches spreading, drooping at the extremities; branchlets slightly compressed...........................7. *C. lusitanica*
AA. Branchlets regularly pinnately ramified, ultimate branchlets in one plane, slender, drooping.
  B. Cone ½-¾ inch across: branchlets not or slightly compressed.
    C. Leaves of branchlets acute, often free at tip: branchlets slightly compressed..................................7. *C. lusitanica* var. *Benthami*
    CC. Leaves obtusish: branchlets terete......................8. *C. torulosa*
  BB. Cone ⅓-½ inch across: branchlets distinctly flattened, dark green...9. *C. funebris*

1. **Cupressus sempervirens.** ITALIAN or MEDITERRANEAN CYPRESS. Fig. 72. The cypress of history, planted since ancient times: tree to 80 feet with erect or horizontal branches and dark green foliage; trunk with thin gray bark, smooth or slightly longitudinally fissured: leaves closely appressed, ovate, obtuse, glandular: staminate flowers with 10-12 stamens: cones short-oblong or nearly globose, 1 inch or more long; scales 8-14, with a short boss on the back, bract free at the apex; seeds 8-20 under each scale. Southern Europe and western Asia. Much planted in southern Europe particularly in its columnar form (var. *stricta*). It is hardy only in the southern states and California.—*Cupressus sempervirens*, Linnæus, Species Plantarum, 1002 (1753).

Var. **stricta.** COLUMNAR ITALIAN CYPRESS. Plate XXXIV. Tree with erect branches, forming a narrow columnar head. The classical cypress of the Greek and Roman writers.—*Cupressus sempervirens* var. *stricta*, Aiton, Hortus Kewensis, iii, 372 (1789); *C. fastigiata*, DeCandolle, Flore Française, v, 336 (1815); *C. sempervirens* var. *pyramidalis*, Nyman, Conspectus Floræ Europeæ, 675 (1881).

Var. **indica.** GLOBECONE ITALIAN CYPRESS. Similar to var. *stricta* in habit: cones globose, with 10 scales; bract acutely mucronate at the apex.— *Cupressus sempervirens* var. *indica*, Parlatore in DeCandolle, Prodromus, xvi, II, 469 (1868); *C. Roylei*, Carrière, Traité Général des Conifères, 128 (1855); *C. Whitleyana*, Hort.

Var. **horizontalis.** SPREADING ITALIAN CYPRESS. Branches horizontally spreading, forming a broad pyramidal head.—*Cupressus sempervirens* var. *horizontalis*, Gordon, Pinetum, 68 (1858); *C. horizontalis*, Miller, Gardeners Dictionary, ed. 8, no. 2 (1768).

72. Cupressus sempervirens. (× ½)

Related species is **C. Duclouxiana** from western China, differing from *C. semper-virens* var. *horizontalis* in its more slender and glaucous spreading branches, branchlets compressed, leaves very small (less than 1 line long), somewhat obtuse: cones nearly globular, about 1 inch across. It bears the name of Ducloux who collected it in Yunnan.

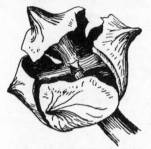

—*Cupressus Duclouxiana*, Hickel in Camus, Les Cyprès, 91 (1914); *C. torulosa*, Rehder & Wilson, Plantæ Wilsonianæ, ii, 54 (1916), not D. Don.

2. **C. macrocarpa.** MONTEREY CYPRESS. Plate XXXV. Fig. 73. Tree to 40, occasionally to 70 feet tall, with horizontal branches forming a broad spreading head; bark ridged, dark reddish-brown, separating into thick persistent scales; branchlets stout: leaves rhombic-ovate, swollen toward the tip, obtuse, closely appressed, not or obscurely glandular, dark or bright green: staminate flowers with 6–8 stamens: cones globular or oblong, to 1½ inches long; scales 8–12, with a short obtuse boss on the back; seeds about 20. Known in two native groves on the coast of central California near Monterey, the trees becoming irregular and picturesque when exposed to the sea and much visited by travelers; well known as a planted tree in many parts of the world, making a symmetrical and attractive subject.—*Cupressus macrocarpa*, Hartweg ex Gordon in Journ. Hort. Soc. Lond. iv, 296 (1849); *C. Hartwegii*, Carrière in Rev. Hort. 233 (1855).

73. Cone of Cupressus macrocarpa, after opening. Somewhat over-size.

Var. **Crippsii.** A juvenile form with rigid short branchlets and spreading sharp-pointed leaves; the tips of young branchlets silvery-white. Originated in nursery of Thomas Cripps at Tunbridge Wells, England.—*Cupressus macrocarpa* var. *Crippsii*, Masters.

Var. **fastigiata.** Branches ascending, forming a compact fastigiate head.—*Cupressus macrocarpa* var. *fastigiata*, Carrière.

Var. **lutea.** An upright fastigiate form with yellow foliage changing to green the second year.—*Cupressus macrocarpa* var. *lutea*, Dickson.

Var. **variegata.** Young foliage blotched with white.—*Cupressus macrocarpa* var. *variegata*, Lemaire.

C. Leylandii is described as a hybrid between *C. macrocarpa* and *Chamæcyparis nootkatensis:* tree and branchlets like *nootkatensis:* cones globose, to ¾ inch diameter, with 8 scales and about 5 seeds to each.—*Cupressus Leylandii*, Jackson & Dallimore, Kew Bull. 114 (1926); named for C. J. Leyland, Northumberland, England.

3. **C. Macnabiana.** MACNAB CYPRESS. Fig. 74. Shrub with several stems, or small tree to 20 feet, forming a dense pyramidal head; bark dark reddish-brown, thin, broken into ridges and separating into slightly attached scales: leaves ovate, obtuse, thickened at the apex, conspicuously resinous-glandular, dark green or glaucous: cones short-oblong, ¾–1 inch high, dark red-brown, often glaucous; scales usually 6, with prominent conical and curved bosses on the back. Bears the name of James McNab, 1810–1878, British gardener and botanist. Hillsides and canyons in California, north of San Francisco. Thought to be the hardiest of the true cypresses.—*Cupressus Macnabiana*, Murray in Edinb. New Phil. Journ. n. s. i, 293 (1855); *C.*

glandulosa, Hooker ex Gordon, Pinetum, 64 (1858); *C. Bakeri*, Jepson, Flora of California, 61 (1909); *C. nevadensis*, Abrams in Torreya, xix, 92 (1919).

Var. **sulphurea**. Branchlets with golden tips.—*Cupressus Macnabiana* var. *sulphurea*, Berckmans.

4. C. Goveniana. GOWEN or DWARF CYPRESS. Tree to 50 or seldom 75 feet or more tall but usually a shrub less than 20 feet and in its native place often only 1–2 feet high and coning; branches slender, erect or spreading, forming a broad, open or pyramidal head; bark bright reddish-brown, separating into thin thread-like scales; branchlets slender: leaves ovate, acute, closely appressed, inconspicuously glandular: abundant staminate flowers in spring: cones subglobose or short-oblong, ½– ¾ inch across; scales 6–8, with short blunt bosses; seed brown or nearly black. The name commemorates James Robert Gowen, died 1862, Secretary to the Horticultural Society of London when the plant was introduced. Coastal species in Monterey and Mendocino counties, California.—*Cupressus Goveniana*, Gordon in Journ. Hort. Soc. Lond. iv, 295 (1849); *C. californica*, Carrière, Traité Général des Conifères, 127 (1855); *C. pygmœa*, Sargent in Coult. Bot. Gaz. xxxi, 239 (1901).

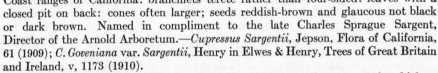

74. Cupressus Macnabiana.
(× ½)

Var. **glauca** has glaucous foliage.—*Cupressus Goveniana* var. *glauca*, Hort.

Some of the stock in cultivation as *C. Goveniana* may be **C. Sargentii**, a species of dry slopes in the Coast ranges of California: branchlets terete rather than four-sided: leaves with a closed pit on back: cones often larger; seeds reddish-brown and glaucous not black or dark brown. Named in compliment to the late Charles Sprague Sargent, Director of the Arnold Arboretum.—*Cupressus Sargentii*, Jepson, Flora of California, 61 (1909); *C. Goveniana* var. *Sargentii*, Henry in Elwes & Henry, Trees of Great Britain and Ireland, v, 1173 (1910).

5. C. guadalupensis. GUADALUPE CYPRESS. Wide-spreading tree, 40 feet high or more; bark grayish-brown, lustrous, exfoliating, brownish-red below; branchlets drooping, slender: leaves bluish-green, scentless, acute or acutish, obscurely glandular: cones globose, 1 inch across or more, with 6–8 very thick strongly bossed scales. Guadeloupe Islands, southern and Lower California. Introduced about 1880 to Europe.—*Cupressus guadalupensis*, S. Watson in Proc. Amer. Acad. xiv, 300 (1879); *C. macrocarpa* var. *guadalupensis*, Masters in Gard. Chron., ser. 3, xviii, 62 (1895).

Var. **glauca** has bluer foliage.—*Cupressus guadalupensis* var. *glauca*, Hort.

6. C. arizonica. ARIZONA CYPRESS. Tree to 40, and rarely to 70 feet tall, with horizontal short branches, forming a narrow, pyramidal, or broad open head; bark on young trees separating into large thin deciduous scales leaving a smooth red surface, on older trunks fibrous and dark red-brown; branchlets stout: leaves pale green or glaucous, ovate, obtuse, thickened at the apex, usually without glands: cones sub-globose to broadly ellipsoidal, dark red-brown and bloomy, ¾–1 inch across; scales 6–8, with stout pointed often curved bosses. Eastern Arizona, New Mexico, and

northern Mexico. Probably not generally planted: see var. *bonita.*—*Cupressus arizonica*, Greene in Bull. Torr. Bot. Club, ix, 64 (1882); *C. Benthamii* var. *arizonica*, Masters in Journ. Linn. Soc. xxxi, 340 (1896).

Var. bonita. SMOOTH CYPRESS. Mature leaves with conspicuous resinous gland on back, more or less glaucous: cones 1–1⅓ inches across; the scales with a short mucro. Central and southern Arizona. This is, next to *C. Macnabiana*, the hardiest cypress and probably hardy as far north as New York. The plant in cultivation as *C. arizonica* is apparently var. *bonita.*—*Cupressus arizonica* var. *bonita*, Lemmon, Handbook Western American Cone-bearers, ed. 3, 76 (1895); *C. glabra*, Sudworth in American Forestry, xvi, 88 (1910).

Var. compacta. A low roundish form.—*Cupressus arizonica* var. *compacta*, Schneider.

Var. glauca. A juvenile stage with silvery-gray foliage.— *Cupressus arizonica* var. *glauca*, Woodall.

7. C. lusitanica. MEXICAN CYPRESS; frequently known as PORTUGUESE CYPRESS. Fig. 75. Tree to 50 feet, with spreading branches and more or less pendulous, irregularly ramified, slightly compressed branchlets; trunk with reddish-brown bark fissured into long narrow strips: leaves ovate, acutish, appressed, slightly free at tips, glaucous: cones pedun-cled, about ½ inch across, covered with glaucous bloom; scales 6–8, with an elongated, pointed and usually hooked boss. Early introduced into Europe without record of nativity; long established in Portugal, territory anciently known as Lusitania, whence the specific name. In the meantime a Mexican cypress cultivated in Europe had been described as *Cupressus Benthamii* (in honor of George Bentham, 1800–1884, one of the ablest of British botanists). It is now established that *C. lusitanica* is native at high elevations in Mexico and Guatemala, and that *Benthamii* is one of the various forms of it (see A. Bruce Jackson, Gard. Chron. ser. 3, lvii, 206, 259, 1915). The name *lusitanica* continues to hold even though seemingly a misnomer, but it records the history and the long association of the tree with Portugal and is therefore not inappropriate.—*Cupressus lusitanica*, Miller, Gardeners Dictionary, ed. 8, no. 3 (1768); *C. pendula*, L'Héritier, Stirpes Novæ, 15 (1784); *C. glauca*, Lamarck, Encyclopédie Méthodique, ii, 243 (1786); *C. Lindleyi*, Klotzsch ex Endlicher, Synopsis Coniferarum, 59 (1847); *C. sinensis*, Hort.

Var. Benthami. BENTHAM CYPRESS. Narrow pyramidal tree with spreading or deflexed branches; branchlets pinnately and regularly ramified in one plane, the ultimate branchlets slightly compressed: leaves acute, free at the tips, with a glandular pit on back.—*Cupressus lusitanica* var. *Benthamii*, Carrière, Traité Général des Conifères, ed. 2, 155 (1867); *C. thurifera*, Schlechtendal in Linnaea, xii, 493 (1838); *C.*

75. Cupressus lusi-tanica. About natural size.

Benthamii, Endlicher, Synopsis Coniferarum, 59 (1847); *C. excelsa*, Scott ex Carrière, Traité Général des Conifères, 128 (1855).

Var. **Knightiana**. KNIGHT CYPRESS. Similar to the preceding variety, but branchlets more compressed and very regularly pinnately branched, the ultimate branchlets of nearly equal length, green to glaucous. Named for Joseph Knight, English nurseryman.—*Cupressus lusitanica* var. *Knightiana*, Rehder in Journ. Arnold Arb. i, 52 (1919); *C. Knightiana*, Knight & Perry ex Gordon, Pinetum, 61 (1858); *C. Benthami* var. *Knightiana*, Masters in Journ. Linn. Soc. xxxi, 340 (1896).

8. **C. torulosa**. BHUTAN CYPRESS. Tall pyramidal tree to 150 feet high, with short horizontal branches ascending at the extremities; trunk with brown bark peeling off in long narrow fibrous strips; branchlets slender, drooping: leaves rhombic-ovate, acutish or obtusish, appressed or slightly spreading at the apex, bright or bluish-green: cones globular, nearly sessile, ½-¾ inch across; scales 8–10 with a short obtuse inconspicuous boss. Himalayas.—*Cupressus torulosa*, D. Don, Prodromus Floræ Nepalensis, 55 (1825); *C. nepalensis*, Loudon, Encyclopædia of Trees and Shrubs, 1118 (1842).

Var. **Corneyana**. Branches and branchlets pendulous; the branchlet-systems not distinctly distichous. Introduced before 1850.—*Cupressus torulosa* var. *Corneyana*, Carrière; *C. Corneyana*, Knight & Perry, *nomen*, "Mr. Corneys' cypress."

9. **C. funebris**. MOURNING CYPRESS. Fig. 76. Tree to 60 feet tall, with wide-spreading pendulous branches and branchlets; branchlets flattened; trunk with brown smooth bark: leaves deltoid-ovate, acute, light green, often slightly spreading at the apex: cones short-peduncled, globose, ⅓–½ inch across; scales 8, with a short-pointed boss. China.—

76. Cupressus funebris. (×½)

Cupressus funebris, Endlicher, Synopsis Coniferarum, 58 (1847); *C. pendula*, Lambert, A Description of the Genus Pinus, i, 97 (1803), not Thunber.

A related species is **C. cashmeriana**. KASHMIR CYPRESS. Tree with ascending branches and pendulous branchlets; branchlets compressed: lateral leaves spreading: cones dark brown, ellipsoidal, nearly ½ inch across; scales 10 with triangular reflexed umbo. Kashmir.—*Cupressus cashmeriana*, Royle ex Carrière, Traité Général des Conifères, ed. 2, 161 (1867); *C. torulosa* var. *kashmiriana*, Kent in Veitch, Manual of the Coniferæ, ed. 2, 234 (1900); *C. funebris* var. *glauca*, Masters in Kew, Hand-list of the Coniferæ, 37 (1896), *nomen*.

21. CHAMÆCYPARIS. FALSE-CYPRESS. Monœcious evergreen aromatic trees of six species in North America and eastern Asia closely allied to Cupressus and sometimes combined with that genus but differ in the smaller cones which mature the first year and bear 5 or fewer seeds to each scale and also in flat branches and entire leaves, popular in cultivation; bark scaly or fissured on old wood; leading shoots nodding; branchlets usually flattened and pinnately ramified: leaves scale-like (only in the juvenile state subulate), opposite and decussate, densely clothing the branchlets: flowers small; the fertile ones inconspicuous, globose; staminate yellow or red, oblong, often conspicuous by their abundance: cones small, globular, with 6–11 bracts, each bearing 2, rarely up to 5, winged seeds, ripening the first season. The name Chamæcyparis (chamecyp′-aris) is apparently an adaptation from Pliny's Chamæcyparissus, "ground-cypress," derived from Greek *chamai*, on the ground, and *kuparissos*, cypress, although its species are not lower but generally taller than the true cypresses.— *Chamæcyparis*, Spach, Histoire Naturelle des Végétaux, Phan. xi, 329 (1842).

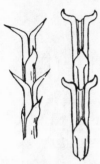

77. Axial leaves of Chamæcyparis. (× 2½). C. pisifera left, C. obtusa right.

The false-cypresses are hardy trees although some of them become ragged and irregular in very exposed places. They abound in dwarf forms and therefore have increased in popularity in recent years. The many named kinds are propagated by cuttings (which may be slow and difficult) and also by grafting.

The old genus Retinispora or Retinospora represents juvenile forms of Chamæcyparis and Thuja.

On seedling or juvenile plants of Chamæcyparis the leaves may be all awl-shaped or subulate, and also spreading away from the twig. In certain horticultural forms, particularly those to which the name *ericoides* (heath-like) is applied, the juvenile stage may persist and become a character of the variety. Such states, propagated asexually, may be difficult to place in the proper species when labels and records are lost, although the specific marks may remain evident to the botanist. The spray, or branchlets, of the false-cypresses usually has a distinct upper and lower surface, as if these sprays were compound leaves; along the axes or stems of these sprays of *C. Lawsoniana* and *C. obtusa* the little scale-like leaves on the two sides are distinctly larger or longer than those on the face, or on top and bottom (Fig. 77), and these distinctions separate the species into two groups (A and AA in the key). These leaves are perhaps ⅛ inch or less long.

KEY to the species of Chamæcyparis:

A. Leaves on the sides and on the (lower and upper) faces of the branchlets of practically equal size, readily distinguished under a good hand-lens (left, Fig. 77).
  B. Branchlets not distinctly pinnately placed; each branchlet flattened, slender: leaves glandular and bluish-green..........................1. *C. thyoides*
  BB. Branchlets arranged in one plane as if a pinnate leaf.
    c. Under side of leaf with white or glaucous markings: branchlets themselves flattened...2. *C. pisifera*

cc. Under side of leaf without white markings.
    D. Back of leaf bearing a pit or groove..........................3. *C. formosensis*
      DD. Back of leaf keeled or without gland or pit.....................4. *C. nootkatensis*
AA. Leaves on the two sides of the twig distinctly larger than those on the faces,
    the body of leaf closely appressed (right, Fig. 77).
  B. Without a gland on the back, manifestly obtuse at apex..............5. *C. obtusa*
  BB. With a gland or a pit on back, acute or nearly so at apex.............6. *C. Lawsoniana*

1. **Chamæcyparis thyoides.** WHITE-CEDAR. Fig. 78. Widespread tree near the
Atlantic and Gulf coasts, hardiest but least ornamental in cultivation of the species
probably in part because its wet or swampy habitat is not available; to 70–80 feet,
with erect-spreading branches; trunk with reddish-brown fissured bark divided into
flat connected ridges; branchlets irregularly arranged, spreading, not pendulous, very
thin and slender, flattened: leaves closely imbricate on the leading shoots, spreading
at the apex, acute, keeled, glaucous or light green, with a conspicuous gland on the
back, fragrant: cones small, ¼ inch diameter, bluish-purple, with glaucous bloom;
seeds 1 or 2, with wings as broad as the seed. From Maine southward near the coast
to Florida and west to Mississippi.—*Chamæcyparis thyoides*, Britton, Sterns & Poggenburg, Preliminary Catalogue... of New York City, 71 (1888); *C. sphæroidea*, Spach,
Histoire Naturelle des Végétaux, Phan. xi, 331 (1842); *Cupressus thyoides*, Linnæus,
Species Plantarum, 1003 (1753).

Var. **andelyensis.** ANDELY RETINISPORA. Intermediate form between var.
ericoides and the type; bluish-green and of erect growth, with loosely appressed lanceolate leaves; often some branchlets with leaves of the type and some with leaves of
var. *ericoides*. Originated in Andeleys, France, at nursery of Couchois.—*Chamæcyparis thyoides* var. *andelyensis*, Schneider; *C. sphæroidea andelyensis*, Carrière; *C.
leptoclada*, Hochstetter; *Retinispora leptoclada*, Hort.

Var. **ericoides.** CEDAR RETINISPORA. Compact shrub of erect dense habit; leaves
linear-lanceolate, spreading,
with 2 glaucous lines be-
neath, coloring in winter
usually reddish-brown.—
Chamæcyparis thyoides var.
ericoides, Sudworth; *C. ericoides*, Carrière; *Retinispora
ericoides*, Hort.

Var. **glauca.** Of com-
pact habit, very glaucous,
with silvery hue.—*Chamæ-
cyparis thyoides* var. *glauca*,
Sudworth; *C. sphæroidea
glauca*, Endlicher; *C. sphæroidea* var. *kewensis*, Hort.

Var. **Hoveyi.** Slender,
with dense terminal tufts.—
Chamæcyparis thyoides var.
Hoveyi, Hort.; *C. sphæroidea*
var. *Hoveyi*, Beissner.

78. Chamæcyparis thyoides. (× ⅓)

Var. **variegata.**   Branchlets   partially   colored   golden-yellow.—*Chamœcyparis thyoides* var. *variegata*, Sudworth; *Cupressus thyoides variegata*, Loudon.

2. **C. pisifera.**   SAWARA CYPRESS.   Figs. 77 left, 79.   A large tree in Japan, much

79. Chamæcyparis pisifera. (× 1)

planted in temple grounds, and in many forms in this country, the leaves conspicuously sharppointed; to 100 feet, with horizontal branches; trunk with red-brown thin rather smooth bark peeling off in thin strips; branchlets flattened, distichously arranged in horizontal planes and somewhat pendulous: leaves ovate-lanceolate, with mucronate tips, slightly spreading, obscurely glandular, shining above, with whitish lines beneath: cones globular, ¼–⅓ inch diameter, brown; scales 10, rarely 12, with a small mucro at the depressed center, each scale with 1–2 broad-winged seeds. Japan. Hardy as far north as southern Ontario and New England. A tree of fairly rapid growth with a narrow-pyramidal rather loosely branched head, the horizontal branches more or less ascending at the extremities; it is a thinner tree than the other species of the genus and is likely to lose its lower branches rather early. — *Chamœcyparis pisifera*, Siebold & Zuccarini in Endlicher, Synopsis Coniferarum, 64 (1847); *Cupressus pisifera*, Koch, Dendrologie, ii, II, 170 (1873); *Retinispora pisifera*, Siebold & Zuccarini, Flora Japonica, ii, 39 (1842).

Color cultivars are *aurea, filifera aurea* and *aureo-variegata, nana aureo-variegata, sulphurea*, and also forms of *plumosa* and *squarrosa;* dwarf or suppressed forms, *nana, filifera nana, squarrosa minima;* odd or pendulous, the *filifera* forms; juvenile forms, retaining awl-leaves for years, the *plumosa* and *squarrosa* kinds.

Var. **aurea.**   A form with golden-yellow foliage.—*Chamœcyparis pisifera* var. *aurea*, Carrière.

Var. **filifera**. THREAD RETINISPORA. Branches elongated and slender, thread-like, gracefully pendulous, with distant branchlets and leaves.—*Chamæcyparis pisifera* var. *filifera*, Beissner; *C. obtusa filifera*, Hort.; *C. pisifera filifera pendula*, Hort.; *Retinispora filifera*, Standish.

Var. **filifera aurea**. A form of var. *filifera* with the young growth golden-yellow.—*Chamæcyparis pisifera* var. *filifera aurea*, Beissner.

Var. **filifera aureo-variegata**. A form of var. *filifera* with the branchlets variegated with yellow, but less elongated and less thread-like.— *Chamæcyparis pisifera* var. *filifera aureo-variegata*, Beissner.

Var. **filifera nana**. A var. *filifera* form of bushy habit less than 3 feet high.—*Chamæcyparis pisifera* var. *filifera nana*, Hesse.

Var. **nana**. Very low flat-topped form with dark blue-green leaves.—*Chamæcyparis pisifera* var. *nana*, Beissner.

Var. **nana aureo-variegata**. A form of var. *nana* having foliage tipped with yellow.—*Chamæcyparis pisifera* var. *nana aureo-variegata*, Hornibrook.

Var. **plumosa**. PLUME RETINISPORA. Fig. 80. Habit conical; branches almost erect, with slender branchlets of feathery appearance: leaves subulate, pointed and slightly spreading, bright green. Intermediate between the type and var. *squarrosa*. —*Chamæcyparis pisifera* var. *plumosa*, Beissner; *Retinispora plumosa*, Veitch.

Var. **plumosa argentea**. A form of the above with tips of branchlets whitish.—*Chamæcyparis pisifera* var. *plumosa argentea*, Beissner.

Var. **plumosa aurea**. Plate XXIX. A very showy form with young growth of golden-yellow color.—*Chamæcyparis pisifera* var. *plumosa aurea*, Beissner; *Retinispora plumosa aurea*, Standish.

80. Chamæcyparis pisifera var. plumosa. About full size.

Var. **plumosa flavescens**. Tips of young branchlets yellowish. — *Chamæcyparis pisifera* var. *plumosa flavescens*, Beissner; *Retinispora plumosa sulphurea*, Hort.

Var. **plumosa lutescens**. Low form of var. *plumosa* with yellow-tipped branchlets. —*Chamæcyparis pisifera* var. *plumosa lutescens*, Hort.

Var. **squarrosa**. MOSS RETINISPORA. Densely branched bushy tree or shrub with spreading feathery branchlets: leaves linear, spreading, glaucous above, silvery below; one of the forms that long holds its essential juvenile character, yet now and then it produces branches with mature or scale-like leaves in the midst of the awl-like leaves. —*Chamæcyparis pisifera* var. *squarrosa*, Beissner & Hochstetter; *C. squarrosa Veitchii*, Hort.; *Retinispora squarrosa*, Siebold & Zuccarini; *R. leptoclada*, Zuccarini.

Var. **squarrosa dumosa.** Of more compact and slower-growing habit than the preceding.—*Chamæcyparis pisifera* var. *squarrosa dumosa*, Beissner.

Var. **squarrosa intermedia.** Globose form with juvenile foliage, or often sending up a leading shoot with intermediate foliage at top giving a spire-like effect. This has been known as var. *nana* but should not be confused with *C. pisifera* var. *nana* or *C. pisifera* var. *filifera nana*.—*Chamæcyparis pisifera* var. *squarrosa intermedia*, Hornibrook; *C. pisifera* var. *squarrosa pygmœa*, Hort.

Var. **squarrosa minima.** Very dwarf with leaves recurving at right angles to the branchlet.—*Chamæcyparis pisifera* var. *squarrosa minima*, Hornibrook.

Var. **squarrosa Sieboldii.** A dwarf globose form.—*Chamæcyparis pisifera* var. *squarrosa Sieboldii*, Hort.

Var. **squarrosa sulphurea.** A form of var. *squarrosa* with yellow foliage.—*Chamæcyparis pisifera* var. *squarrosa sulphurea*, Beissner.

Var. **sulphurea.** A form with light yellow foliage.—*Chamæcyparis pisifera* var. *sulphurea*, Schelle.

3. **C. formosensis.** FORMOSA CYPRESS. A titanic tree in its native mountains, planted in Europe but probably not yet appearing in American lists; occasionally to 190 feet high, with a trunk 20 feet in diameter and with spreading branches pendulous at the extremities; branchlets dull green on both sides or slightly bloomy below: leaves appressed, free at the incurved apex, obscurely glandular: cones short-ellipsoidal, ¼–⅓ inch across; scales with a conspicuous broadly triangular boss; seeds 2 under each scale, narrow-winged. Formosa.—*Chamæcyparis formosensis*, Matsumura in Bot. Mag. Tokyo, xv, 137 (1901); *Cupressus formosensis*, Henry in Elwes & Henry, Trees of Great Britain and Ireland, v, 1149 (1910).

4. **C. nootkatensis.** NOOTKA CYPRESS. YELLOW-CEDAR. Plate XXXVII. Fig. 81. Probably the hardiest of the false-cypresses in the East excepting *C. thyoides*, attractive in cultivation: tree to 120 feet, with ascending branches, pendulous at the extremities; trunk with brownish-gray irregularly fissured bark separating into large thin scales; branchlets distichously arranged, on the upper part of the tree in vertical planes, slightly flattened or nearly quadrangular, pendulous: leaves densely imbricate, usually dark green, acute, on the leading shoots spreading at apex, mostly without glands: cones subglobose, nearly ½ inch diameter, dark red-brown, with glaucous bloom; scales 4–6 with erect pointed bosses, each with 2–4 broad-winged seeds. Southwestern Alaska to Oregon. First made known from Nootka Sound, Vancouver Island. Hardy as far north as Ontario and New England. Handsome tree of pyramidal shape with dark green lustrous foliage, the branchlets with more or less pendulous tips.—*Chamæcyparis nootkatensis*, Sudworth, Nomenclature of the Arborescent Flora of the United States, 79 (1897); *C. nutkaensis*, Spach, Histoire Naturelle des Végétaux, Phan. xi, 333 (1842); *Cupressus nootkatensis*, Lambert, A Description of the Genus Pinus, ii, 18 (1824).

Var. **compacta.** A dwarf compact form.—*Chamæcyparis nootkatensis* var. *compacta*, Beissner.

Var. **glauca.** With very glaucous foliage.—*Chamæcyparis nootkatensis* var. *glauca*, Beissner; *Thujopsis borealis* var. *glauca*, Jaeger.

Var. **lutea.** The young growth colored light yellow.—*Chamæcyparis nootkatensis* var. *lutea*, Beissner.

CEDARS, LARCHES, CYPRESSES, AND OTHERS   163

Var. **pendula.** A form with distinctly pendulous branches.—*Chamæcyparis nootkatensis* var. *pendula*, Beissner.

5. **C. obtusa.** HINOKI CYPRESS. Figs. 77 right, 82. Handsome large tree with dark green lustrous foliage and leaves conspicuously blunt, known in cultivation mostly in many varieties; to 120 feet tall, with horizontal branches; trunk with reddish-brown rather smooth bark, peeling off in thin strips; branchlets frond-like, arranged in horizontal planes, flattened, pendulous: leaves bright green and shining above, with whitish lines beneath, thickish, the facial ones rhombic-ovate, obtuse, and very closely appressed, with a gland on the back, the lateral ones free at the acutish apex: cones globose, nearly ½ inch diameter, brown; scales 8, rarely 10, with a small mucro on the depressed back, each with 2, rarely 3–5 narrowly winged seeds. Japan. Hardy as far north as Ontario and New England. A handsome tree with dark green lustrous foliage.—*Chamæcyparis obtusa*, Siebold & Zuccarini in Endlicher, Synopsis Coniferarum, 63 (1847); *Cupressus obtusa*, Koch, Dendrologie, ii, II, 168 (1873); *Retinispora obtusa*, Siebold & Zuccarini, Flora Japonica, ii, 38 (1842).

81. Chamæcyparis nootkatensis. Somewhat enlarged.

Color cultivars are *albo-spicata, aurea, aurea Youngii, Crippsii, gracilis aurea, nana aurea, tetragona;* dwarf or low forms, *compacta, lycopodioides, nana, nana aurea, pygmæa, tetragona* and subvar. *minima, Tsatsumi;* main stature and habit forms, *breviramea, erecta, ericoides* (juvenile), *filicoides, filiformis, gracilis* and *gracilis aurea, lycopodioides* (mostly low), *magnifica, pendula.*

Var. **formosana.** Tree to 130 feet tall; branchlets slenderer and thinner: cones subglobose, about ⅓ inch across; seeds smaller. Formosa. Introduced to the Arnold Arboretum by E. H. Wilson in 1918. Probably hardy only in the southern states and California.—*Chamæcyparis obtusa* var. *formosana*, Hayata in Journ. Coll. Sci. Tokyo, xxv, 208 (1908).

Var. **albo-spicata.** Young shoots at first creamy-white, changing later to pale green.—*Chamæcyparis obtusa* var. *albospicata*, Beissner.

Var. **aurea.** Young foliage golden-yellow.—*Chamæcyparis obtusa* var. *aurea*, Beissner.

Var. **aurea Youngii.** Similar to var. *aurea* but the branchlets are more pendulous and the color less bright.—*Chamæcyparis obtusa* var. *aurea Youngii*, Nash.

Var. **breviramea.** Pyramidal form with short branches.—*Chamæcyparis obtusa* var. *breviramea*, Hort.

Var. **compacta.** FOOTBALL CYPRESS. Of dwarf and dense broadly conical habit with much crowded short branchlets at the end of the short branches.—*Chamæcyparis obtusa* var. *compacta*, Hartweg & Ruempl.; *Retinispora obtusa gracilis compacta*, Hort.

Var. **Crippsii.** With pale yellow foliage. Bears the name of the Cripps Nursery, England.—*Chamæcyparis obtusa* var. *Crippsii*, Rehder.

82. Chamæcyparis obtusa. (× 2)

Var. **erecta.** Fastigiate form with ascending branches and bright green foliage.—
Chamæcyparis obtusa var. *erecta*, Beissner; *Retinispora obtusa erecta*, Waterer.

Var. **ericoides.** SANDER RETINISPORA. Of low subglobose habit with bluish-gray
linear spreading blunt leaves about ⅛ inch long, thickish,˙marked with a green line
above.—*Chamæcyparis obtusa* var. *ericoides*, Boehmer; *Retinispora Sanderi*, Sander;
Juniperus Sanderi, Hort.

Var. **filicoides.** FERNSPRAY RETINISPORA. Of slow growth, with short and densely
frond-like arranged branchlets.—*Chamæcyparis obtusa* var. *filicoides*, Beissner.

Var. **filiformis.** Branches thick and thread-like, drooping.—*Chamæcyparis obtusa*
var. *filiformis*, Hort.

Var. **gracilis.** Compact pyramidal form with dark green foliage; branchlets with
slightly pendulous tips.—*Chamæcyparis obtusa* var. *gracilis*, Nash; *Cupressus obtusa
gracilis*, Lav.

Var. **gracilis aurea.** Graceful form, foliage bright yellow when young, changing
later to greenish-yellow.—*Chamæcyparis obtusa* var. *gracilis aurea*, Beissner.

Var. **lycopodioides.** CLUBMOSS RETINISPORA. Low form of somewhat irregular
habit, with spreading rigid branches and thick nearly terete dark green branchlets:
leaves very crowded and disposed in more than 4 ranks.—*Chamæcyparis obtusa* var.
lycopodioides, Carrière.

Var. **magnifica.** A vigorous form with stout branchlets and lustrous bright green
foliage.—*Chamæcyparis obtusa* var. *magnifica*, Beissner.

Var. **nana.** Low form of slow growth with short deep green branchlets.—*Chamæcyparis obtusa* var. *nana*, Carrière.

Var. **nana aurea.** A form of the above with the young growth golden-yellow.—
Chamæcyparis obtusa var. *nana aurea*, Carrière.

Var. **pendula.** Habit drooping.—*Chamæcyparis obtusa* var. *pendula*, Hort.

Var. **pygmæa.** Very dwarf form with horizontal almost creeping densely frond-like
branches; exceedingly interesting form for rockeries.—*Chamæcyparis obtusa* var.
pygmæa, Carrière.

Var. **tetragona.** A dwarf broad-pyramidal form with crowded irregular branchlet-systems, the branchlets more or less 4-angled and partly golden-yellow, the shaded
parts green.—*Chamæcyparis obtusa* var. *tetragona*, Rehder; *C. obtusa* var. *tetragona
aurea*, Nicholson.

Var. **tetragona minima.** Cushion-like form with light green foliage.—*Chamæcyparis obtusa* var. *tetragona minima*, Hornibrook.

Var. **Tsatsumi.** Low spreading form with somewhat twisted dense thread-like
branchlets and scale-like dark green leaves.—*Chamæcyparis obtusa* var. *Tsatsumi*, Slavin.
Other listed names are *acuta* and *decussata*.

6. **C. Lawsoniana.** LAWSON CYPRESS. Plate XXXVI. Fig. 83. Noble forest tree of
the Northwest, known in cultivation in great numbers of named forms but in nature
not represented in recognized botanical varieties, one of the most beautiful conifers for
planting; to 200 feet, with horizontally spreading and usually pendulous branches;
bark reddish-brown, thick, divided into rounded ridges covered with small scales;
branchlets flattened, frond-like, arranged in horizontal planes: leaves closely appressed,
obtuse or somewhat acute, usually bright green, marked below with often indistinct
white streaks, with a gland on the back: staminate catkins bright red (yellow in **all**

other species): cones globose, about ⅓ inch across, red-brown and often glaucous; scales 8, with a thin reflexed mucro, each with 2–4 broad-winged seeds. Seeds of this cypress were sent in 1854 by William Murray to the Lawson nurseries at Edinburgh, Charles Lawson, 1794–1873, being then head of the firm. Moist hillsides and canyons, southwestern Oregon and northern California; known also as Port Orford cedar, from a place in Oregon. Hardy as far north as New York and in sheltered positions to Massachusetts. This is one of the most beautiful conifers and it forms in cultivation usually narrow pyramidal trees densely furnished to the ground with branches; it is very

83. Chamæcyparis Lawsoniana
Spray natural size.

variable, and about 80 garden forms are known in European nurseries and collections. —*Chamæcyparis Lawsoniana*, Parlatore in Ann. Mus. Stor. Nat. Fir. i, 181 (1864); *Cupressus Lawsoniana*, Murray in Edinb. New Phil. Journ. n. s., i, 292 (1855).

There are numerous forms of *C. Lawsoniana* which may be classified as follows: color forms, *albo-spica, argentea, aurea, glauca, lutea, Stewarti, versicolor, Westermanni;* forms of upright or columnar habit, *Allumii, erecta, Fletcheri, Fraseri, pyramidalis, Wisseli, Youngii;* forms of spreading, pendulous or contorted habit, *filiformis, Forsteckiana, gracilis, intertexta, Krameri, lycopodioides, nidiformis, patula, pendula;* compact or dwarf forms, *Bowleri, darleyensis, minima glauca, nana.*

Var. **albo-spica**. CREAM CYPRESS. Tip of branchlets creamy-white, of slender habit.—*Chamæcyparis Lawsoniana* var. *albo-spica*, Beissner.

Var. Allumii. Scarab Cypress. Of columnar habit, foliage very glaucous with a bluish metallic hue; the best blue columnar form.—*Chamæcyparis Lawsoniana* var. *Allumii*, Beissner.

Var. argentea. Of slender habit, with very glaucous almost silvery foliage; here belongs "Silver Queen."—*Chamæcyparis Lawsoniana* var. *argentea*, Beissner.

Var. aurea. Foliage golden-yellow when young.—*Chamæcyparis Lawsoniana* var. *aurea*, Hort.

Var. Bowleri. A dense compact form with the tips of the branchlets elongated and pendulous.—*Chamæcyparis Lawsoniana* var. *Bowleri*, Hort.

Var. darleyensis. Of low loose habit, foliage slightly golden-yellow.—*Chamæcyparis Lawsoniana* var. *darleyensis*, Hort.

Var. erecta. Dense columnar habit and bright green foliage; one of the most beautiful varieties but somewhat tender.—*Chamæcyparis Lawsoniana* var. *erecta*, Sudworth; *C. Lawsoniana* var. *erecta viridis*, Beissner.

Var. erecta glauca. Similar in habit to the above, but with glaucous foliage.—*Chamæcyparis Lawsoniana* var. *erecta glauca*, Beissner.

Var. filiformis. Branches spreading, the branchlets drooping.—*Chamæcyparis Lawsoniana* var. *filiformis*, Beissner.

Var. Fletcheri. A dense columnar form with glaucous leaves. Originated at Fletcher's Nurseries, Chertsey, England.—*Chamæcyparis Lawsoniana* var. *Fletcheri*, Fletcher & Sons.

Var. Forsteckiana. Branchlets twisted into cockscomb-like heads.—*Chamæcyparis Lawsoniana* var. *Forsteckiana*, Beissner.

Var. Fraseri. Similar to var. *Allumii* but less narrow in habit and with dark blue foliage.—*Chamæcyparis Lawsoniana* var. *Fraseri*, Beissner.

Var. glauca. Steel Cypress. Foliage of metallic glaucous tint; one of the hardier forms; here belongs "Triomphe de Boskoop."—*Chamæcyparis Lawsoniana* var. *glauca*, Beissner.

Var. gracilis. Elegant light green form with graceful pendulous branchlets.—*Chamæcyparis Lawsoniana* var. *gracilis*, Beissner; *C. Lawsoniana* var. *gracilis pendula*, Hort.

Var. intertexta. Glaucous growth, with remote pendulous branches and distant thickish branchlets.—*Chamæcyparis Lawsoniana* var. *intertexta*, Beissner.

Var. Krameri. Of thin habit with slender whip-like branches.—*Chamæcyparis Lawsoniana* var. *Krameri*, Beissner.

Var. lutea. Of compact habit, young growth clear yellow.—*Chamæcyparis Lawsoniana* var. *lutea*, Beissner.

Var. lycopodioides. Branches irregular, branchlets twisted.—*Chamæcyparis Lawsoniana* var. *lycopodioides*, Beissner.

Var. minima glauca. Dwarf and compact conical form with dark steel-blue foliage. —*Chamæcyparis Lawsoniana* var. *minima glauca*, Beissner.

Var. nana. Dwarf globose habit.—*Chamæcyparis Lawsoniana* var. *nana*, Beissner.

Var. nana glauca. A form of the above with young growth bluish-green.—*Chamæcyparis Lawsoniana* var. *nana glauca*, Beissner.

Var. nidiformis. Horizontal branches radiating from a dense center, branchlets drooping at tips.—*Chamæcyparis Lawsoniana* var. *nidiformis*, Beissner.

Var. patula. Of compact habit with spreading branches and glossy dark green leaves.—*Chamæcyparis Lawsoniana* var. *patula*, Hort.

Var. pendula. With pendulous branches.—*Chamæcyparis Lawsoniana* var. *pendula*, Beissner.

Var. pyramidalis. Of columnar habit, the young growth white in its form alba.— *Chamæcyparis Lawsoniana* var. *pyramidalis*, Hort.

Var. Stewarti. Foliage of young shoots deep yellow.—*Chamæcyparis Lawsoniana* var. *Stewarti*, Hort.

Var. versicolor. A particolored form having some leaves creamy-white and those near tips of shoots yellow below and light green above.—*Chamæcyparis Lawsoniana* var. *versicolor*, Hort.

Var. Westermanni. Leaves light yellow; of stiff pyramidal habit.—*Chamæcyparis Lawsoniana* var. *Westermanni*, Hort.

Var. Wisseli. Columnar, foliage glaucous.—*Chamæcyparis Lawsoniana* var. *Wisseli*, Hort.

Var. Youngii. Of pyramidal habit with spreading sometimes twisted branches.— *Chamæcyparis Lawsoniana* var. *Youngii*, Hort.

Other listed names under this species are: *Drummondii, elegans, elegantissima, globosa, Hollandi, lutescens, monumentalis, Ribunei, Rosenthalii, semper-horizontalis, stricta, sulphurea, tortuosa, Veitchii glauca.*

22. THUJA. ARBOR-VITÆ. Trees and shrubs, two species in North America, four in Asia, all but one (*T. sutchuensis* of China) in cultivation, evergreen mostly aromatic monœcious plants much prized in cultivation for ornament and running into numerous cultivars; bark thin, the outer parts irregularly scaling; branches relatively short, horizontal, or in *T. orientalis* ascending, the smaller branchlets deciduous: leaves on seedlings and on certain cultivars needle-like and spirally placed, but the usual ones small and scale-like and imbricate in four rows or ranks (2 pairs of opposite leaves), appressed, sometimes gland-bearing on the back: flowers small, globose, terminal on short branchlets; staminate yellow and consisting of 6–12 decussate stamens each with 2–4 anther-cells; fertile flowers consisting of 8–12 scales in opposite pairs, of which only the middle ones, or in the section Biota the lower ones, are fertile, each scale with 2 ovules inside at the base: cones globose-ovoid to oval-oblong; scales with a thickened ridge or umbo at the apex; seeds 2 or 3 under each scale, thin with broad lateral wings or thick and wingless; cotyledons 2. Name derived from Greek *thya* or *thyia*, a resinous tree. The name is spelled both Thuja and Thuya, but the pronunciation (thù-ya) is the same in either case; also Thuia and Thya. It was written Thuja by Linnæus in Species Plantarum, 1002 (1753) and therefore so adopted, but also spelled Thuya by him in the Genera Plantarum of 1754; such variations in orthography were not so important in those days. The name arbor-vitæ is Latin meaning *tree-of-life*, early applied to *T. occidentalis* when introduced to Europe.

The branchlets in Thuja are arranged more or less in the form of pinnate leaves. The branchlets are deciduous: one may find them under the tree, 1 to 4 or 5 inches long. Each branchlet is covered with small closely appressed scale-leaves; the main little axis of these systems of branchlets bears rather larger and longer more pointed leaves, and the shape and position of these axial leaves are important points in identification of species.

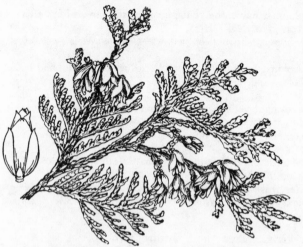

Thuja is distinguished from Chamæcyparis and Cupressus at once by the character of the cones: in those genera the cone-scales are peltate or shield-shaped whereas in Thuja the scales are thin and attached at base, making a different shaped cone.

84. Thuja occidentalis. Spray about one-half natural size, with dehisced cones. Separate cone not discharged, somewhat enlarged.

Some authors include Thujopsis (with its single species, *dolabrata*) in Thuja. Segregating this species in a separate genus, Thuja as commonly accepted yet contains two well-marked groups, Thuja proper, and Biota with the single species *orientalis* still sometimes listed under that name. The group Biota is probably biologically worthy to stand as an independent genus. Some of the plants known as Retinospora (Retinispora) are forms of Thujas.

Arbor-vitæ of one kind or another are almost everywhere planted. The native *T. occidentalis* is completely hardy and adaptable; its variability from seeds has produced almost endless forms, very many of which have been named and propagated by means of cuttings; the small and compact kinds abound and are now prized with the demand for dwarf conifers. *T. orientalis* is less hardy in the North, although some forms of it stand well in parts of New England and New York. The three other species now introduced are also hardy and desirable. Cuttings root readily.

The two American arbor-vitæ are important timber trees. The wood is durable in posts, poles and ties. Trunks of *T. plicata* are used by Indians for canoes; called canoe-cedar.

KEY to the species of Thuja:

I. The Thujas proper, represented in cultivation by four species and a multi-
tude of cultivars: sprays or branchlet-systems usually in horizontal planes
and flat, edges of branchlets lying practically horizontally: leaves often
lighter colored underneath: cones oblong to conical, light brown or yellow
when ripe, with thin scales only the middle ones of which have seeds and
the seeds winged.

  A. Back of leaf bearing a large conspicuous gland or grain toward the top:
    axis of the branchlet-group flat....................................1. *T. occidentalis*

  AA. Back of leaf glandless, or at least not prominently modified: axis of
    branchlet-groups terete or nearly so.

    B. Leaves on main axes terminating in a long free point appressed or
      parallel to the axis...2. *T. plicata*

    BB. Leaves on main or primary axes ending in short thick or triangular
      more or less spreading points.

      C. Under surface of leaf slightly concave if at all, with white lines on
        lower half: tree..3. *T. Standishii*

      CC. Under surface of leaf concave or grooved, glaucous or white-marked:
        bush...4. *T. koraiensis*

II. The Biotas, represented by one species and many varieties: sprays or
branchlet-group vertical or erect, edges of branchlets standing more or
less towards the tree or away from it: leaves bright green on both surfaces:
cones more or less ovate, fleshy when partly grown, woody at maturity,
the scales ending in a hook or rolled horn and only lower ones fertile;
seeds wingless...5. *T. orientalis*

1. **Thuja occidentalis.** AMERICAN
ARBOR-VITÆ, often but erroneously called
white-cedar, which is *Chamæcyparis thyoides.* Figs. 84, 85 left. Widespread tree
in North America, and probably the
most frequently planted in this country
of any conifer, forming very dense forests
in swampy and springy areas or along
streams; to 60 or 70 feet and 5 feet diameter, with exfoliating bark and trunk
fluted with age, with short horizontal
branches ascending at the end and forming a narrow pyramidal rather compact
head; bark light red-brown, shallowly
fissured into narrow connected ridges
covered with elongated scales: leaves
ovate, acute, or apiculate, usually glandular, bright green above, yellowish-green
beneath, in winter dull brownish-green:
cones oval to oval-oblong, about ½ inch
long, with usually 2 pairs of fertile scales;
seeds ⅛ inch long. Nova Scotia to Manitoba, south to North Carolina, Tennessee,
and Illinois.—*Thuja occidentalis,* Linnæus,
Species Plantarum, 1002 (1753).

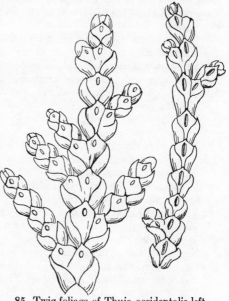

85. Twig foliage of Thuja occidentalis left,
showing the globular gland on back of each
leaf; T. orientalis, right, showing grooved
leaves. Enlarged.

In nature *T. occidentalis* is not recognized in botanical varieties. The trunks are utilized for posts, railroad ties and other purposes because of the durability of the wood. It is a favorite tree for shelter-belts and hedges about premises. In cultivation, however, the species has yielded a marvelous range of forms, much planted for ornament, the listed kinds in North America falling into the following groups: color forms, *alba, aurea, aureo-variegata, Burrowii, Columbia, Douglasii aurea, lutea, lutescens, semper-aurea, variegata, Vervœneana;* pyramidal or fastigiate forms, *Buchanani, compacta, conica, Douglasii pyramidalis, fastigiata, filicoides, plicata, Riversi, robusta, Rosenthali, theodonensis, viridis;* globose or dwarf forms, *Boothii, densiforma, dumosa, globosa, Hoveyi, intermedia, nana, pumila, pygmœa, recurva nana, Reidii, umbraculifera, Wagneriana, Woodwardii;* of pendulous, irregular or abnormal habit, *cristata, filiformis, Ohlendorffi, pendula, spiralis;* juvenile forms, *Ellwangeriana, ericoides.*

Var. **alba.** Tips of young branchlets white; "Queen Victoria" belongs here.— *Thuja occidentalis* var. *alba,* Gordon; *T. occidentalis* var. *albo-spica,* Beissner.

Var. **aurea.** Broad bushy form with deep yellow foliage; also Meehan's Golden has yellow foliage.—*Thuja occidentalis* var. *aurea,* Nelson.

Var. **aureo-variegata.** Foliage variegated with golden-yellow.—*Thuja occidentalis* var. *aureo-variegata,* Henkel & Hochstetter; *T. occidentalis* var. *aurea maculata,* Hort.; *T. occidentalis* var. *Wareana aurea,* Hort.

Var. **Bodmeri.** Monstrosity form with thick clumpy growth due to shortened more or less curved branchlets and dense overlapping foliage green underneath.— *Thuja occidentalis* var. *Bodmeri,* Hort. The plant known as *T. Batemani* is said to be this variety.

Var. **Boothii.** Low and compact with rather large leaves.—*Thuja occidentalis* var. *Boothii,* Hort.

Var. **Buchanani.** Graceful narrow-pyramidal form with slender branches and rather remote and irregularly arranged thin branchlets clothed with grayish-green foliage; a very distinct form.—*Thuja occidentalis* var. *Buchanani,* Parsons.

Var. **Burrowii.** Leaves yellow.—*Thuja occidentalis* var. *Burrowii,* Hort.

Var. **Columbia.** Strong habit: foliage broad, with a beautiful silvery variegation. —*Thuja occidentalis* var. *Columbia,* Parsons.

Var. **compacta.** Pyramidal form of denser habit and slower growth than type.— *Thuja occidentalis* var. *compacta,* Carrière.

Var. **conica.** Cone-shaped form.—*Thuja occidentalis* var. *conica,* Hort.

Var. **cristata.** Dwarf pyramidal form with stout crowded branchlets.—*Thuja occidentalis* var. *cristata,* Carrière.

Var. **densiforma.** Very dense form.—*Thuja occidentalis* var. *densiforma,* Hort.

Var. **Douglasii aurea.** A vigorously growing form with bronzy-yellow foliage.— *Thuja occidentalis* var. *Douglasii aurea,* Hort.

Var. **Douglasii pyramidalis.** Dense pyramidal form with short fern-like branches often cristate at the ends.—*Thuja occidentalis* var. *Douglasii pyramidalis,* Spaeth.

Var. **dumosa.** Dwarf and dense.—*Thuja occidentalis* var. *dumosa,* Hort.

Var. **Ellwangeriana.** A low broad pyramid with slender branches clothed with two kinds of foliage, adult leaves and primordial acicular spreading leaves; it is an intermediate form between var. *ericoides* and the type. Named for George Ellwanger, American nurseryman.—*Thuja occidentalis* var. *Ellwangeriana,* Beissner.

Var. **Ellwangeriana aurea.** Like the preceding but with yellow foliage.—*Thuja occidentalis* var. *Ellwangeriana aurea*, Beissner.

Var. **ericoides.** HEATH RETINISPORA. Dwarf globose or broadly pyramidal form with slender branchlets clothed with needle-shaped soft spreading leaves, dull green above, grayish-green beneath and assuming a brownish tint in winter.—*Thuja occidentalis* var. *ericoides*, Beissner & Hochstetter; *Retinispora dubia*, Carrière; *R. ericoides*, Hort.

Var. **fastigiata.** Columnar form with short branches.—*Thuja occidentalis* var. *fastigiata*, Jaeger; *T. occidentalis* var. *pyramidalis*, Hort.; *T. occidentalis* var. *columnaris*, Hort.; *T. occidentalis* var. *stricta*, Hort.

Var. **filicoides.** Densely branched narrow pyramidal form with the ultimate branchlets short and regularly pinnately arranged.—*Thuja occidentalis* var. *filicoides*, Beissner.

Var. **filiformis.** Plate XXXVIII. Bushy form with long and slender sparingly ramified branches nodding at the tips, partly 4-angled and clothed with sharply pointed leaves; a very distinct form somewhat similar to *Chamæcyparis pisifera* var. *filifera.*—*Thuja occidentalis* var. *filiformis*, Beissner; *T. occidentalis* var. *Douglasii*, Rehder.

Var. **globosa.** Dwarf globose form with bright green leaves; here belongs "Tom Thumb."—*Thuja occidentalis* var. *globosa*, Gordon; *T. occidentalis* var. *Spihlmannii*, P. Smith; *T. occidentalis* var. *Froebeli*, Hort.

Var. **Hoopesii.** Habit broad-pyramidal or dome-shaped: foliage dense, coarse, light green. Named for Josiah Hoopes, author "Book of Evergreens."—*Thuja occidentalis* var. *Hoopesii*, Hort.

Var. **Hoveyi.** Dwarf dense ovate-globose form with bright green foliage.—*Thuja occidentalis* var. *Hoveyi*, Gordon.

Var. **intermedia.** Of dwarf compact habit.—*Thuja occidentalis* var. *intermedia*, Hort.

Var. **lutea.** Pyramidal form with bright yellow foliage, "George Peabody Golden." —*Thuja occidentalis* var. *lutea*, Kent; *T. occidentalis* var. *elegantissima*, Hort.

Var. **lutescens.** A form of var. *robusta* with bright or dark yellow foliage.—*Thuja occidentalis* var. *lutescens*, Hesse; *T. occidentalis* var. *Wareana lutescens*, Hesse.

Var. **nana.** Dwarf and compact.—*Thuja occidentalis* var. *nana*, Hort.

Var. **Ohlendorffi.** Peculiar form with two kinds of foliage; the younger and lower branchlets with spreading acicular leaves like those of var. *ericoides*, but thicker in texture; the upper branchlets slender and sparingly ramified much like those of var. *filiformis.*—*Thuja occidentalis* var. *Ohlendorffi*, Beissner; *T. occidentalis* var. *Spaethii*, P. Smith.

Var. **pendula.** With the branches bending downward and the branchlets more tufted.—*Thuja occidentalis* var. *pendula*, Gordon.

Var. **plicata.** MOSS ARBOR-VITÆ. Pyramidal tree, darker and denser than the type; branchlets short, rigid, much flattened: foliage distinctly glandular, brownish dark green above, bluish-green beneath.—*Thuja occidentalis* var. *plicata*, Masters.

Var. **pumila.** Very dwarf dark green form, growing broader than high; here belongs "Little Gem."—*Thuja occidentalis* var. *pumila*, Beissner.

Var. **pygmæa.** Dwarf form.—*Thuja occidentalis* var. *pygmæa*, Hort.

Var. **recurva nana.** Dwarf with recurved branchlets.—*Thuja occidentalis* var. *recurva nana*, Hort.

Var. **Reidii.** Dwarf broad form.—*Thuja occidentalis* var. *Reidii*, Hort.

Var. **Riversi.** Compact pyramidal form with yellowish-green foliage.—*Thuja occidentalis* var. *Riversi*, Beissner.

Var. **robusta.** SIBERIAN ARBOR-VITÆ. Pyramidal tree lower and denser than the type, with stouter branchlets: foliage bright green; a very desirable form.—*Thuja occidentalis* var. *robusta*, Carrière; *T. occidentalis* var. *Wareana*, Nelson; *T. occidentalis* var. *densa*, Gordon; *T. caucasica*, Hort.; *T. tatarica*, Hort.; *T. sibirica*, Hoopes.

Var. **Rosenthali.** Columnar form with dark green lustrous foliage.—*Thuja occidentalis* var. *Rosenthali*, Ohlendorff.

Var. **semperaurea.** A vigorous form with golden-yellow foliage.—*Thuja occidentalis* var. *semperaurea*, Hort.

Var. **Smithiana.** Low compact form with dark green foliage becoming nearly purple in autumn.—*Thuja occidentalis* var. *Smithiana*, Hort.

Var. **spiralis.** Compact form with upright branches and very close-set short branchlets; the branchlet-systems concave and twisted, suggesting a spiral arrangement if seen from above.—*Thuja occidentalis* var. *spiralis*, Hort.

Var. **theodonensis.** Vigorous form of upright habit with broad thickish branchlets and dark green foliage.—*Thuja occidentalis* var. *theodonensis*, Beissner; *T. occidentalis* var. *magnifica*, Hort.

Var. **umbraculifera.** Compact, depressed-globose, of umbrella-like shape with dark green foliage.—*Thuja occidentalis* var. *umbraculifera*, Beissner.

Var. **variegata.** Branchlets variegated silvery-white.—*Thuja occidentalis* var. *variegata*, West; *T. occidentalis* var. *argentea*, Carrière; *T. occidentalis* var. *albo-variegata*, Beissner.

Var. **Vervæneana.** Of smaller and denser habit than the type; branchlets slenderer, with yellowish foliage, bronzy in winter.—*Thuja occidentalis* var. *Vervæneana*, Gordon.

Var. **viridis.** Compact pyramidal form with upright branches and dark green lustrous foliage.—*Thuja occidentalis* var. *viridis*, Beissner; *T. occidentalis* var. *erecta viridis*, Nicholson.

Var. **Wagneriana.** Globose, with dark green foliage.—*Thuja occidentalis* var. *Wagneriana*, Hort.

Var. **Woodwardii.** Dense globose form with deep green foliage.—*Thuja occidentalis* var. *Woodwardii*, Spaeth.

Other names occasionally listed under this species are: *Brinkerhoffi*, *gallica*, *hudsonica*, *nigra*, *pulcherrima*.

2. **T. plicata.** GIANT ARBOR-VITÆ. Plate **XXXVIII**. One of the great trees of the forests of northwestern America, and also one of the best in grounds for ornament; attaining 200 feet, with short horizontal branches often pendulous at the ends, forming a narrow pyramid; trunk with a much-buttressed base and clothed with cinnamon-red bark; branchlets slender, regularly and closely set: leaves bright green and glossy above, dark green beneath and with whitish triangular spots: leaves of vigorous shoots widely spaced, ending in long points parallel to axis of the lateral branchlets, acute and scarcely glandular: cones cylindric-ovoid, little over ½ inch long; scales 8–10, elliptic-oblong, usually the 3 middle pairs fertile; seeds winged, notched at the apex. Alaska to northern California and Montana. The Rocky Mountain form is hardy as far north as Massachusetts. Handsome pyramidal tree of rapid growth with bright

green lustrous foliage which retains its color in winter.—*Thuja plicata*, Don, Hortus Cantabrigiensis, ed. 6, 249 (1811); *T. gigantea*, Nuttall in Journ. Acad. Philadel. vii, 52 (1834); *T. Menziesii*, Douglas ex Endlicher, Synopsis Coniferarum, 52 (1847); *T. Lobbii*, Hort. ex Gordon, Pinetum, 323 (1858).

Var. **atrovirens**. Foliage dark green.—*Thuja plicata* var. *atrovirens*, Sudworth; *T. gigantea atrovirens*, Beissner; *T. Lobbii* var. *atrovirens*, Hort., *T. occidentalis Vervæneana atrovirens*, Hort.

Var. **aurea**. Leaves yellowish.—*Thuja plicata* var. *aurea*, Hort.

Var. **fastigiata**. Columnar form.—*Thuja plicata* var. *fastigiata*, Schneider; *T. gigantea fastigiata*, Beissner; *T. gigantea pyramidalis*, Bean.

Var. **pendula**. Form with slender pendulous branches.—*Thuja plicata* var. *pendula*, Schneider; *T. gigantea pendula*, Beissner.

3. **T. Standishii**. JAPANESE or STANDISH ARBOR-VITÆ. Plate XXXVII. Handsome ornamental tree, hardy in western New York and in Massachusetts, making a dense rather broad head; to 50 feet, with spreading or somewhat ascending branches forming a broad pyramid; bark reddish-brown, thin, separating into small scales leaving pale gray blotches; branchlets rather thick, compressed: leaves bright green above with triangular white marks below, glandless, those of the main axes with rigid free points, those of the lateral branchlets obtuse, ovate: cones ovoid, ⅓–½ inch long; scales 10–12, broad-ovate, the two middle pairs fertile; seeds 3 to each scale with narrow wings not notched at apex. Japan. Made known from gardens in Tokyo in 1860, whence seeds were sent to the Standish Nursery at Ascot in England.—*Thuja Standishii*, Carrière, Traité Général des Conifères, ed. 2, 108 (1867); *T. japonica*, Maximowicz in Bull. Acad. Sci. St. Petersb., ser. 3, x, 490 (1866); *T. gigantea* var. *japonica*, Franchet & Savatier, Enumeratio Plantarum in Japonia, i, 469 (1875); *Thujopsis Standishii*, Gordon, Pinetum, Suppl. 100 (1862).

4. **T. koraiensis**. KOREAN ARBOR-VITÆ. Plate XL. Low shrub, usually with decumbent branches, rarely a slender narrow-pyramidal tree to 12 feet tall, with spreading branches ascending at the ends; bark thin, scaly, chocolate-brown; branchlets much flattened: leaves of main branches triangular-ovate, acuminate, glandular, of lateral branchlets deltoid or rhombic, acutish or obtuse, glandular, bright green above, glaucous beneath: cones elliptic-ovoid, about ⅓ inch long, light brown; scales 8, those of the 2 middle fertile pairs oval to narrow-obovate; seeds with the wing emarginate at apex. Korea. Probably hardy as far north as Massachusetts.— *Thuja koraiensis*, Nakai in Bot. Mag. Tokyo, xxxiii, 196 (1919).

5. **T. orientalis**. CHINESE or ORIENTAL ARBOR-VITÆ. Plate XXXVII. Fig. 86. In its typical form, a graceful and symmetrical tree with slender ascending branches, mostly known in the southern and Pacific states but certain races hardy in New York and Massachusetts, as well as some of the varieties; pyramidal or bushy tree branching from near the base, attaining 60 feet, with spreading and ascending branches; bark thin, separating into papery scales, reddish-

86. Cones of Thuja orientalis, somewhat enlarged; lower figure is an old dehisced cone such as frequently clings on the tree.

brown; branchlets thin: leaves of main axes with a free rather spreading apex, those of the lateral branchlets closely appressed, rhombic-ovate, acute, bright green, with a small gland on the back: cones globose-ovate, ½–1 inch long, fleshy and bluish before ripening; usually 6 ovate scales, each with a horn-like process, the uppermost pair sterile; seeds 2 to each scale, ovoid, brown. Much planted in China and Japan, native in Korea, Manchuria and northeastern China, its full natural range not well determined; it thrives in warm climates.—*Thuja orientalis*, Linnæus, Species Plantarum, 1002 (1753); *Biota orientalis*, Endlicher, Synopsis Coniferarum, 47 (1847).

Var. **argenteo-variegata.** Tips of young shoots creamy-white.—*Thuja orientalis* var. *argenteo-variegata*, Hort.; *Biota orientalis* var. *argentea*, Gordon.

Var. **aurea.** Low compact globose shrub, golden-yellow in spring, changing to bright green.—*Thuja orientalis* var. *aurea*, Dauvesse; *Biota orientalis aurea nana*, Sénéclauze.

Var. **Bakeri.** Foliage pale green; adapted to hot dry locations.—*Thuja orientalis* var. *Bakeri*, Hort.

Var. **beverleyensis.** A columnar form with the tips of the branchlets golden-yellow.—*Thuja orientalis* var. *beverleyensis*, Rehder; *T. beverleyensis*, Hort.

Var. **bonita.** A broad slow-growing cone-shaped form with shining bright green leaves tipped with golden-yellow.—*Thuja orientalis* var. *bonita*, Hort.

Var. **conspicua.** Compact fastigiate form, the intense golden foliage partially suffused with green.—*Thuja orientalis* var. *conspicua*, Berckmans; *T. orientalis* var. *aurea conspicua*, Hort.

Var. **decussata.** Dwarf globose juvenile form: leaves linear-lanceolate, spreading, stiff, acute, bluish-green.—*Thuja orientalis* var. *decussata*, Masters; *Biota orientalis* var. *decussata*, Beissner & Hochstetter; *Retinispora juniperoides*, Carrière; *Chamæcyparis decussata*, Hort.

Var. **elegantissima.** A low columnar form, bright yellow in spring, yellowish-green afterward.—*Thuja orientalis* var. *elegantissima*, Vos.

Var. **flagelliformis.** Branches pendulous, thread-like, sparingly ramified, and with the leaves wide apart and acuminate.—*Thuja orientalis* var. *flagelliformis*, Jacques; *T. orientalis* var. *pendula*, Masters; *T. pendula*, Lambert; *T. filiformis*, Lindley; *Biota orientalis* var. *pendula*, Parlatore; *B. orientalis* var. *filiformis*, Henkel & Hochstetter.

Var. **funiculata.** Intermediate between the above and the juvenile form; branchlets drooping.—*Thuja orientalis* var. *funiculata*, Nicholson.

Var. **gracilis.** A slender pyramidal form.—*Thuja orientalis* var. *gracilis*, Hort.

Var. **intermedia.** A form intermediate between var. *flagelliformis* and the juvenile stage; branchlets pendulous.—*Thuja orientalis* var. *intermedia*, Carrière.

Var. **meldensis.** Of columnar pyramidal somewhat irregular growth: leaves acicular, bluish-green, sometimes passing into the normal form: intermediate between var. *decussata* and the type.—*Thuja orientalis* var. *meldensis*, Masters.

Var. **nana compacta.** A dwarf columnar or conical form with denser foliage than the type.—*Thuja orientalis* var. *nana compacta*, Hort.

Var. **semperaurescens.** Dwarf, globose: the golden hue of the foliage remains throughout the whole year.—*Thuja orientalis* var. *semperaurescens*, Nicholson.

Var. **Sieboldii.** Globose compact low form, bright green. Bears the name of Philipp Franz von Siebold, 1796–1866.—*Thuja orientalis* var. *Sieboldii*, Lawson; *T.*

orientalis var. *japonica,* Siebold; *T. orientalis* var. *nana,* Carrière; *T. orientalis* var. *Zuccariniana,* Veitch; *T. orientalis* var. *compacta,* Beissner; *Biota orientalis* var. *Sieboldii,* Endlicher.

Var. **stricta.** Of pyramidal habit, with bright green foliage: one of the tallest and hardiest varieties.—*Thuja orientalis* var. *stricta,* Loudon; *T. pyramidalis,* Tenore; *Biota orientalis* var. *pyramidalis,* Endlicher.

Other varietal names listed under *T. orientalis* are: *Berckmanniana, columnaris, conica, excelsa, texana glauca.*

23. THUJOPSIS. Hiba Arbor-vitæ. Fig. 87. A single monœcious evergreen tree in moist dense forests of Japan, by some authors included in Thuja but differing in its very flat and broad branchlets, dolabrate (axe-shaped) lateral leaves, nearly flat-topped cones as broad as long with 5 seeds at each wedge-form scale; large tree with spreading branches; branchlets broad, much flattened and frond-like, arranged in horizontal planes: leaves opposite and in 4 rows, with white markings below: staminate flowers with 6–10 pairs of stamens: cones subglobose; scales 6–10, rhomboidal, imbricate, flat, woody, usually with a mucro below the apex, the upper pair sterile, the fertile scales with 3–5 winged seeds each; cotyledons 2. Name derived from Thuja and Greek, *opsis,* likeness; referring to its close relation to that genus. Also spelled Thuyopsis or Thyopsis but not originally.—*Thujopsis* (thuyóp-sis), Siebold & Zuccarini, Flora Japonica, ii, 32 (1842).

Thujopsis dolabrata. Fig. 87. Attractive pyramidal tree in several forms, attaining 50 feet, or sometimes shrubby; bark thin, reddish-brown, fissured longitudinally into long narrow strips; branches irregularly whorled or scattered, horizontally spreading and often nodding at the ends; branchlets ⅛–¼ inch broad: leaves glossy green above, marked with a broad white band beneath, those of the upper and under side obovate-oblong, obtuse, adnate except at the apex, the lateral ones spreading, ovate-lanceolate and curved (hatchet-shaped), obtusish: cones globose-ovoid, about ½–⅝ inch long; scales with a prominent often curved umbo below the apex. Central Japan. It has not proved very successful in the eastern states

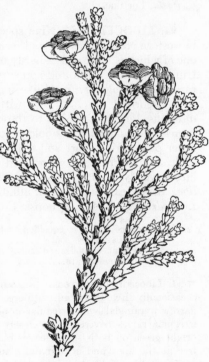

87. Thujopsis dolabrata. (× 1) Cones not mature.

and is not hardy much farther north than New York, though at Mattapoisett, Cape Cod, some fine specimens are growing. When well developed it is a handsome tree of dense broad-pyramidal habit, with bright green lustrous foliage.—*Thujopsis dolabrata*, Siebold & Zuccarini, Flora Japonica, ii, 32 (1842); *T. dolabrata* var. *australis*, Henry in Elwes & Henry, Trees of Great Britain and Ireland, ii, 202 (1907); *Thuja dolabrata*, Linnæus f., Supplementum Plantarum, 420 (1781).

Var. **Hondai.** Tree to 70, or occasionally to 90 feet tall; branches more densely ramified and the branchlets placed close together and overlapping one another by their edges more than in the type: leaves smaller and whiter beneath: cones subglobose, ⅗–¾ inch across; scales less thickened at the apex and with the umbo reduced to a short mucro or narrow ridge. Northern Japan; has not proved hardy in Massachusetts, although it may be somewhat hardier than the type.—*Thujopsis dolabrata* var. *Hondai*, Makino in Bot. Mag. Tokyo, xv, 104 (1901); *T. Hondai*, Henry in Elwes & Henry, Trees of Great Britain and Ireland, ii, 202 (1907).

Var. **nana.** Dwarf form, with more slender and narrower branchlets of a lighter green.—*Thujopsis dolabrata* var. *nana*, Siebold & Zuccarini; *T. lætevirens*, Lindley.

Var. **variegata.** Tips of branchlets creamy-white.—*Thujopsis dolabrata* var. *variegata*, Fortune.

24. LIBOCEDRUS. Nine species of evergreen mostly monœcious trees in western North America, southern Chile, New Zealand, China, and Oceanica, one of which is more or less hardy in the northeastern states to Massachusetts; trunk with scaly bark and spreading or erect branches; branchlets flattened, rarely quadrangular, frond-like in arrangement: leaves decussate, scale-like, with decurrent base, with or without glands: flowers monœcious or rarely diœcious, terminal, similar to those of Thuja; the staminate ones with 12–16 decussate stamens: cones oblong to ovate, with 4, rarely 6, woody scales, the lower pair sterile, short and reflexed, the second one much larger and fertile, each scale bearing 2 long-winged seeds, the third pair, if present, connate into a woody septum, cotyledons 2. Name (libocéd-rus) derived from Greek *libas*, drop, tear, and *Cedrus;* alluding to the resinous character of the tree.—*Libocedrus*, Endlicher, Synopsis Coniferarum, 42 (1847).

A. Facial or median leaves equalling or perhaps slightly exceeding the lateral
  leaves, all dark green...1. *L. decurrens*
AA. Facial leaves much smaller and usually shorter than lateral ones, the latter with
  white lines underneath.. 2. *L. chilensis*

1. Libocedrus decurrens. INCENSE-CEDAR. Fig. 88. An ornamental tree to 100, occasionally to 200 feet tall, with erect or spreading short branches, forming a rather narrow pyramidal head, irregular in old age; bark bright cinnamon-red, broken into irregular ridges covered with closely appressed scales; branchlets much flattened, bright green on both sides: leaves oblong-ovate, adnate, with long decurrent base, free at the apex and acuminate, glandular on the back: cones pendulous, oblong, ¾–1 inch long, light reddish-brown; scales mucronate below the apex, a third connate pair separating the 2 fertile ones; seeds oblong-lanceolate, ⅓–1 inch long. Mountains

XVIII. Two good Asian firs. At left, *Abies homolepis*; Connecticut. Young growth of *Abies recurvata*, two-thirds natural size; New York.

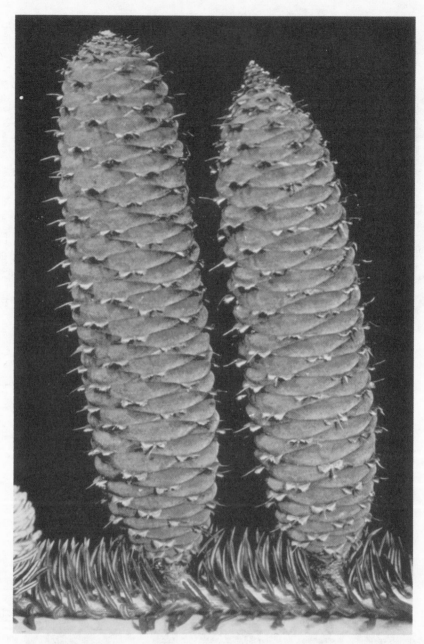

XIX. Greek fir, *Abies cephalonica*, nearly natural size, in midsummer; Connecticut.

XX. Two firs and a spruce. Korean fir, *Abies koreana* lower left, three-fourths size in mid-summer; Connecticut. Fraser fir, *Abies Fraseri* lower right, two-fifths natural size; New York. Colorado spruce, *Picea pungens* above, about two-thirds full size; New York.

XXI. Douglas fir, *Pseudotsuga Douglasii* showing the ornamental cones,
nearly natural size; var. *densa* below. Both in New York.

XXII. Spruce and fir. Red spruce at left, *Picea rubens;* Pisgah National Forest, North Carolina. Alpine fir at right, *Abies lasiocarpa;* San Isabel National Forest, Colorado.

XXIII. Cones of Norway spruce, *Picea Abies*, natural size; New York.

XXIV. Two American spruces. White spruce above, *Picea glauca*, about natural size; Connecticut. Red spruce below, *Picea rubens* (by three-fourths); New Hampshire.

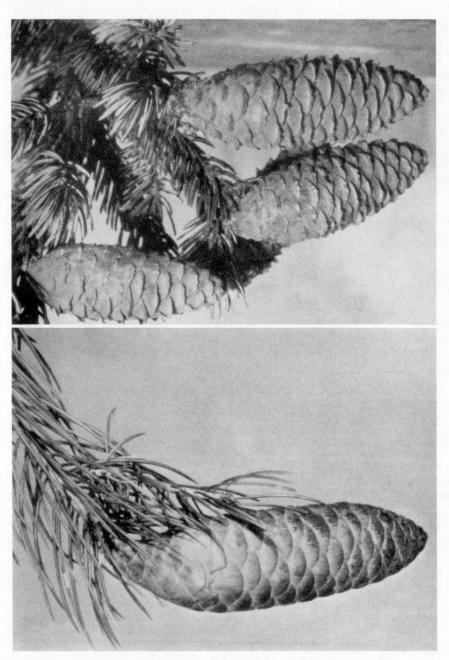

XXV. Two Asian spruces. Left, *Picea Smithiana*, nearly full size; Connecticut. Right, *Picea bicolor*, nearly natural size; Connecticut.

XXVI. Colorado Blue spruce, *Picea pungens* var. *argentea*, often incorrectly known as Koster Blue spruce; New York.

XXVII. Dwarf compact spruces.   Above, *Picea glauca* var. *conica*, often called *Picea albertiana*.   Beneath, *Picea Abies* var. *pygmæa*.   Massachusetts.

XXVIII. Japanese hemlock, *Tsuga diversifolia*; Massachusetts.

XXIX. Hemlock and Sawara cypress. Right, *Tsuga canadensis* var. *pendula*, an old specimen; Pennsylvania. Left, *Chamaecyparis pisifera* var. *plumosa aurea*: Massachusetts.

XXX. Deodar cedar, *Cedrus Deodara*; southern California.

XXXI. Pond-cypress in the Everglades in winter aspect, *Taxodium ascendens;* Florida.

XXXII. Big tree, *Sequoia gigantea*, smaller trees being firs: California.

XXXIII. Araucaria. Characteristic tree and cones (by two-fifths) of *Araucaria angustifolia*; Brazil:

and canyons, Oregon to Lower California and western Nevada, in the Cascade, Coast and Sierra Nevada mountains. Hardy as far north as Massachusetts in sheltered positions. A handsome thuja-like tree of narrow-pyramidal or columnar habit with deep green lustrous foliage, the upper branchlet-systems in vertical planes. A few garden forms are cultivated in Europe.—*Libocedrus decurrens*, Torrey, Plantæ Fremontianæ, 7 (1854); *L. Craigiana*, Low ex Gordon, Pinetum, Suppl. 102 (1862); *Thuja gigantea*, Carrière in Rev. Hort. 224 (1854); *T. Craigiana*, Murray in Botany of Oregon Expedition, 2 (1854); *Heyderia decurrens*, K. Koch, Dendrologie, ii, II, 179 (1873).

Var. **compacta** is dwarf and more compact. —*Libocedrus decurrens* var. *compacta*, Beissner.

2. **L. chilensis.** CHILEAN INCENSE-CEDAR. Tree to 60 feet tall, with compact pyramidal head and short trunk; branchlets much compressed, compactly placed or aggregated: facial leaves minute, obtuse, gland-bearing at tip, sometimes almost concealed by the lateral ones which are much larger, boat-shaped, keeled, acute and spreading at apex, with a silvery line beneath: cones ovate-oblong, ½ inch long. Chile on lower slopes of Andes; planted in California. Introduced in 1847 to Great Britain.—*Libocedrus chilensis*, Endlicher, Synopsis Coniferarum, 44 (1847).

The following species are occasionally seen in European collections, but are apparently unknown in American gardens; they are all tender and could be grown only in the southern states and California:

L. Bidwillii. Differs from *L. plumosa* in being a smaller tree, with mature branches 4-angled and leaves almost uniform. New Zealand. Dedicated to J. C. Bidwill, 1815–1853, botanical explorer.—*Libocedrus Bidwillii*, Hooker f., Handbook of New Zealand Flora, 257 (1867).

L. macrolepis. Tree to 100 feet tall; branchlets compressed, glaucous below with white markings: leaves of equal length, acute, the lateral strongly keeled, the facial ones obovate, apiculate: cones obovate-oblong, about ¾ inch long, consisting of 6 truncate scales. Southwestern China, Formosa. Introduced to Great Britain in 1899.—*Libocedrus macrolepis*, Bentham & Hooker, Genera Plantarum, iii, 426 (1880).

L. plumosa. Tree to 100 feet tall, with dense pyramidal head; branchlets much compressed: facial leaves ovate, acute, scarcely glandular, lateral leaves longer, spreading and acute at apex, with a white band below: cones about ½ inch long; scales 4, with a large curved spine on the back. New Zealand. Introduced to Great Britain

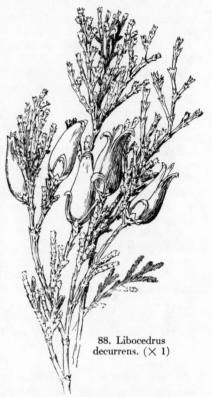

88. Libocedrus decurrens. (× 1)

in 1847.—*Libocedrus plumosa*, Sargent, Silva of North America, x, 134 (1896); *L. Doniana*, Endlicher, Synopsis Coniferarum, 43 (1847); *Dacrydium plumosum*, D. Don ex Lambert, A Description of the Genus Pinus, ed. 2, ii, Appx. 143 (1828).

L. uvifera. Tree to 100 feet tall, with compact pyramidal head, sometimes shrubby; branchlets almost tetragonal: leaves all alike, spreading, ovate or ovate-lanceolate, acute or obtuse, $\frac{1}{12}$ inch long: cones ovate; scales with a large curved spine on the back. Chile to Patagonia.—*Libocedrus uvifera*, Pilger in Engler & Prantl, Die Natürlichen Pflanzenfamilien, ed. 2, 389 (1926); *L. tetragona*, Endlicher, Synopsis Coniferarum, 44 (1847); *L. cupressoides*, Sargent, Silva of North America, x, 134 (1896), not *Pinus cupressoides*, Molina (Fitzroya); *Juniperus uvifera*, Don ex Lambert, A Description of the Genus Pinus, ed. 2, ii, 116 (1828).

A related genus apparently not in cultivation in this country is **Fokienia**; it is intermediate in its characters between Chamæcyparis and Libocedrus, resembling the latter in the foliage and in the seeds having 2 very unequal lateral wings; the cone is subglobose and composed of numerous peltate scales, each bearing 2 seeds. Two species in southeastern China. **F. Hodginsii** is a tree to 40 feet; branchlets much flattened: the lateral leaves with spreading acute apex, green above and with white markings below: cones 1 inch across, ripening the second year. Introduced into England; would probably be adapted only to warmer parts of the United States. Named for Captain Hodgins who obtained the cones from Foochow.—*Fokienia Hodginsii*, Henry & Thomas in Gard. Chron., ser. 3, xlix, 67 (1911); *Cupressus Hodginsii*, Dunn in Journ. Linn. Soc., Bot. xxxviii, 367 (1908).

25. **CALLITRIS.** CYPRESS-PINE. About twenty species of evergreen monœcious trees and shrubs in the southern hemisphere belonging to the cypress subfamily, a few of them met as planted subjects in Florida and California; branchlets articulate and brittle, 3- or rarely 4-angled or nearly terete: leaves in whorls of 3, or rarely 4, reduced to minute scales: staminate catkins ovoid to cylindric, the stamens in whorls of 3 or 4: cones on short and thick peduncles, without bracts at base, subglobose to oblong, usually ripening the second season; scales 6 or rarely 8, unequal, those of the outer whorl smaller; seeds many to each scale, winged; cotyledons 2, rarely 3. Name probably derived from Greek (callì-tris) *beauty* and *thrice*, referring to the ternate whorls of leaves and cones.—*Callitris*, Ventenat, Decas Generum Novorum, 10 (1808); *Octoclinis*, F. Mueller in Trans. Phil. Inst. Vict. ii, 21 (1858).

KEY to the species of Callitris:

A. Plant glaucous.
   B. Cone verrucose or rugose...1. *C. verrucosa*
   BB. Cone (valves) not verrucose..2. *C. glauca*
AA. Plant green (*C. verrucosa* may sometimes be sought here).
   B. Tip of leaves a short point.......................................3. *C. cupressiformis*
   BB. Tip of leaves blunt or obtuse.
      c. Internodes with angular ribs...................................4. *C. Muelleri*
      cc. Internodes not prominently angled or ribbed..................5. *C. robusta*

1. **Callitris verrucosa.** TURPENTINE-PINE. Tall tree or sometimes shrubby, with thick bark, usually glaucous, the spray composed of thin branchlets, internodes very short: leaves very small, appressed with short free points: cones solitary or in clusters, globose, about 1 inch or less in diameter, the 6 valves or scales warted on the outside. Australia.—*Callitris verrucosa*, R. Brown ex F. M. Bailey, Queensland Flora, v, 1496 (1902); *C. verrucosa*, R. Brown ex Mirbel in Mem. Mus. Hist. Nat. Par. xiii, 74 (1825), *nomen; Frenela verrucosa*, A. Cunningham ex Mirbel, l. c.

2. **C. glauca.** To 100 feet and 2–3 feet diameter, or sometimes shrubby, with a narrow head when young, the spray fine: leaves glaucous-green, short and acute: cones clustered or single, short-stalked, ¾ inch or less in diameter; scales thin, with distinct projection near apex. Australia; perhaps a form of *C. robusta.—Callitris glauca*, R. Brown ex Mirbel in Mem. Mus. Hist. Nat. Par. xiii, 74 (1825), *nomen*.

3. **C. cupressiformis.** Tree to 50 feet tall; branchlets slender, angular, often drooping: cones often clustered, subglobose, about ½ inch across, furrowed at the junctions of the valves, the larger valves dilated into a broadly rhombical apex, with a conical process at the center and usually rugose. Australia. Introduced into this country by the Department of Agriculture in 1912 and 1919.—*Callitris cupressiformis*, Ventenat, Decas Generum Novorum, 10 (1808); *C. rhomboidea*, R. Brown in Richard, De Coniferis, 47 (1826); *Frenela rhomboidea*, Endlicher, Synopsis Coniferarum, 36 (1847).

89. Callitris robusta. (× ¾)

4. **C. Muelleri.** ILLAWARRA-PINE. Tree to perhaps 50 feet, with dense narrow head, the long internodes angled from the leaf-bases: leaves spreading, long for the genus, olive-green: cones solitary or clustered, globular but somewhat flattened at top, 1 inch across more or less, not angled or furrowed, the 6 thick scales with point. New South Wales. Dedicated to Baron Ferdinand von Mueller, German-Australian botanist, 1825–1896, author of numerous species.—*Callitris Muelleri*, Bentham ex F. Mueller, Systematic Census of Australian Plants, 109 (1882).

5. **C. robusta.** Fig. 89. Tree to 100 feet tall; branchlets short and erect, often glaucous, with terete or obscurely angled internodes: scale-like leaves small and acute, ternate: staminate flowers solitary or in 3's, ⅙–⅓ inch long: cones solitary or few together, subglobose, about 1 inch across, not furrowed; valves 6, smooth on back or somewhat tuberculate. Australia; cultivated in California and Florida. The tree somewhat resembles red-cedar, and is reported as useful for tall hedges and windbreaks. This is one of the "pines" of Australia, the wood being used in building and for the making of furniture.—*Callitris robusta*, R. Brown ex F. M. Bailey, Queensland Flora, v, 1496 (1902); *C. robusta*, R. Brown ex Mirbel in Mem. Mus. Hist. Nat. Par. xiii, 74 (1825), *nomen; Frenela robusta*, A. Cunningham ex Mirbel, l. c.

Other species may be planted within our territory:

C. calcarata. Branchlets angular: cones ovoid, furrowed at junction of the valves, about ½ inch diameter, the larger valves little or not dilated at apex. Australia.— *Callitris calcarata*, R. Brown ex F. M. Bailey, Queensland Flora, v, 1497 (1902); *C. calcarata*, R. Brown ex Mirbel in Mem. Mus. Hist. Nat. Par. xiii, 74 (1825), *nomen;* *Frenela Endlicheri*, Parlatore in DeCandolle, Prodromus, xvi, II, 449 (1868).

C. Drummondii. Shrub or small tree; branchlets angular: cones usually solitary, globose, not furrowed, about ½ inch across, smooth or slightly rugose on back, with a minute mucro below the apex. Australia. Introduced by the Department of Agriculture in 1920 and recommended as an ornamental evergreen of dwarf globose habit with bright green branchlets.—*Callitris Drummondii*, F. Mueller, Systematic Census of Australian Plants, 109 (1882); *Frenela Drummondii*, Parlatore in Journ. Bot. i, 35 (1863).

C. oblonga. Tree to 25 feet tall; branchlets angular: cones usually clustered, ovoid or oblong, ¾–1 inch long, furrowed at the junction of the valves, the larger valves not dilated at apex, the smaller valves slightly overlapping the larger ones. Tasmania.—*Callitris oblonga*, Richard, De Coniferis, 49 (1826); *C. australis*, Sweet, Hortus Britannicus, ed. 2, 474 (1830); *Frenela Gunnii*, Endlicher, Synopsis Coniferarum, 38 (1847).

90. Juvenile foliage of Widdringtonia Whytei. (× about 1)

26. ACTINOSTROBUS. Two evergreen monœcious shrubs of west Australia, differing from Callitris in technical characters, as the presence of many sterile scale-like appressed bracts about the base of the cone (whence the generic name) and cone-scales of different shape: leaves ternate, scale-like, sometimes needle-shaped: cones ripening the first year, with 6 acute valvate scales surrounding a conical production of the central axis; each scale with 2 winged seeds.—*Actinostrobus* (actinós-trobus), Miquel in Lehmann, Plantæ Preissianæ, i, 644 (1845).

Actinostrobus pyramidalis. Densely branched shrub to 8 feet, branchlets erect and glabrous: leaves spreading at tip: cones ovoid, about ½ inch diameter, with triangular pointed scales. Introduced in Europe and to be expected in the mild parts of the United States and under glass.—*Actinostrobus pyramidalis*, Miquel in Lehmann, Plantæ Preissianæ, i, 644 (1845); *Callitris Actinostrobus*, F. Mueller, Essay on the Plants Collected by Mr. Eugene Fitzalan during Lieut. Smith's Expedition to the Estuary of the Burdekin, 19 (1860).

27. WIDDRINGTONIA. Half dozen African evergreen monœcious or sometimes diœcious trees of the cypress subfamily, with terete branches, one of which is planted in southern California: leaves opposite, scale-like or linear, on leading shoots alternate and linear: staminate flowers solitary and terminal:

cones ripening the second year; scales 4, valvate, equal, usually tuberculate and angular on back; each scale with 1 to many winged seeds. Named for Samuel Edward Widdrington [formerly Cook] 1787–1856, wrote on conifers.—*Widdringtonia* (widdringtò-nia), Endlicher, Genera Plantarum, Suppl. ii, 25 (1842).

A. Leaves tetrastichous,—arranged in 4 rows on the twig.
  B. Cone-scales warted or tubercled...................................1. *W. Schwarzii*
  BB. Cone-scales smooth..2. *W. cupressoides*
AA. Leaves, at least the juvenile ones, spirally arranged, the mature or scale-like ones sometimes opposite: scales of cone warted, or variously tubercled.
  B. Juvenile leaves to ¾ inch long: cone about as broad as long..........3. *W. juniperoides*
  BB. Juvenile leaves to 1 inch long: cone mostly narrower than long........4. *W. Whytei*

1. **Widdringtonia Schwarzii.** Pyramidal much-branched tree to 80 feet, with densely ascending branchlets: leaves in 4 rows and closely covering the shoots, less than ⅛ inch long, thickish, acute: cones clustered at end of branchlets, to ¾ inch across when open; scales 4, thick and woody, warted on back and more or less glandular, about ½ inch across. Cape Province, 2,500 to about 4,000 feet; named for Schwarz, who collected it.— *Widdringtonia Schwarzii*, Masters in Journ. Linn. Soc., Bot. xxxvii, 269 (1905).

2. **W. cupressoides.** Shrub or small tree to 12 feet, with main branches to 8 inches diameter and branchlets compactly erect: leaves in 4 rows, those on young plants to ½ inch long, the adult ones small and closely appressed, also obtuse and triangular: cone-scales 4, convex and nearly or quite smooth, to ¾ inch long, one pair narrower than the other, mucro below apex and obtuse. South Africa.— *Widdringtonia cupressoides*, Endlicher, Synopsis Coniferarum, 32 (1847); *Thuja cupressoides*, Linnæus, Mantissa, i, 125 (1767).

3. **W. juniperoides.** Widely branched tree to 60 feet: juvenile leaves spirally placed, glaucous-green, to ¾ inch long; scale-like leaves alternating in pairs, covering branchlets, obtuse or blunt: cones solitary or several on short side shoots, globose, about ¾ inch long; scales most-

91. Mature foliage of Widdringtonia Whytei, showing clustered cones about one-third full size, and detail of mature foliage.

ly 4, woody and coarsely tuberculate, spurred near apex. South Africa.—*Widdringtonia juniperoides*, Endlicher, Synopsis Coniferarum, 32 (1847); *Cupressus juniperoides*, Linnæus, Species Plantarum, ed. 2, 1422 (1763).

4. **W. Whytei.** MLANJI-CEDAR. Figs. 90, 91. A large tree to 140 feet tall, with a straight clear trunk and very thick bark: leading shoots with spirally arranged imbricate leaves free at the apex and triangular and subpungent; ultimate branchlets with opposite closely appressed leaves deltoid and with a thickened apex; young seedling plants with linear spreading leaves to 1 inch long: cones 4–6 together on short lateral branchlets, ovoid, about ¾ inch across; scales oblong, obtuse, tuberculate on back and with a short mucro below the apex. Tropical East Africa, at 6,000–8,000 feet altitude where it was first reported from the Mlanji Mountains in 1891 by Alexander Whyte (1834–1908). It is recommended for reforestation purposes in tropical and subtropical countries; its wood is dull reddish-white and strongly aromatic.—*Widdringtonia Whytei*, Rendle in Trans. Linn. Soc., ser. 2, iv, 60 (1894); *Callitris Whytei*, Engler, Die Pflanzenwelt Afrikas, ii, 89 (1908).

92. Tetraclinis articulata, one cone dehisced. About natural size.

28. TETRACLINIS. One evergreen monœcious tree of the cypress subfamily, native on mountains and dry hills in southern Spain, Malta, and northern Africa, known by the 4-ranked leaves and flattened articulate branchlets, and technical cone characters: leaves scale-like, minute, in whorls of 4: cones tetragonal, consisting of 4 valvate scales of nearly equal size, the outer pair concave on back, the inner pair depressed on back and usually sterile, all with a small mucro below the apex; fertile scales with 2 or 3 broad-winged seeds. Name (tetraclì-nis) from Greek, *four*, and *bed*, referring to the number and shape of the cone-scales.—*Tetraclinis*, Masters in Journ. Linn. Soc., Bot. xxx, 14 (1893).

Tetraclinis articulata. ARAR-TREE. ALERCE. Fig. 92. Small tree to 20 feet tall, with slender spreading branches: the free apex of leaves triangular, glandular: cones about ½ inch across; scales oval. Mountains of northwestern Africa. Sometimes cultivated in European gardens and in California. It is probably not hardy north of the southern states and California. The arar-tree has some resemblance to *Thuja orientalis*, but the habit is looser and the branchlets slenderer. It furnishes gum sandarach, a varnish resin.—*Tetraclinis articulata*, Masters in Journ. Linn. Soc., Bot. xxx, 14 (1893); *Callitris quadrivalvis*, Ventenat, Decas Generum Novorum, 10 (1808); *Thuja articulata*, Vahl, Symbolæ Botanicæ, ii, 96 (1790).

29. FITZROYA. FITZROY-CYPRESS. One evergreen diœcious tree from southern Chile; ramification of branchlets irregular; branchlets angled: leaves ternate, decurrent, their free part spreading: staminate flowers cylindric, solitary, axillary, consisting of 15–24 stamens in ternate whorls: cones small, globose, with 3 ternate whorls of valvate scales, the lower whorl small and sterile, slightly imbricate, the middle whorl sterile or fertile and the upper one fertile; each fertile scale with a prominent compressed umbo on back and with 2–6 2- or 3-winged seeds. The name (fitzròy-a) honors Captain R. Fitzroy of the British Navy; died in 1855. —*Fitzroya*, Hooker f. in Journ. Hort. Soc. Lond. vi, 264 (1851).

93. Fitzroya cupressoides. (× 1)

Fitzroya cupressoides. Fig. 93. Tree to 100 feet tall, in cultivation usually shrubby; bark thick, fibrous, deeply furrowed: leaves ternate or occasionally opposite, spreading or somewhat imbricate, ovate-oblong to narrow-oblong, with incurved mucronate tip, about ⅛ inch long, dark green and concave above, keeled on back, with 2 white stomatic bands beneath: cones globose, ⅓ inch across. Southern Chile. It may be hardy as far north as the Middle Atlantic states in sheltered positions. In cultivation it is usually a shrub of slow growth and unsymmetrical habit, apparently without special ornamental merits.—*Fitzroya cupressoides*, Johnston in Contr. Gray Herb. n. s. lxx, 91 (1924); *F. patagonica*, Hooker f. ex Lindley in Journ. Hort. Soc. Lond. vi, 264 (1851); *Pinus cupressoides*, Molina, Saggio Sulla Storia Naturale del Chile, 168 (1782).

DISELMA, a genus closely related to Fitzroya, in the mountains of western Tasmania, was once introduced in Great Britain but not reported from this country. It differs chiefly in the cones with 2 pairs of scales, the inner scales each with 2 3-winged seeds, and in the opposite scale-like closely appressed leaves. The only species is **D. Archeri,** a small tree or bush to 20 feet.—*Diselma Archeri*, Hooker f., Flora Tasmaniæ in The Botany of the Antarctic Voyage of H. M. Ships Erebus and Terror, i, 353 (1857); *Fitzroya Archeri*, Bentham & Hooker f., Genera Plantarum, iii, 426 (1880). It bears the name of William Archer, Jr., who thought the plant to be *Microcachrys tetragona* of Hooker (in Hooker Journal of Botany, ii, 51, 1850).

CHAPTER VI

THE TRUE CONE-BEARERS—JUNIPERS

THE junipers are so unlike other familiar conifers in producing berry-like bodies rather than dry more or less open cones, and are so many and diverse that they may well be presented horticulturally in a chapter by themselves. Morphologically the berries are modified cones, the few scales having become fleshy and cohering, and usually completely inclosing the seeds; there are small scaly bracts at the base; it is apparent that they do not have the structure or the external character of the true berry, as the currant or grape.

30. **JUNIPERUS.** JUNIPER. SAVIN. RED-CEDAR. Diœcious and rarely monœcious evergreen shrubs and trees, sometimes very low and mat-like, about forty species in cold and warm parts of the northern hemisphere, many of them planted for ornament and some of them very variable under cultivation, the wood aromatic and of the arboreous kinds employed in the arts; the berries yield oil, spirits, and medicine; branchlets spreading, ascending, or irregular, the trunk usually not single and continuous and head not pyramidal or conical as in firs and spruces, bark usually shredding: leaves small, opposite or in 3's, of two kinds, awl-like or needle-shaped and variously spreading in some species and on main axial growths of other species and with whitish or bluish lines on upper surface, also scale-like and appressed to the twig on shorter or fruiting branchlets of some of the species and those species therefore bearing both kinds or forms: staminate flowers yellow, consisting of numerous anthers united into a little ovoid or oblong catkin; fertile flowers greenish, minutely globular, with several bracts, each or some bearing 1 or 2 ovules; the bracts become fleshy and unite into a berry-like cone (galbulus), usually wholly inclosing the 1–6, rarely 12, seeds. The fruit ripens either the first year, as in *J. virginiana*, or the second, as in *J. Sabina* and most species, or in the third, as in *J. communis*. Juniperus (junip'-erus) is the ancient Latin name of these plants.—*Juniperus*, Linnæus, Species Plantarum, 1038 (1753).

Juniperus resembles Cupressus in many ways, and sometimes is difficult to distinguish without fruit; but young plants with needle-shaped leaves can usually be told apart, since Juniperus has the whitish bands or marks on the upper surface of the leaves, while the similar juvenile forms of allied genera have the whitish marks underneath. Often it is difficult to determine between species of junipers themselves, unless one has mature fruits.

Some writers prefer to regard the junipers as of two genera, Juniperus with leaves all awl-shaped or subulate and articulated to the twig and flower-clusters axillary, and Sabina with leaves of two kinds (subulate and scale-like) and decurrent or running down the stem, flower-clusters terminal. These contrasts are represented by the main divisions, A and AA, in the key.

The junipers comprise many kinds hardy and desirable for planting in the North. They abound in dwarf forms and are therefore in demand for small places, covering banks, and for foundation planting. Those of southern Europe, the Canary Islands and other warm regions constitute another set, suitable for California and the southern parts of the country. Junipers are relatively free from diseases and pests. They are propagated from seeds, which are commonly produced abundantly when both sexes are together, and also by cuttings.

Other species-names of juniper than those treated in this account are likely to appear in the lists. Some of them may be only varietal names erroneously raised to specific rank.

In the brown-fruited section with denticulate or ciliolate leaf-margins two other species may be mentioned, apparently not yet regularly in cultivation:

J. Pinchotii. Shrubby tree to 20 feet tall; branchlets thick: leaves usually in 3's, obtusely pointed, rounded and conspicuously glandular-pitted on back, about $\frac{1}{16}$ inch long: fruit subglobose, $\frac{1}{4}$–$\frac{1}{3}$ inch long, reddish-brown, 1–2-seeded. Texas.—*Juniperus Pinchotii*, Sudworth in Forestry and Irrigation, xi, 203 (1905); named for Gifford Pinchot, forester, Governor of Pennsylvania.

J. flaccida. A tree to 30 feet tall, with spreading branches and slender drooping branchlets: leaves opposite, acuminate, spreading at apex, glandular or eglandular on back: fruit subglobose, $\frac{1}{3}$–$\frac{1}{2}$ inch across, dark red-brown, bloomy, with thick resinous flesh, 4–12-seeded. Southern Texas and northeastern Mexico; hardy only in the southern states.—*Juniperus flaccida*, Schlechtendal in Linnaea, xii, 495 (1838).

With fruits blue or black, and denticulate leaves are:

J. pseudosabina. Low shrub closely related *J. Wallichiana*, but leaves less acute and fruit smaller, recurved, often globose. Altai Mountains, Turkestan; hardy North.—*Juniperus pseudosabina*, Fischer & Meyer, Index Seminum quæ Hortus Botanicus Imperialis Petropolitanus, viii, 65 (1841).

J. saltuaria. Tree to 50 feet tall: leaves bright green, closely appressed, slightly incurved at the acute or obtusish apex, slightly glandular: flowers monœcious: fruit erect, subglobose or ovoid, about $\frac{1}{4}$ inch long, black, not bloomy, 1-seeded. Western China.—*Juniperus saltuaria*, Rehder & Wilson in Sargent, Plantæ Wilsonianæ, ii, 61 (1914).

Species-names without recognized botanical standing, that have been listed as introduced in North America, are *J. flacciformis*, *Luptoni*, *Smithiana*, *Wilsoni* which is probably *J. squamata* var. *Wilsoni*.

KEY to the species of Juniperus:

A. Leaves needle-shaped and in 3's, jointed or definitely articulated to the twig, not running down on it, most clearly observed on parts bearing needle-like foliage (Fig. 94, left): plants producing distinct winter-buds: staminate flowers axillary.
   B. Seeds separate in the small or medium fruit: leaves very narrow.
      C. Upper surface of leaf bearing one prominent white longitudinal line or band: fruit usually black or blue.
         D. Leaf linear to lanceolate (relatively broad), concave above and white band broad, obscurely keeled underneath............. 1. *J. communis*
         DD. Leaf narrow-linear and stiff, sulcate or grooved above, keeled underneath.
            E. Plant upright, with trunk and ascending or spreading branches that are pendulous only at tips or with drooping side branchlets... 2. *J. rigida*
            EE. Plant prostrate or procumbent, without tree-like habit....... 3. *J. conferta*
      CC. Upper surface of leaf bearing two longitudinal white bands: fruit orange or brown.
         D. White bands on upper side of leaf broader than the green margin: branchlets slender and pendulous......................... 4. *J. formosana*
         DD. White bands narrower than green margin or at least not broader: branchlets upright, or pendulous in No. 7.
            E. Stature mostly shrub-like: leaves conspicuously spreading or even horizontal.
               F. Leaf tapering from the base........................... 5. *J. macrocarpa*
               FF. Leaf tapering from middle.............................. 6. *J. Oxycedrus*
            EE. Stature arboreous: leaves pointing toward apex of drooping branchlets.. 7. *J. Cedrus*
   BB. Seeds connate or grown together in the very large fruit making a 3-celled stone or pit: leaves to ⅛ inch broad......................... 8. *J. drupacea*
AA. Leaves scale-like and opposite or needle-like and in 3's, not regularly jointed to the twig but decurrent on it (Fig. 94, right), often each one bearing a gland on its back: plants without distinct or definite winter-buds: staminate flowers terminal (*Sabina*).
   B. Species with only needle-like leaves in 3's, rather loose on the twig or not flatly appressed, with two white longitudinal lines on upper surface.
      C. Branchlets green (or not glaucous): leaves green or only light glaucous underneath: fruit 1-seeded.
         D. Leaves about ⅙ inch long, with a channel from base to near the apex.. 9. *J. squamata*
         DD. Leaves to ¼ inch long, with channel only near the base........10. *J. recurva*
      CC. Branchlets with glaucous lines along the edges of the ridges running from a whitish spot at base of leaf on either side: fruit 2-seeded..11. *J. procumbens*
   BB. Species with leaves scale-like and opposite or perhaps also needle-like on certain growths (exceptions in vars. of No. 22).
      C. Margin of leaves minutely denticulate or fringed (distinguished against the light with a strong lens).
         D. Color of ripe fruit reddish-brown beneath the bloom.
            E. Fruit 3-9-seeded: the scale-like leaves irregularly ovate or rhombic, obtuse, furrowed on back......................12. *J. phœnicea*
            EE. Fruit 3-4-seeded: the scale-like leaves opposite, obtusish and apiculate: trunk with scaly bark.......................13. *J. pachyphlœa*
            EEE. Fruit 1-2-seeded: the scale-like leaves acute or acuminate, opposite or in 3's: trunk usually with shreddy bark.
               F. Leaves glandular-pitted on the back, obtuse, commonly in 3's...14. *J. californica*

ғғ. Leaves not glandular or only inconspicuously so and not
pitted, commonly in 2's..................................15. *J. utahensis*
DD. Color of ripe fruit under bloom blue or almost black.
  E. Leaves conspicuously glandular on the back, usually in 3's:
seeds 2 or 3...16. *J. occidentalis*
  EE. Leaves glandless or in No. 19 sometimes with a gland: seeds
1 or 2.
    F. Size of fruit large, about ½ inch diameter................17. *J. Wallichiana*
    FF. Size of fruit about ¼ inch diameter or long: seed solitary,
with 2 or 3 depressions.
      G. Branchlets terete with reddish or copper-colored bark:
seeds mostly solitary, with 2 or 3 ridges, sometimes
flattened...18. *J. monosperma*
      GG. Branchlets 4-angled, gray: seeds without ridges, not
flattened when single............................19. *J. Ashei*
  CC. Margin of leaves entire.
    D. Color of fruit brown or purplish-brown under the bloom (if any
bloom); perhaps an exception in No. 23.
      E. Scale-like leaves acute; acicular leaves opposite (except on
leading shoots).
        F. Seeds of fruit 3-6: leaves ovate with free ends...........20. *J. excelsa*
        FF. Seeds of fruit 2-3: leaves lanceolate....................21. *J. procera*
      EE. Scale-like leaves (if present) obtuse; acicular leaves often
ternate.
        F. Fruit globular.......................................22. *J. chinensis*
        FF. Fruit ovoid-globose.................................23. *J. morrisonicola*
    DD. Color of fruit blue under the bloom.
      E. Plant usually a distinct tree with fruit on erect or ascending
pedicels.
        F. Branchlets pinnately ramified and slender, mostly in one
plane...24. *J. thurifera*
        FF. Branchlets stout and short, thickly set: acicular leaves
rigid and spiny-pointed...........................25. *J. barbadensis*
        FFF. Branchlets slender, not appearing pinnate.
          G. Fruit ripening the first season.
            H. Diameter of fruit $\frac{1}{12}$-$\frac{1}{6}$ inch: leaves acute: branchlets
very slender, usually pendulous: southern tender
tree..26. *J. lucayana*
            HH. Diameter of fruit ¼-⅓ inch: leaves acute or acumi- (*silicicola*)
nate: branchlets usually upright or spreading:
northern tree...............................27. *J. virginiana*
          GG. Fruit ripening the second season, ¼-⅓ inch across.....28. *J. scopulorum*
      EE. Plant a shrub: fruit on curved pedicels, pendulous.
        F. Leaves bluish-green or steel-blue, acute, of slight aromatic
odor: prostrate shrub.............................29. *J. horizontalis*
        FF. Leaves dark or bluish-green, acutish or obtuse, of disagree-
able odor when bruised: shrub with usually ascending or
spreading branches...............................30. *J. Sabina*

1. **Juniperus communis.** COMMON JUNIPER. Fig. 94, left. Upright shrub or tree,
sometimes attaining to 40 feet: leaves linear or linear-lanceolate, tapering from the
base into a sharp point, concave and with a broad white band above, sometimes divided
at base by a green midrib, bluntly keeled below, ½-¾ inch long: fruit almost sessile,
dark blue, glaucous, ¼-⅓ inch across, ripening the second or third year. The typical
form is common in northern and central Europe and extends through northern and
western Asia to Korea and Japan; in North America it occurs only occasionally from

New England to Pennsylvania and North Carolina. A variable species with several geographical and climatic varieties and various garden forms.—*Juniperus communis*, Linnæus, Species Plantarum, 1040 (1753).

This circumterrestrial species exhibits many regional forms, some of which have been regarded as separate species but which, for the purposes at least of this book, may be kept together.

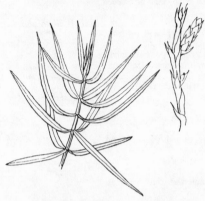

Var. **depressa**. PROSTRATE JUNIPER. Plate XXXIX. Forming broad patches, the stems ascending from a procumbent base, rarely exceeding 4 feet in height. Common low juniper of eastern North America. A form of this is var. **aureo-spica**. Tips of branchlets golden-yellow. —*Juniperus communis* var. *depressa*, Pursh, Flora Americæ Septentrionalis, ii, 646 (1814); *J. canadensis*, Burgsdorf, Anleitung .... Holzarten, ii, 124 (1787); *J. communis* var. *canadensis*, Loudon, Arboretum et Fruticetum Britannicum, iv, 2490 (1838); *J. communis* var. *nana canadensis*, Carrière, Traité Général des Conifères, ed. 2, 15 (1867).

94. The two sections of Juniperus, somewhat enlarged. At left, true juniper class; right, Sabina.

Var. **hibernica**. IRISH JUNIPER. Narrow columnar form, with upright branches, deep green, tips of branchlets erect: leaves shorter, less spreading.—*Juniperus communis* var. *hibernica*, Gordon, Pinetum, 94 (1858); *J. communis* var. *stricta*, Carrière, Traité Général des Conifères, 22 (1855).

Var. **Jackii**. Prostrate, with flagelliform trailing branches often to 3 feet long, and almost unbranched except for occasional clusters of short lateral branchlets 1-2 inches long: leaves linear-lanceolate, incurved. Oregon, northern California, collected by J. G. Jack of the Arnold Arboretum.—*Juniperus communis* var. *Jackii*, Rehder in Mitteil. Deutsch. Dendrol. Ges. xvi, 70 (1907).

Var. **montana**. MOUNTAIN JUNIPER. Low, spreading or procumbent shrub, seldom over 2 feet high: leaves oblong-linear, abruptly pointed, usually incurved, densely clothing the branches, with a broad silvery-white line above, ¼-½ inch long. Arctic and mountainous regions.—*Juniperus communis* var. *montana*, Aiton, Hortus Kewensis, iii, 414 (1789); *J. sibirica*, Burgsdorf, Anleitung .... Holzarten, ii, 124 (1787); *J. nana*, Willdenow, Species Plantarum, iv, 854 (1806); *J. alpina*, S. F. Gray, A Natural Arrangement of British Plants, ii, 226 (1821); *J. communis* var. *alpina*, Gaudin, Flora Helvetica, vi, 301 (1830); *J. communis* var. *nana*, Loudon, Arboretum et Fruticetum Britannicum, 2486 (1838).

Var. **nipponica**. NIPPONESE JUNIPER. Similar to the preceding, but leaves deeply sulcate above and keeled below. High mountains of Japan.—*Juniperus communis* var. *nipponica*, Wilson, Conifers and Taxads of Japan, 81 (1916); *J. nipponica*, Maximowicz in Bull. Acad. Sci. St. Petersb. xii, 230 (1868).

Var. **suecica**. SWEDISH JUNIPER. Narrow columnar form, growing sometimes into a tree to 40 feet high, with rather long spreading leaves, the branchlets with drooping tips: of lighter and more bluish color than the following variety.—*Juniperus communis* var. *suecica*, Aiton, Hortus Kewensis, iii, 414 (1789); *J. suecica*, Miller, Gardeners Dictionary, ed. 8, no. 2 (1768); *J. communis* var. *fastigiata*, Parlatore in DeCandolle, Prodromus, xvi, II, 479 (1868).

There are also several cultivars of *J. communis*, among them the following:

Var. **aurea.** Young growth golden-yellow turning green the second year.— *Juniperus communis* var. *aurea*, Nicholson; *J. communis* var. *aureo-variegata*, Beissner.

Var. **compressa.** Dwarf shrub with short crowded branchlets.—*Juniperus communis* var. *compressa*, Carrière.

Var. **cracovia.** POLISH JUNIPER. Terminal branchlets pendulous.—*Juniperus communis* var. *cracovia*, Knight; *J. cracovia*, Loddiges ex Loudon.

Var. **echinoformis.** HEDGEHOG JUNIPER. To 2 feet, with densely crowded branchlets.—*Juniperus communis* var. *echinoformis*, Beissner; often but not originally spelled *echinæformis* and *echiniformis*.

Var. **hemisphærica.** A dense rounded shrub to 3 feet.—*Juniperus communis* var. *hemisphærica*, Parlatore.

Var. **oblongo-pendula.** An upright shrub of broadly columnar outline with pendulous branchlets; a very graceful form.—*Juniperus communis* var. *oblongo-pendula*, Sudworth.

Var. **pendula.** Shrub with spreading recurving branches and pendulous branchlets. —*Juniperus communis* var. *pendula*, Carrière.

Var. **prostrata.** A prostrate form with smaller foliage.—*Juniperus communis* var. *prostrata*, Hort.

Var. **suecica nana.** A dwarf columnar form of var. *suecica*, usually not exceeding 3 feet.—*Juniperus communis* var. *suecica nana*, Hort.

Other listed names under *J. communis* are *Ashfordi*, *columnaris*, *compacta*, *Dayi*, *koraiensis*, *pyramidalis*.

2. **J. rigida.** NEEDLE JUNIPER. Fig. 95. Small pyramidal tree to 30 feet, or spreading shrub with the slender branches pendulous at the extremities: leaves in closely set whorls, narrow-linear, tapering from the middle into a spiny point, stiff, sulcate and with a narrow white band above, prominently keeled below, yellowish-green, ½–1 inch long: fruit globose, ¼–⅓ inch across, brownish-black, bloomy, finally somewhat shining, ripening the second year. Japan, Korea, and Manchuria. Graceful narrow-pyramidal tree, loosely branched with pendulous branchlets; hardy as far north as New England and Ontario.—*Juniperus rigida*, Siebold & Zuccarini, Flora Japonica, ii, 109 (1842).

3. **J. conferta.** SHORE JUNIPER. Procumbent shrub: leaves crowded, narrow-linear, tapering into a spiny point, sulcate and with a narrow white band above, keeled below: fruit globose, ¼–½ inch across, bloomy black at maturity, 3-seeded. Japan and Saghalin, on sandy seashores. Hardy at least as far north as Massachusetts; it should make a good ground-cover and be particularly suited for planting on sand-dunes.—*Juniperus conferta*, Parlatore, Coniferas Novas, 1 (1863); *J. litoralis*, Maximowicz in Bull. Acad. Sci. St. Petersb. xii, 230 (1868).

4. **J. formosana.** FORMOSA JUNIPER. Tree to 40 feet usually dividing into several stems from the base, with spreading or ascending branches and pendulous branchlets:

leaves more or less directed forward, linear, spiny-pointed, ½–1 inch long and $\frac{1}{16}$–$\frac{1}{12}$ inch wide, with 2 broad white bands above, confluent near apex, keeled below: fruit subglobose to broadly ovoid, about ⅓ inch across, reddish or oránge-brown. Formosa,

China. Handsome tree with pendulous branch-lets, hardy as far north as Massachusetts.— *Juniperus formosana*, Hayata in Journ. Coll. Sci. Tokyo, xxv, art..19, 209 (1908); *J. taxifolia*, Parlatore in DeCandolle, Prodromus, xvi, II, 481 (1868).

A related species is **J. taxifolia** which is easily distinguished by the obtuse or obtusish leaves ¼–½ inch long, and the lustrous light chestnut-brown subglobose or depressed-globose fruit. Bonin Islands. Probably hardy only in the southern states and California.—*Juniperus taxifolia*, Hooker & Arnott, Botany of Captain Beechey's Voyage, 271 (1841).

5. **J. macrocarpa.** PLUM JUNIPER. Shrub or small tree to 12 feet high, of dense pyram-idal habit: leaves crowded, linear-lanceolate, tapering from the base, spiny-pointed, spread-ing, ½–¾ inch long and about $\frac{1}{12}$ inch broad: fruit to ½ inch across, dark brown, glaucous. Mediterranean region. Probably hardy as far north as New York.—*Juniperus macrocarpa*, Sibthorp & Smith, Floræ Græcæ Prodromus, ii, 263 (1813); *J. neaboriensis*, Gordon, Pinetum, 96 (1858); *J. Oxycedrus* subsp. *macrocarpa*, Ascherson & Graebner, Synopsis der Mitteleu-ropaischen Flora, i, 294 (1897).

95. Juniperus rigida. Tree with drooping spray but rigid-pointed leaves. (× ¾)

6. **J. Oxycedrus.** PRICKLY JUNIPER. Mostly a dense shrub, but sometimes a stocky tree to 30 feet tall, with angled slender erect or ascend-ing branchlets: leaves linear-awl-shaped, $\frac{1}{16}$ inch or less broad and ½–¾ inch long, tapering from the middle to a very sharp or prickle-like point (whence the pre-Linnæan nomen Oxycedrus, *sharp cedar*), swollen or expanded at base, spreading from the twig, the white bands on upper surface nearly or quite equal to the green mar-ginal area: fruit ripening the second year, solitary on short stalk in the leaf-axils, globose, ½ inch or less diameter, shining reddish-brown at maturity, mostly not glaucous. Mediterranean region to Persia; several regional forms are known abroad.—*Juniperus Oxycedrus*, Linnæus, Species Plantarum, 1038 (1753).

7. **J. Cedrus.** CANARY ISLAND JUNIPER. Differs from *J. Oxycedrus* in being a real tree attaining the height of 80–100 feet, with wide-spreading branches and drooping branchlets: leaves less rigid and scarcely spine-tipped, pointing forward: fruit ½ inch or less long, orange-brown and glaucous at maturity. Canary Islands.—*Juniperus Cedrus*, Webb & Berthelot, Phytographia Canariensis, iii, 277 (1836–1840).

8. **J. drupacea.** SYRIAN JUNIPER. Pyramidal tree with narrow head, to 45 feet; branchlets triangular, with prominent ridges: leaves decurrent, linear-lanceolate, spiny-pointed, ½–¾ inch long and ⅛–⅙ inch broad (the broadest of all species), with 2 white lines above and broad green midrib, keeled below: fruit bluish-black or brown, glaucous, ¾–1 inch across, edible. Greece, Asia Minor. Handsome ornamental tree of columnar habit; thrives in limestone soil. Probably not hardy north of the Middle Atlantic states.—*Juniperus drupacea*, Labillardière, Icones Plantarum Syriæ Rariorum, Decas ii, 14 (1791).

9. **J. squamata.** HIMALAYAN JUNIPER. Decumbent shrub, sometimes ascending; branchlets thick, ascending at the apex, green: leaves crowded, loosely appressed, linear-lanceolate or lanceolate, straight or slightly curved, finely pointed, grayish- or bluish-green, with 2 grayish-white bands above, convex below and grooved from the base to near apex, ⅙–¼ inch long: fruit changing from reddish-brown to purplish-black, globose-ovoid, ¼–⅓ inch long. This species, of wide distribution in Asia from Afghanistan eastward, appears in various geographical forms.—*Juniperus squamata*, Buchanan-Hamilton in Lambert, A Description of the Genus Pinus, ii, 17 (1824); *J. densa*, Gordon, Pinetum, Suppl. 32 (1862); *J. recurva* var. *squamata*, Parlatore in DeCandolle, Prodromus, xvi, II, 482 (1868); *J. recurva* var. *densa*, Hort.

Var. **Fargesii.** Tree to 70 feet: leaves longer and narrower, linear-lanceolate, more spreading, usually about ⅓ inch long, acuminate: fruit ovoid, ¼ inch long. Named for R. P. Farges, collector.—*Juniperus squamata* var. *Fargesii*, Rehder & Wilson in Sargent, Plantæ Wilsonianæ, ii, 59 (1914); *J. Fargesii*, Komarov in Not. Syst. Herb. Hort. Petrop. v, 30 (1924).

Var. **Meyeri.** Upright shrub much branched with short straight branchlets: leaves narrow-lanceolate, straight, ¼–⅓ inch long, very glaucous on back. China. Introduced in 1914 by F. N. Meyer through the Department of Agriculture. Very handsome on account of its dense habit and the bluish-white color of its foliage.—*Juniperus squamata* var. *Meyeri*, Rehder in Journ. Arnold Arb. iii, 207 (1922).

Var. **Wilsonii.** Upright shrub to 6 feet, densely clothed with short branchlets recurved at the tips: leaves shorter and broader, crowded, broadly lanceolate, about ⅙ inch long. Western China. Introduced to the Arnold Arboretum by the late E. H. Wilson in 1909.—*Juniperus squamata* var. *Wilsonii*, Rehder in The Cultivated Evergreens, 200 (1923).

Var. **prostrata.** Prostrate with more spreading leaves having brighter bluish-white bands.—*Juniperus squamata* var. *prostrata*, Hornibrook.

The varietal names *albo-variegata* and *variegata* occur.

10. **J. recurva.** DROOPING JUNIPER. Graceful shrub or small tree to 30 feet, with broadly pyramidal crown and spreading curved branches and drooping branchlets, the thin light brown bark peeling in strips: leaves dull green, awl-shaped, imbricated, in 3's, appressed, to ¼ inch long, concave above and grooved below the middle, with hard sharp point: fruit ovoid, to ½ inch long, ripening second year, dark purplish-brown; seed single and pitted. Eastern Himalaya; hardy probably only in southern states and little known in this country.—*Juniperus recurva*, Buchanan-Hamilton ex D. Don, Prodromus Floræ Nepalensis, 55 (1825); *Sabina recurva*, Antoine, Die Cupressineen-Gattungen, 67 (1857).

11. **J. procumbens.** CREEPING JUNIPER. Low spreading shrub with stiff ascending

branchlets, about 2 feet high: leaves in 3's, linear-lanceolate, spiny-pointed, concave above and glaucous with a green midrib toward the apex, below bluish with 2 white spots near the base from which 2 glaucous lines run down the edges of the pulvini, ¼-⅓ inch long: fruit subglobose, 2-3-seeded, about ⅖ inch across. Recorded as wild in mountains of Japan, but known mostly in Japanese gardens; much grown in this country, particularly California, and hardy as far north as Massachusetts; useful as ground-cover.—*Juniperus procumbens*, Siebold in Ann. Soc. Hort. Pays-Bas, 31 (1844); *J. chinensis* var. *procumbens*, Endlicher, Synopsis Coniferarum, 21 (1847).

12. **J. phœnicea.** PHENICIAN JUNIPER. Shrub or a small tree to 20 feet or more, known in several varieties, but little planted in North America, erect or ascending with slender much ramified branches often appearing as if pinnate: leaves scale-like, very small, dull dark or bluish-green, opposite or in 3's, obtuse or nearly so, appressed to twig, rounded on back: fruit nearly or quite globose, to ½ inch diameter, yellowish- or reddish-brown; seeds 3-6 or 9. Canary Islands and Mediterranean region; probably not hardy in northern states.—*Juniperus phœnicea*, Linnæus, Species Plantarum, 1040 (1753); *Sabina phœnicea*, Antoine, Die Cupressineen-Gattungen, 42 (1857).

13. **J. pachyphlæa.** CHECKER JUNIPER. Handsome tree with heavy checkered bark (*pachyphlœa:* thick-barked) and young awl-shaped leaves usually glaucous or silvery white: tree to 60 feet tall, with a short trunk and stout spreading branches forming a broad-pyramidal or round-topped head; bark dark brown, thick, broken into small closely appressed scales; branchlets slender: leaves usually scale-like, opposite, rhombic-ovate, rounded or apiculate at apex, obscurely keeled on back and glandular, bluish-green, 1⁄16 inch long: fruit globose or broadly ellipsoidal, tuberculate, reddish-brown, glaucous, about ½ inch long, with 3-4 seeds. Arizona and New Mexico to southwestern Texas and Mexico. Introduced to Europe before 1875. One of the handsomest of the American junipers, remarkable for its checkered bark; the acicular foliage of young plants is usually glaucous to nearly silvery-white. Not hardy north of the Middle Atlantic states.—*Juniperus pachyphlœa*, Torrey in U. S. Rept. Expl. Miss. Pacif. iv, 142 (1857); *Sabina pachyphlœa*, Antoine, Die Cupressineen-Gattungen, 39 (1857).

14. **J. californica.** CALIFORNIA JUNIPER. Mostly a tree-like shrub but sometimes a tree to 40 feet and then perhaps with a conical head: leaves scale-like and closely appressed, mostly in 3's, ovate to oblong, obtusely pointed, conspicuously glandular-pitted and slightly keeled on back: fruit ellipsoidal, ¾ inch or less long, nearly smooth, reddish-brown beneath the bloom, flesh thick, dry and sweetish. California and Lower California, on hills and mountains in Coast range; listed in California.— *Juniperus californica*, Carrière in Rev. Hort., ser. 4, iii, 352 (1854); *Sabina californica*, Antoine, Die Cupressineen-Gattungen, 52 (1857).

15. **J. utahensis.** UTAH JUNIPER. Plate XL. Bushy tree, rarely exceeding 20 feet, with short trunk and erect to ascending branches forming a roundish open head; branchlets slender: leaves light yellow-green, usually scale-like and closely appressed, opposite or occasionally in 3's, rhombic-ovate, acute and often acuminate, rounded at back and usually glandless, about 1⁄12 inch long; acicular leaves usually in 3's: fruit subglobose or broadly ellipsoidal, ⅙-¼ inch long, marked by the tips of the scales, reddish-brown, glaucous, with thin sweet flesh, 1- or rarely 2-3-seeded. Wyoming to California, Arizona and New Mexico. Rarely planted and of no particular ornamental

value.—*Juniperus utahensis*, Lemmon in Rept. Calif. State Bd. For. iii, 183 (1890); *J. californica* var. *utahensis*, Engelmann in Trans. St. Louis Acad. Sci. iii, 588 (1877); *Sabina utahensis*, Rydberg in Bull. Torr. Bot. Club, 598 (1905).

Var. **megalocarpa.** Tree to 50 feet with a single trunk; the scale-like leaves in 3's: fruit ½–⅜ inch across. Arizona, New Mexico. Introduced in 1916.—*Juniperus utahensis* var. *megalocarpa*, Sargent in Bot. Gaz. lxvii, 208 (1919); *J. megalocarpa*, Sudworth, Forestry and Irrigation, xiii, 307 (1907).

16. **J. occidentalis.** WESTERN JUNIPER. Tree to 40 feet, rarely to 60 feet tall, with spreading branches forming a broad low head, or shrub with several upright stems; branchlets stout, about $\frac{1}{12}$ inch thick: leaves usually scale-like, in 3's, closely appressed, ovate, acute, grayish-green, conspicuously glandular on back, rarely acicular: fruit subglobose or ovoid, ¼–⅓ inch long, bluish-black, glaucous, 2–3-seeded; seeds eaten by Indians. Washington and western Idaho to southern California. Introduced to Europe about 1840.—*Juniperus occidentalis*, Hooker, Flora Boreali-Americana, ii, 166 (1838); *Sabina occidentalis*, Heller, Muhlenbergia, i, 47 (1904).

17. **J. Wallichiana.** BLACK JUNIPER. Tree to 60 feet, sometimes shrubby, with the branchlets very slender and 4-sided: scale-like leaves narrowly ovate, small with free and acute tips, bright green, furrowed and glandular on back, margins whitish; awl-shaped leaves in 3's, sharp, glaucous on upper surface, channelled on the other surface: fruit ovoid and upright, to about ½ inch long, blue the second year when mature; seed single, flattened. Dedicated to Nathaniel Wallich (1786–1854), authority on Asian plants. Himalayas, at high elevations; little known in North America.—*Juniperus Wallichiana*, Hooker f. ex Brandis, Forest Flora of .... India, 537 (1874); *J. pseudosabina*, Hooker f., Flora of British India, v, 646 (1888), not Fischer & Meyer.

18. **J. monosperma.** CHERRYSTONE JUNIPER or CEDAR. A tree occasionally to 50 feet tall, with stout ascending branches or branching from the base and shrubby; branchlets slender, about $\frac{1}{24}$ inch thick: leaves mostly scale-like, opposite, rarely in 3's, acute or acuminate, often slightly spreading at apex, thickened and rounded on back and conspicuously glandular, grayish-green; acicular leaves in 3's, often ½ inch long, inconspicuously glandular: fruit globose or ovoid, ⅛–¼ inch long, dark blue, glaucous, 1-seeded, rarely 2–3-seeded; the seeds sometimes exserted, pale chestnut-brown, obtuse and prominently ridged, sometimes flattened. Colorado to Nevada, western Texas and northern Mexico. Of little ornamental value and probably not hardy north of the Middle Atlantic states.—*Juniperus monosperma*, Sargent, Silva of North America, x, 89 (1896); *J. occidentalis* var. *monosperma*, Engelmann in Trans. St. Louis Acad. Sci. iii, 590 (1877); *Sabina monosperma*, Rydberg in Bull. Torr. Bot. Club, 598 (1905).

Related species is **J. mexicana.** Tree to 30 or occasionally to 100 feet tall: leaves obtuse or acute, thickened and keeled on back, usually eglandular: fruit ¼–½ inch long; seed ovoid, acute, slightly ridged. Western and southern Texas to central Mexico. Hardy only in the southern states.—*Juniperus mexicana*, Schlechtendal in Linnaea, v, 77 (1830); *J. sabinoides*, Nees in Linnaea, xix, 706 (1847); *J. tetragona*, Schlechtendal in Linnaea, xii, 495 (1838).

19. **J. Ashei.** OZARK WHITE CEDAR. Tree of shrubby aspect, to 20 feet high and usually with several trunks, making a broad, globular or open head, with gray shreddy

bark and angular branchlets: leaves scale-like, in 2's or sometimes in 3's, ovate and acute, dark gray-green, with or without a gland on back, those on seedlings and terminal twigs awl-shaped, acuminate, spreading, ⅓ inch or less long: fruit globose-ovoid, ¼–⅓ inch long, dark blue and glaucous, with thin sweet flesh; seeds 1 or sometimes 2, broad-ovate, lacking ridges or angles and not flattened when single. Southern Missouri and western Arkansas on outcrops and bluffs; sparingly planted in its region. Dedicated to the late W. W. Ashe of the United States Forest Service.—*Juniperus Ashei*, Buchholz in Bot. Gaz. xc, 329 (1930).

20. **J. excelsa.** GREEK JUNIPER. Pyramidal tree to 60 feet tall, with upright or spreading branches: leaves usually scale-like, on smaller branchlets opposite, closely appressed, rhombic-ovate, with incurved acute apex, glandular on back, dark or bluish-green, on leading shoots usually in 3's, acute, free at apex; acicular leaves opposite, with 2 glaucous bands above, ⅕–¼ inch long: fruit globose, ⅓–½ inch across, dark purplish-brown, covered with bluish bloom, 4–6-seeded. Greece, western Asia, and Caucasus. Apparently will not stand in the northern parts of the country.—*Juniperus excelsa*, Bieberstein, Flora Taurico-Caucasica, ii, 425 (1808); *Sabina excelsa*, Antoine, Die Cupressineen-Gattungen, 45 (1857).

Var. **stricta.** SPINY GREEK JUNIPER. Columnar form with juvenile glaucous foliage.—*Juniperus excelsa* var. *stricta*, Rollisson; *J. excelsa* var. *Perkinsii*, Gordon;

96. Juniperus chinensis. (× about ½)

J. excelsa var. *venusta*, Gordon. Plant grown in the North under this name is *J. chinensis* var. *pyramidalis*.

Var. **variegata.** Leaves variegated with yellowish-white.—*Juniperus excelsa* var. *variegata*, Hort.

21. **J. procera.** AFRICAN JUNIPER. Tree to 100 or 150 feet tall, similar to the preceding: leaves in 3's, or opposite, lanceolate and spreading or loosely appressed and ovate-lanceolate: fruit globose, small, about ¼ inch across, 2–3-seeded. Mountains of eastern Africa. Probably the tallest species of the genus.—*Juniperus procera*, Hochstetter ex Endlicher, Synopsis Coniferarum, 26 (1847).

22. **J. chinensis.** CHINESE JUNIPER. Fig. 96. Hardy and variable species much planted and known in many forms aside from the separation of the sexes (as *fœmina* and *mas*): tree to 60 feet, or shrub, sometimes procumbent; branches rather slender: acicular leaves opposite or in 3's,

linear, pointed and spreading, with 2 white bands above, or scale-like, appressed, rhombic, obtuse: flowers diœcious; the staminate ones numerous, yellow, often on branchlets with juvenile foliage: fruit globular, brownish-violet, with bloom, ¼–⅓ inch across, with 2 or 3 seeds, ripening the second year. Himalayas, China, Japan.— *Juniperus chinensis*, Linnæus, Mantissa, 127 (1767); *J. sinensis*, Hort. ex Carrière, Traité Général des Conifères, ed. 2, 33 (1867); *Sabina chinensis*, Antoine, Die Cupressineen-Gattungen, 54 (1857).

Var. **japonica**. JAPANESE JUNIPER. Low shrub with spreading sometimes procumbent branches and usually acicular leaves in 3's. Introduced in 1862 from Japan into this country. Variegated forms are "japonica aurea," the foliage tinged with golden-yellow, var. "**japonica aureo-variegata**," with part of the foliage golden-yellow, and var. **japonica alba**, leaves variegated with white.—*Juniperus chinensis* var. *japonica*, Lavallée, Arboretum Segrezianum, 290 (1877); *J. japonica*, Carrière, Traité Général des Conifères, 33 (1855); *J. chinensis* var. *nana*, Hochstetter, Die Coniferen oder Nadelhölzer, 90 (1882); *J. chinensis* var. *decumbens*, Hornibrook, Dwarf and Slow-Growing Conifers, 66 (1923).

Var. **Sargentii**. SARGENT JUNIPER. Plate XLIII. A prostrate shrub with long creeping stem and ascending branchlets forming dense mats: adult plants with the leaves mostly scale-like and bluish-green, acicular and grass-green on young plants: fruit bluish, slightly bloomy. Japan, Saghalin, and Kurile Islands. Introduced in 1892 by the late C. S. Sargent to America. A handsome form valuable as a ground-cover. This and the preceding variety have been confused often with *J. procumbens*, Siebold, but that species has the leaves always acicular and in 3's and marked on the back with 2 conspicuous white spots near the base from which glaucous bands extend down the edges of the pulvini.—*Juniperus chinensis* var. *Sargentii*, Henry in Elwes & Henry, Trees of Great Britain and Ireland, vi, 1432 (1912); *J. procumbens*, Sargent, in Garden and Forest, x, 421 (1897), not Siebold; *J. chinensis* var. *procumbens*, Takeda in Journ. Linn. Soc. xlii, 486 (1914).

Horticultural forms of *J. chinensis* are numerous, some of which follow; they may be grouped as follows:

Color cultivars, *aurea, aureo-globosa, plumosa aurea, pyramidalis glauca, variegata;* narrow, columnar and pyramidal forms, *columnaris, Fortunei, pyramidalis, Smithii;* conical and globose kinds are *aureo-globosa, globosa, mas, oblonga;* drooping habit or branches pendulous or twisted are *oblonga, pendula, Sheppardi, Smithii, torulosa;* open spreading growth, *Pfitzeriana, plumosa* and *plumosa aurea;* juvenile or prevailingly with awl-leaves, *columnaris, Fortunei, mas, pyramidalis, Sheppardi;* ground-cover, *japonica, Sargentii.*

Var. **aurea**. An upright form with scale-like foliage, the young growth golden-yellow.—*Juniperus chinensis* var. *aurea*, Young; *J. chinensis* var. *mascula aurea*, Hort.

Var. **aureo-globosa**. A form with habit similar to var. *globosa* but with the younger branchlets more or less golden-yellow.—*Juniperus chinensis* var. *aureo-globosa*, Rehder.

Var. **columnaris**. A very hardy narrow-pyramidal form with awl-shaped leaves.— *Juniperus chinensis* var. *columnaris*, Hort.

Var. **Fortunei**. Of columnar habit with bright green mostly awl-shaped leaves. Bears the name of Robert Fortune.—*Juniperus chinensis* var. *Fortunei*, Hort.

Var. **globosa**. A dwarf and dense subglobose form with short crowded thickish branchlets clothed with bright green scale-like leaves, with only few small branchlets with awl-shaped leaves on lower part of the branches.—*Juniperus chinensis* var. *globosa*, Hornibrook; *J. virginalis globosa*, Hort.

Var. **mas.** A dense conical form usually with staminate flowers and awl-shaped leaves.—*Juniperus chinensis* var. *mas*, Gordon; *J. chinensis* var. *mascula*, Carrière; *J. chinensis* var. *neaboriensis*, Beissner; *J. struthiacea*, Knight.

Var. **oblonga.** Subglobose, forming a distinct leading shoot with branches reflexed at tips.—*Juniperus chinensis* var. *oblonga*, Bobbink & Atkins.

Var. **pendula.** Branches spreading, pendulous at tips.—*Juniperus chinensis* var. *pendula*, Franchet.

Var. **Pfitzeriana.** Pfitzer Juniper. Plate XLI. Forming a broad pyramid with horizontally spreading branches and nodding branchlets, grayish-green. Originated in Spaeth Nurseries, Germany.—*Juniperus chinensis* var. *Pfitzeriana*, Spaeth.

Var. **plumosa.** Low form with arching branches and branchlets forming plumose sprays.—*Juniperus chinensis* var. *plumosa*, Hornibrook.

Var. **plumosa aurea.** Similar to var. *plumosa* with young leaves golden-yellow.— *Juniperus chinensis* var. *plumosa aurea*, Hornibrook; *J. chinensis* var. *japonica aurea*, Masters.

Var. **pyramidalis.** Narrow-pyramidal form with bluish-green mostly awl-shaped leaves.—*Juniperus chinensis* var. *pyramidalis*, Beissner. Grown sometimes as *J. excelsa* var. *stricta*.

Var. **pyramidalis glauca.** A glaucous form of the above.—*Juniperus chinensis* var. *pyramidalis glauca*, Slavin.

Var. **Sheppardi.** Juvenile form of bushy drooping habit and awl-shaped leaves.— *Juniperus chinensis* var. *Sheppardi*, Hornibrook.

Var. **Smithii.** Of broad pyramidal habit with terminal branchlets pendulous, and scale-like leaves.—*Juniperus chinensis* var. *Smithii*, Hort.

Var. **sphærica.** Fruit not glaucous, with numerous seeds.—*Juniperus chinensis* var. *sphærica*, Hort.

Var. **torulosa.** Branchlets twisted.—*Juniperus chinensis* var. *torulosa*, Hort.

Var. **variegata.** Whiteleaf Chinese Juniper. Compact shrub with tips of branchlets creamy-white, leaves mostly scale-like.—*Juniperus chinensis* var. *variegata*, Fortune; *J. chinensis* var. *albo-variegata*,Veitch; *J. chinensis* var. *argenteo-variegata*,Hort.

Other listed names are *dentata, monumentalis, stricta, sylvestris, viridis.*

23. **J. morrisonicola.** Mt. Morrison Juniper. Much like *J. chinensis* in habit but distinguished by longer or ovate-globose fruit, black and glabrous at maturity (dried) and by technical characters: young twigs angled and green: leaves all lanceolate, sharp-pointed, spreading, about $\frac{1}{8}$ inch long and very narrow, somewhat glaucous. Formosa, at high elevations; has been introduced in North America, but little known. —*Juniperus morrisonicola*, Hayata in Gard. Chron., ser. 3, xliii, 194 (Mar. 1908); Journ. Linn. Soc., Bot. xxxviii, 298 (June 1908).

24. **J. thurifera.** Spanish or Frankincense Juniper. Tree to 30 or 40 feet, trunk becoming of large girth, the crown usually narrow-pyramidal in cultivation, the slender growth pinnately branched: scale-like leaves appressed and opposite, ovate with pointed free tips, small, furrowed and glandular on the back; awl-shaped leaves also opposite: fruit subglobose, about $\frac{1}{3}$ inch across, blue, glaucous at maturity the

second year; seeds 2–4, with pits at base. *Thurifera*, incense-bearing, alluding to qualities of the wood. Southwestern Europe, northern Africa; little known in cultivation in North America.—*Juniperus thurifera*, Linnæus, Species Plantarum, 1039 (1753); *J. hispanica*, Miller, Gardeners Dictionary, ed. 8, no. 13 (1768); *J. sabinoïdes*, Endlicher, Synopsis Coniferarum, 24 (1847), partly; *Sabina thurifera*, Antoine, Die Cupressineen-Gattungen, 51 (1857).

25. **J. barbadensis.** BARBADOS or BERMUDA JUNIPER or CEDAR. Probably not planted in the United States and not expected to be hardy except in the warmest parts: tree to 40 feet tall, in habit much like *J. virginiana*, but branches much stouter and foliage pale bluish-green; branchlets thickly set, quadrangular, stout and short: leaves mostly imbricate, thick or acicular, spiny-pointed, rigid, erect-spreading: staminate catkins larger: fruit usually 2-seeded and depressed-globular. Bermuda, Barbados, Antigua. Hardy only in the southern states, but probably not in cultivation in this country.—*Juniperus barbadensis*, Linnæus, Species Plantarum, 1039 (1753); *J. bermudiana*, Linnæus, l. c.

26. **J. lucayana.** WEST INDIAN RED-CEDAR. Tree to 50 feet tall, with spreading branches and slender pendulous 4-angled branchlets: leaves light green, closely appressed, ovate, sharp-pointed, glandular: fruit reniform, about ⅙ inch thick, dark blue, glaucous, 1–2-seeded. Jamaica, Cuba, Bahamas, Haiti. The species-name is from Lucaya, an aboriginal name for the Bahama Islands.—*Juniperus lucayana*, Britton, North American Trees, 121 (1908); *J. virginiana* var. *barbadensis*, Gordon, Pinetum, 114 (1858); *J. australis*, Pilger in Urban, Symbolæ Antillanæ, vii, 479 (1913); *J. barbadensis*, of authors, not Linnæus.

Var. **Bedfordiana.** An English juvenile form with light green acicular foliage and slender pendulous branchlets.—*Juniperus lucayana* var. *Bedfordiana*, Rehder in Journ. Arnold Arb. iii, 208 (1922); *J. virginiana Bedfordiana*, Knight & Perry, Synopsis of Coniferous Plants, 12 (1850), *nomen; J. virginiana* var. *gracilis*, Sargent, Silva of North America, x, 96 (1896).

The tree juniper or cedar native on the coastal plain from South Carolina to Florida and Texas, often planted, formerly known as *J. barbadensis* (*bermudiana*) and later as *J. lucayana* is probably all **J. silicicola,** which grows on dunes, sandy land and clay outcrops, differing from *J. lucayana* in the ovoid rather than reniform cones or fruit and from *J. virginiana* in the usually more slender twigs, larger staminate catkins, and smaller narrower cones. The tree is conic in outline when young but in age is widely branched and more or less rounded or even depressed in outline, frequently much wind-worn on coastal exposures: twigs slender: scale-leaves ovoid or triangular-ovoid, acute or sometimes blunt: staminate catkins ellipsoid, $\frac{3}{16}$ inch or less long: cones or berries with slight bloom at maturity.—*Juniperus silicicola*, new comb.; *Sabina silicicola*, Small in Journ. N. Y. Bot. Gard. xxiv, 5 (1923).

27. **J. virginiana.** RED-CEDAR. Plate XLII. Fig. 94, right. Well-known field and pasture tree of dry and rocky places, of narrow head, with red fragrant heartwood, long cultivated in many forms; to 100 feet, with conical head and spreading or upright branches: leaves spiny-pointed, spreading, or scale-like, rhombic, acute or subacute, imbricate: fruit brownish-violet, glaucous, globular or ovoid, ¼–⅓ inch across. Canada to Florida, east of Rocky Mountains.—*Juniperus virginiana*, Linnæus, Species Plantarum, 1039 (1753); *Sabina virginiana*, Antoine, Die Cupressineen-Gattungen, 61 (1857).

Color cultivars of *J. virginiana* are *albo-spica, argentea, aurea, Burkii, elegantissima, glauca, plumosa, pyramidalis glauca, pyramidiformis Hillii, variegata;* columnar and narrow-pyramidal forms are *Burkii, Canaertii, elegantissima, Keteleeri, plumosa, pyramidalis* and subvars., *pyramidiformis* and subvar., *Schottii, venusta;* spreading, open or pendulous, *Chamberlaynii, filifera, Kosteri, pendula, reptans, tripartita.*

Var. **albo-spica.** Tips of branchlets white; here belongs "Triomphe d'Angers" with the variegation more constant and more conspicuous.—*Juniperus virginiana* var. *albo-spica,* Beissner.

Var. **argentea.** Leaves and young shoots silvery.—*Juniperus virginiana* var. *argentea,* Hort.

Var. **aurea.** Foliage dark green with bronzy tips.—*Juniperus virginiana* var. *aurea,* Hort.

Var. **Burkii.** Of columnar habit with steel-blue foliage.—*Juniperus virginiana* var. *Burkii,* Hort.

Var. **Canaertii.** A compact pyramidal form with dark green foliage and bluish bloomy fruits.—*Juniperus virginiana* var. *Canaertii,* Sénéclauze; *J. virginiana* var. *Cannarti,* Beissner.

Var. **Chamberlaynii.** With spreading branches and elongated pendulous branchlets: leaves dimorphic, grayish-green.—*Juniperus virginiana* var. *Chamberlaynii,* Carrière.

Var. **elegantissima.** Pyramidal tree with the tips of the branchlets golden-yellow. —*Juniperus virginiana* var. *elegantissima,* Hochstetter.

Var. **filifera.** Broad-pyramidal form with slender much divided branchlets and blue-gray foliage.—*Juniperus virginiana* var. *filifera,* D. Hill.

Var. **glauca.** Vigorous form with very glaucous foliage.—*Juniperus virginiana* var. *glauca,* Carrière.

Var. **globosa.** A compact-globose form with bright green scale-like foliage.— *Juniperus virginiana* var. *globosa,* Beissner.

Var. **Keteleeri.** Compact pyramidal form with ascending branches and dark green scale-like foliage.—*Juniperus virginiana* var. *Keteleeri,* Hort.

Var. **Kosteri.** Low and spreading, with glaucous leaves.—*Juniperus virginiana* var. *Kosteri,* Beissner.

Var. **pendula.** With spreading limbs and slender pendulous branches: leaves usually scale-like.—*Juniperus virginiana* var. *pendula,* Carrière.

Var. **plumosa.** A pyramidal form with mostly acicular foliage and white or whitish tips.—*Juniperus virginiana* var. *plumosa,* Rehder; *J. virginiana* var. *plumosa alba,* Beissner.

Var. **pyramidalis.** Dense columnar form.—*Juniperus virginiana* var. *pyramidalis,* Carrière, a European plant.

Var. **pyramidalis glauca.** A form of the above with glaucous foliage.—*Juniperus virginiana* var. *pyramidalis glauca,* Hort.

Var. **pyramidalis viridis.** A form of var. *pyramidalis* with very dark green foliage. —*Juniperus virginiana* var. *pyramidalis viridis,* Hort.

Var. **pyramidiformis.** HILL JUNIPER. Very narrow pyramidal or columnar, with dark green mostly scale-like leaves densely covering the ascending branchlets.— *Juniperus virginiana* var. *pyramidiformis,* D. Hill; *J. virginiana* var. *pyramidalis,* D. Hill.

Var. pyramidiformis Hillii. DUNDEE JUNIPER. Of columnar habit with ascending branchlets bearing short dense acicular leaves, young growth pale bluish-green, plant becoming plum-colored in autumn.—*Juniperus virginiana* var. *pyramidiformis Hillii*, D. Hill.

Var. reptans. Low shrub with horizontally spreading branches and slender curving branchlets, bright green.—*Juniperus virginiana* var. *reptans*, Beissner; *J. virginiana* var. *horizontalis*, Arb. Kew.

Var. Schottii. A comparatively small columnar tree with bright green scale-like foliage.—*Juniperus virginiana* var. *Schottii*, Gordon.

Var. tripartita. FOUNTAIN RED-CEDAR. A dwarf spreading form of irregular habit, densely branched, with acicular glaucous leaves.—*Juniperus virginiana* var. *tripartita*, R. Smith.

Var. variegata. Branchlets variegated with white.—*Juniperus virginiana* var. *variegata*, Lawson; *J. virginiana* var. *albo-variegata*, Beissner.

Var. venusta. A columnar form with glossy dark green foliage.—*Juniperus virginiana* var. *venusta*, Rehder; *J. venusta*, Ellwanger & Barry.

Other listed names are *corymbosa, cylindrica, fastigiata, Libretoni*.

28. J. scopulorum. ROCKY MOUNTAIN JUNIPER or CEDAR. Very hardy and attractive tree reaching 40 feet but commonly of lesser stature, withstanding dry and difficult conditions, valuable in cultivation; closely allied to *virginiana;* chiefly distinguished by the somewhat larger fruit, ripening not until the second year; by its habit, forming a broad head with stout spreading branches and often dividing into several stems near the base; and by its shredding bark. The branchlets are somewhat shorter and stouter, and the foliage usually glaucous or yellowish-green. British Columbia to California in the Rocky Mountains.—*Juniperus scopulorum*, Sargent in Garden and Forest, x, 420 (1897), in obs.; Silva of North America, xiv, 93 (1902); *J. dealbata*, Loudon, Encyclopædia of Trees and Shrubs, 1090 (1842), not Douglas; *Sabina scopulorum*, Rydberg in Bull. Torr. Bot. Club, 598 (1905).

Var. argentea. A narrow-pyramidal form with silvery-white foliage.—*Juniperus scopulorum* var. *argentea*, D. Hill.

Var. Hilli. Foliage very light blue. Bears the name of Hill Nurseries, Dundee, Illinois.—*Juniperus scopulorum* var. *Hillii*, D. Hill.

Var. horizontalis. Upright form with horizontally spreading branches and bluish-white foliage.—*Juniperus scopulorum* var. *horizontalis*, D. Hill.

Var. viridifolia. A pyramidal form with striking bright green foliage.—*Juniperus scopulorum* var. *viridifolia*, D. Hill.

29. J. horizontalis. CREEPING JUNIPER. Valuable native ground-cover plant for exposed sandy and rocky situations: procumbent, usually with long trailing branches furnished with numerous short branchlets, sometimes to 4 feet high and with spreading branches: leaves of young plants subulate, mature foliage imbricate, scale-like, acute or acutely cuspidate, bluish-green or steel-blue: fruit about $\frac{1}{3}$ inch across, blue, slightly glaucous, on a pedicel shorter than its length. Nova Scotia to British Columbia, south to Massachusetts, New York, Minnesota, and Montana. Hardy to north-western Canada and valued as a ground-cover for sandy and rocky soil in exposed situations. Once supposed to be a form of the European *J. Sabina.*—*Juniperus horizontalis*, Moench, Methodus, 699 (1794); *J. prostrata*, Persoon, Synopsis Plantarum, ii, 632 (1807); *J. Sabina* var. *procumbens*, Pursh, Flora Americæ Septentrionalis, 647 (1814); *J. repens*, Nuttall, Genera of North American Plants, ii, 245 (1818); *J. Sabina* var. *prostrata*, Loudon, Arboretum et Fruticetum Britannicum, iv, 2498 (1838); *J. hudsonica*, Forbes, Pinetum Woburnense, 208 (1839); *J. virginiana* var. *prostrata*, Torrey, Flora of State of New York, ii, 235 (1843); *J. Sabina* var. *horizontalis*, Hort.

Var. **alpina**. Plate XLIII. Upright when young but becoming procumbent with ascending branches.—*Juniperus horizontalis* var. *alpina*, Rehder; *J. Sabina* var. *alpina*, Loudon.

Var. **Douglasii**. WAUKEGAN JUNIPER. Trailing form with steel-blue leaves. Bears name of Douglas Nurseries, Waukegan, Illinois.—*Juniperus horizontalis* var. *Douglasii*, Rehder.

Var. **glomerata**. Dwarf form with branchlets crowded into dense clusters.—*Juniperus horizontalis* var. *glomerata*, Rehder.

Var. **plumosa**. ANDORRA JUNIPER. Depressed shrub with flattened top and linear leaves, rising to about 18 inches, bronze-purple in autumn and winter.—*Juniperus horizontalis* var. *plumosa*, Rehder; *J. horizontalis* var. *depressa plumosa*, Hort.

Var: **procumbens**. Very dwarf, only reaching a few inches in height, foliage becoming bluish-green.—*Juniperus horizontalis* var. *procumbens*, Slavin; *J. horizontalis* forma *procumbens*, Slavin.

Var. **variegata**. A procumbent form with tips of branchlets creamy-white.— *Juniperus horizontalis* var. *variegata*, Slavin; *J. horizontalis* forma *variegata*, Slavin.

30. **J. Sabina**. SAVIN. Hardy European spreading or procumbent shrub, or seldom with erect trunk or stem to 12 feet; branchlets rather slender, of a very strong disagreeable odor when bruised: leaves needle-shaped, acute, and slightly spreading or imbricate, oblong-rhombic, obtuse or subacute, usually dark green: fruit ⅕–¼ inch thick, globular, 1–3-seeded. Mountains of central and southern Europe, western Asia, and Caucasus. Stands as far north as Canada.—*Juniperus Sabina*, Linnæus, Species Plantarum, 1039 (1753); *Sabina officinalis*, Garcke, Flora von Nord- und Mittel-Deutschland, ed. 4, 387 (1858).

Var. **lusitanica**. Upright shrub with scale-like leaves. Southern Europe.— *Juniperus Sabina* var. *lusitanica*, Ascherson & Graebner, Synopsis der Mitteleuropaischen Flora, i, 253 (1897); *J. sabinoides*, Grisebach, Spicilegium Floræ Rumelicæ et Bithynicæ, ii, 352 (1844).

Var. **cupressifolia**. Procumbent, with ascending thickish branchlets: leaves usually imbricate, scale-like, often bluish-green.—*Juniperus Sabina* var. *cupressifolia*, Aiton; *J. Sabina* var. *humilis*, Endlicher.

Var. **fastigiata**. COLUMN SAVIN. Erect shrub of columnar habit, with dark green mostly scale-like leaves.—*Juniperus Sabina* var. *fastigiata*, Beissner.

Var. **tamariscifolia**. TAMARIX SAVIN. Procumbent or ascending, rarely erect: leaves usually all needle-shaped and often in 3's, slightly incurved, free at the tip and sharply pointed, dark green, with a white band above, often bluish-green.— *Juniperus Sabina* var. *tamariscifolia*, Aiton.

Var. **variegata**. HOARFROST SAVIN. Branchlets variegated with creamy-white: leaves mostly imbricate.—*Juniperus Sabina* var. *variegata*, Carrière.

BOOK II

THE GROWING OF CONIFERS FOR ORNAMENT
AND INTEREST

THE GROWING OF CONIFERS

IN THIS part, called Book II, the practical growing and handling of conifers is under consideration, together with discussion of insects and diseases affecting them. These discussions are based on similar chapters in "The Cultivated Evergreens," which was published late in 1923; a new edition, with corrections and additional illustrations, was published in March, 1925; it was reissued in July, 1928, again in June, 1929, and once more in September, 1930. It is now made new. Its application is to the northeastern United States, eastern Canada and the Middle West.

Authors of most of the original articles on growing and protecting conifers, so far as they are fortunately living or available, have revised the articles as they now again appear, bringing them down to date. Their names are with the articles in regular sequence, but they may also be listed here separately: Ralph S. Hosmer, Professor of Forestry and head of the Department of Forestry, New York State College of Agriculture at Cornell University; the late O. C. Simonds, beloved landscape-gardener of Chicago and author of the book "Landscape-Gardening," who reviewed the present article before his last illness; Stephen F. Hamblin, Director of the Lexington Botanic Gardens at Lexington, Massachusetts, and Assistant Professor of Horticulture in Harvard University; George P. Brett, Chairman of the Board of Directors of The Macmillan Company, cultivator and admirer of conifers on his estate in Connecticut; W. T. Macoun, Dominion Horticulturist, Ottawa, Canada; C. R. Crosby, Extension Professor of Entomology in Cornell University, assisted by M. D. Leonard; D. S. Welch, Assistant Professor of Plant Pathology, Cornell University. The contributions of the lamented John Dunbar have been revised and extended by Arthur D. Slavin, Horticulturist of the Parks of Rochester, New York. The part on propagation, originally prepared by Frederick Ahrens, now retired, of the Rochester Parks, has been extended by the aid of Chester J. Hunn, Assistant Professor of Ornamental Horticulture in Cornell University. The article by the late E. Bollinger, of the former Robert Douglas Evergreen Nurseries at Waukegan, Illinois, has been reviewed by A. H. Hill of the D. Hill Nursery Company at Dundee, Illinois. To all these persons will conifer lovers, as well as the author, be grateful.

CHAPTER VII

CONIFERS IN THE LANDSCAPE

W E ARE here considering the conifers in private grounds and on estates, in parks and public places, and as features in landscapes. It is important also to understand the coniferous forest, against which so much of our civilization is set.

Appreciation of forests is essential to the best understanding of trees of any kind and of conifers in particular. The forest is the natural habitat of coniferous trees. In the open, the trees attain a different character, to be sure, and this character is to be assumed as natural to the species; yet the forest has a community expression of its own and illustrates the features of close plantation as compared with isolated trees. Both these adaptabilities of the species should be understood. Moreover, the forest has a place in the association of the human race that must not be overlooked; and in these later times, when many great forests are receding, we should make special effort to keep green the memory of the woods.

With this sensitive appreciation of conifers in woods and fields, the planter has a keener understanding of their requirements and of their place in parks and private properties; and the open country presents a new interest. There is this difference, however: in the native places many and often most of the plants present an attitude of maturity, whereas in grounds we know them mostly as young or even juvenile subjects.

It is surprising how commonly the conifers are prized only for their immaturity. Seldom does one see a picturesque and fruiting conifer in home premises. We think of them as small, compact, and trim plants adapted to minor effects; in the intermediate stage, between juvenility and maturity, they are looked on as misshapen and perhaps as ragged objects unworthy of attention. We prize them mostly for their symmetry; yet strength and distinction come with age.

(205)

The juvenile and junior stages of large species naturally have distinct merit in themselves. Some of these states last indefinite years; yet the exclusive planting of them is not a permanent project. Even small species, as some of the junipers and yews, tend to lose their full-foliaged effect with age; they may be improved thereby, however, in the estimation of many persons. If employed in foundation planting, which is now much stressed, one must be careful to choose only those kinds that are by nature low and compact, or that are known by safe experience to remain long in the dwarf state; and one should also avoid the effect of stage scenery that comes by planting too uniformly of stiff symmetrical objects. If one wishes to maintain a formal foundation planting, new plants may be substituted as old ones fail or become irregular, or the entire plan may be changed after some years with good effect. Reliable nurserymen will give good advice on these subjects.

The intending planter should be cautioned against cheap and poor conifers. Skill, patience, and much time are required to produce good trees in the nursery; this is particularly true of the choice named kinds propagated by cuttings and grafts. Several years of labor are behind these beautiful plants and years of experience behind the labor; the competent propagator is careful to see that his stock is true to name, and that each kind is given the particular attention it needs. Each plant is an entity. It is individually packed for shipment. Such results cannot be produced at bargain-counter prices. Satisfaction in the home planting depends greatly on the discriminating choice of stock at the outset.

Horticulturists think of conifers almost exclusively as comely foliage subjects; yet the characteristic beauty, as trees mature, may lie quite as much in the branching habit, in irregularity of top, and the strong features of bole and bark, particularly in the pines. These striking elements of developed trees seem a long way off to the home planter and are not likely to be taken into account in the planning of a place; yet in most cases they arrive readily within a life time; and persons who purchase large conifers for removal are privileged to choose those that begin to show signs of ruggedness as well as those still in the symmetrical verdurous state. The full-page plates in this book are chosen to show various age characteristics in conifers.

Many of the horticultural varieties of conifers are grotesque rather than ornamental. They should be planted sparingly, as curiosities, as in parks and display grounds. Some of the ragged, inverted, weeping forms have no regular meaning in a landscape plan; if wanted on the premises, they may well be placed at the side or in the rear where they are only incidents in the picture. In fact, the free use of highly colored varieties, as very blue spruces and yellow, white and purple kinds, is not considered an expression of the highest taste in the choice of conifers on a large scale although useful as specimen plants and as accents in a plantation.

Too many persons know the conifers only as unkempt half-dead gloomy objects standing where they never should have been planted. They may be strays in dark corners; dejected subjects under trees; hedges of kinds not adapted to such work and the trees probably far too large when planted and then savagely carpentered; huddled things about outbuildings; sorrowful specimens on land that has never been fertilized and from which perhaps all the leaves have been laboriously raked in autumn; cozy underlings that have outgrown the second-story windows. Against these common spectacles let the reader contrast a few trees or a plantation set where conifers ought to be, that were well chosen, and that have received as thoughtful attention as one would give to corn or decent roses.

If one makes a conetum, the property may be planted exclusively to this class of plants. The primary object is to grow good specimens, with room enough for each bush or tree to attain its maximum characteristics. In general planting for artistic effect, however, conifers may best be parts in a mixed although not miscellaneous assemblage of broad-leaved evergreens and deciduous plants. These combinations add variety, relieve monotony at any point, and insure against failures of particular kinds. Care must be exercised not to choose very rapid-growing large deciduous trees for close planting with conifers because they will crowd the evergreens out. Just because they are so formal and so emphatic, the placing of coniferous evergreens should be in the hands of persons practiced in landscape values.

The background of the forest.—R. S. Hosmer

Among all the trees of the forest, the conifers are the most important from a commercial standpoint. The reason for this is not far to seek. The trees belonging to the coniferous genera —the pines, spruces, firs, cedars, and hemlocks—furnish the material most in demand for construction of all kinds, and also for a great variety of minor uses in which the demand is for strength combined with relative lightness. The so-called "softwoods" are more easily worked and usually are cheaper than are the broad-leaf species, or "hardwoods," at least in the grades suitable for building purposes. It is not strange, then, that in considering the direct economic value of the forests of the United States, those in which conifers predominate are given first place.

Forests are of use to man in three principal ways: They supply timber, wood, and other forest products. They safeguard the catchment basins of streams needed for human use and so tend to maintain regularity of stream-flow. Also they serve as centers for many forms of recreation. Forests have a direct relation to human health. This is most noticeable in the case of coniferous forests. Highly beneficial results often attend a sojourn in a locality in which there are pine or spruce forests. Forest sanatoria, such as those established by the states of New York and Pennsylvania, are usually in sections in which the conifers predominate.

From the standpoint of timber supply, the coniferous species furnish approximately seventy per cent of the timber cut each year in the forests of the United States. Of minor uses, fifty per cent of the box material comes from the two main divisions of the pine family—the white and the yellow pines. Spruce is the best material for the cheap production of paper. In the southern states, long-leaf pine is the chief source of turpentine and naval stores. The uses are manifold to which the wood of the conifers is put. Wood, and, in large part, coniferous wood, is at the foundation of the prosperity of the nation.

The coniferous forests of the United States form a part of the great belt of conifers that characterizes the North Temperate Zone. This belt stretches from Alaska across Canada and the United States and is found again in Scandinavia, northern Europe, Russia, and Siberia. In the United States, coniferous species are the commercially important trees in four of the five natural forest regions: the Northern Forest, the Southern Pineries, the Rocky Mountain, and the Pacific forests. The fifth region is that of the Central Hardwoods.

The Northern Forest includes the North Woods of New England and New York, the pine lands of the Lake States, and the area lying at the higher elevations southward along the Appalachian Mountain ranges. The more important conifers of the Northern Forest are white pine (*Pinus Strobus*), red pine (*P. resinosa*), red spruce (*Picea rubens*), hemlock (*Tsuga canadensis*), and arbor-vitæ (*Thuja occidentalis*). Although at the higher elevations there are pure stands of conifers, the typical Northern Forest is a mixed forest of conifers and broad-leaf trees. White pine is, or was, the outstanding species. Its tall bole, large size, and easily worked wood marked it from colonial times as, perhaps, the most prized American timber tree. The original forest has now disappeared, except for a few small isolated stands. However, white pine reproduces easily, both naturally and artificially, and grows rapidly, so that in the Northeast it has come to be the principal species used in reforestation.

The Southern Pineries, as the name implies, is essentially a coniferous forest. It extends along the Atlantic seaboard from New Jersey southward to the Gulf states. Long-leaf pine (*Pinus palustris*) is the tree of first importance, both for its lumber and for its turpentine. Three other pines are also to be noted: short-leaf (*P. echinata*), loblolly (*P. Tœda*), and Cuban or slash pine (*P. caribœa*). In the swamps of the South is found the bald-cypress (*Taxodium distichum*).

In the Rocky Mountain region the species of commercial importance are the western yellow pine (*P. ponderosa*), lodgepole pine (*P. contorta* var. *latifolia*), Engelmann spruce (*Picea Engelmanni*), and the mountain form of Douglas fir or Pseudotsuga. In the "Inland Empire" of Montana and Idaho, the western white pine (*P. monticola*) is an important timber tree. Regulated grazing plays an important rôle in the national forests in this region.

The Pacific forest comprises the Pacific Coast states. In Washington and Oregon the most important trees are Douglas fir, western hemlock (*Tsuga heterophylla*), several true firs (Abies), western red-cedar (*Thuja plicata*), Sitka spruce (*Picea sitchensis*), and western white pine. In California the species that stand out are redwood (*Sequoia sempervirens*) near the coast, sugar pine (*Pinus Lambertiana*), and western yellow pine in the Sierras. The largest and highest, as well as the oldest trees in the world, the "big trees" (*Sequoia gigantea*), are found on the Pacific slope.

The foregoing list enumerates but a few, of course, of the total number of conifers in the several forest regions. In general, the forests of the United States fall into two main classes, the eastern and western forests. East of the Great Plains, broadleaf species are found in mixture with conifers. There is usually much undergrowth. In the West the forests consist of practically pure stands of conifers, for the most part, except in the Pacific Northwest, of open character and free from undergrowth.

Without the lumber yielded by the coniferous forests, the United States could never have achieved the rapid material progress that has characterized the growth of the nation, especially since the Civil War. The rapid expansion of the Mississippi Valley states was made possible in no small part by the pine forests of Michigan, Wisconsin, and Minnesota. Likewise, southern pine has played a great part, just as now Douglas fir is coming to be one of the most used woods. The coniferous forests have been a great heritage, but, unfortunately, they have been misused and until very recent years no thought has been given to their replacement. The forest has been treated as a mine, not as a crop. The American people will have reason to regret their short-sightedness.

The Pacific Coast forests now constitute the last great storehouse of virgin softwood timber. When that supply is exhausted, the needs of the nation can be met only from second-growth forests. Furthermore, four-fifths of the standing timber that remains is privately owned and as yet but little of this area has been brought under scientific forest management. This gives point to the movement for an adequate national forest policy that aims to bring about the wise use of all forests, both publicly and privately owned, to the end that the people of the United States may have a continuous supply of wood and of other forest products, adequate for their needs, in perpetuity.

The Christmas-tree problem.—R. S. Hosmer

Of all that the forest yields to man, perhaps no gift is more prized than is the Christmas tree. To the children the tree, with its gay decorations, its glittering lights, and at the top the bright star, is the center of the Christmas celebration. To their elders it brings but little less pleasure. In many families the Christmas tree is allowed to stand for a week, or even until Twelfth Night, all the while continuing to give joy to young and old. It is an indispensable part of the happy Christmastide, and, even when dismantled, it may still serve out-of-doors as a feeding station for the birds. Without a tree the Christmas festivities are not complete.

Just how far back in history the Christmas-tree custom goes, no one knows. It is probably of very ancient origin, possibly a survival from the Scandinavian mythology that preceded Christian times. But whatever its origin, the custom is now so wide-spread and deep seated that it has a recognized place in every Christian country. The United States leads the world in the use of Christmas trees. Over eight million trees are needed each year to supply the demand in American homes. The following statement is designed to show that the use of trees for this purpose is a legitimate and, if properly conducted, a wise use, and that the purveying of Christmas trees rests on a basis of sound economics as well as on sentiment.

Many different kinds of trees are used in the United States as Christmas trees, but practically all are conifers. In the Northeast the favorite is the balsam fir. This comes near to being the ideal Christmas tree. As a small tree it is usually symmetrical, with long, horizontal, spreading branches. Its needles are pleasantly fragrant and persist indoors longer than do those of most other evergreens. Spruce comes next in importance and makes a very good substitute for balsam fir. The species most employed is the red spruce, but the introduced Norway spruce is also to be commended. The other native species, the black and the white spruces, are also used.

In the southern and central states red-cedar is often used as a Christmas tree. It has a conical form and develops a dense and attractive crown. Where the firs and spruces are not easily obtainable, pines are not despised. In parts of the South the scrub pine is much in demand. In the southern Appalachians, Fraser fir makes a good Christmas tree.

In the Rocky Mountain states, Douglas fir, Engelmann spruce, and, in places, lodge-pole pine find favor; on the Pacific Coast, white fir, incense-cedar, and western hemlock. Local custom and availability have much to do with the kinds and species which are used as Christmas trees. Santa Claus seems as well satisfied with one kind as another.

Northern New England, northern New York, and Canada are the source of supply for the cities of the Atlantic seaboard as far south as Baltimore and even Washington. Michigan, Wisconsin, and Minnesota furnish the markets of Chicago, St. Paul, and the cities of the plains states. The arrival of the "Christmas-tree ship" is a looked-for event in Chicago harbor.

Christmas trees vary in size from three to five feet up to thirty-five feet or more; the small sizes up to eight to ten feet are tied in bundles. Large trees are shipped as individuals. Prices in the eastern city markets range from twenty-five to fifty cents up to $40 or $50. When carload lots are shipped, particularly if the trees are graded as to size and condition, the returns may be worth while. There is, however, considerable risk in the Christmas-tree business, especially when a local market is overstocked. Each year after Christmas many perfectly good trees are hauled to the city dump to be burned. To be assured of a reasonable return, the rational procedure for the Christmas-tree owner is to find a market in a neighboring town or city and supply the retail stores directly. By this method he will probably gain much more than when the trees are handled by a series of middlemen.

All too often the question is raised as to whether the cutting and use of Christmas trees is not a great waste, and whether steps should not be taken to discourage or prohibit it. In the opinion of the United States Department of Agriculture, the custom is so old, so well grounded, and so venerated, that even if it were economically somewhat indefensible, these aspects would and should continue to outweigh economic considerations. But, say the foresters, the cutting of trees for Christmas is proper and wholly justifiable. No other use to which these trees could be put is any more worthy than to make them add to the joy of mankind through their use by children on this great festival of the year. True conservation of the forest is not found in abstaining from the use of trees, but in a rational system of forest management. The Christmas tree is a legitimate by-product of the forest. If the spruce and fir trees that are so used were left standing, to be cut later for the manufacture of paper pulp, it is wholly pertinent to inquire whether the joy of a group of children in their Christmas tree does not outbalance the value of a page or two of the comic section of a Sunday supplement.

There are two ways by which Christmas trees can be supplied to meet the demand. Both are in perfect accord with the best principles and practices of forestry. One is by means of intermediate or improvement cuttings, whereby the value and quality of a given stand of forest can be bettered; the other is through the establishment of Christmas-tree plantations, where firs or spruces are grown for this special purpose.

At present the larger number of Christmas trees, both in the United States and Canada, are cut on privately owned lands. Many farmers take advantage of the opportunity thus afforded to clean up pastures where the forest is starting to come back, or to clear land that should be kept open. In parts of New England and in other regions where it is the desire of the owner that abandoned pastures should revert to forest, the taking out of small trees, especially balsam fir, may be of distinct advantage to the stand. The practice of making thinnings is, when judiciously applied, an integral part of forest management. The demand for Christmas trees often makes it possible for the owner to sell the trees removed at a price sufficient to cover the cost of such thinnings, if indeed he does not make an actual profit. Small trees of the coniferous genera have little value for other purposes. Comparatively few owners feel that they can afford to make thinnings which require an outlay for labor, without some immediate return. The indiscriminate clearing of any area of forest land, without making adequate provision for its restocking by young growth is, of course, to be discouraged. True conservation of the forest is its perpetuation through wise use.

The other method, that of establishing commercial plantations of Christmas trees, is already attracting the attention of many owners of non-agricultural land. As the trees are to be removed while still small, close spacing is indicated; three by three feet is good. A rectangular spacing of three feet requires 4,840 trees to the acre. With a triangular spacing of three feet between trees each way, the number is 5,584 to the acre. In New York state, spruce transplants, four years old, can normally be obtained from the nurseries of the Conservation Department, Albany, for around $5 a thousand. In other states that maintain state nurseries, a similar arrangement usually obtains. Specific information may be secured by addressing the State Forester. Directions as to how to plant the trees may also be secured from the State Forester, or from the State College of Agriculture. To give such assistance is a part of the duty of these state officers.

In a Christmas-tree plantation made by the Department of Forestry of the Michigan State College, where four-year-old Norway spruce transplants were used, the average height of the trees in the plantation was six feet at the end of six years. A few of the best trees averaged nine and one-half feet for this period. The soil was a stiff clay, full of stones, and wet in the spring. It was found "that if the trees grow faster than one foot a year they become spindly. The best Christmas trees are those which have grown rather slowly. They are bushier and better shaped."* From such a plantation some trees are cut each year, giving those left a better chance to develop.

A careful estimate of possible returns from Christmas-tree plantations in New York state, made in 1919 by G. Harris Collingwood, then Extension Specialist in Forestry at Cornell University,† showed for a ten-year period an expected net annual profit of $68 an acre. Costs of nursery stock and of planting, the value of the land, and taxes were all counted in and carried forward at six per cent compound interest. This

*Mich. Agr. Coll. Exp. Sta. Special Bull. No. 78. Apr. 1916. "Christmas Tree Plantations," by A. K. Chittenden.
†Two articles in the *Rural New Yorker*, Mar. 1 and 8, 1919. "Christmas Tree Farming," by G. Harris Collingwood.

figure should be taken only as a general indication of the money return to be expected, but it points to the conclusion that when the local conditions are favorable, the growing of Christmas trees can be made a profitable commercial venture. Further information on this subject is contained in a bulletin of the New York Conservation Department, Albany, New York, "Christmas Tree Plantations," by A. F. Amadon, 1929. Copies may be obtained on application to that office.

In growing Christmas trees, it should always be borne in mind that the most important item is to be sure that there exists a market, preferably not far distant, where it is reasonably certain that the trees can be sold when they are of the right size. Where this condition obtains, the establishment of a Christmas-tree plantation should not only be a good investment, but, also, to an owner with imagination, a very satisfying way of using a part of his land. In some cases a living rooted tree may be employed and set out afterwards, thus adding to the interest taken in that tree in the future.

From quite another side there is one point that, unfortunately, has to find a place now-a-days in any discussion of Christmas trees. This is the all too common practice of stealing Christmas trees and Christmas greens. Particularly has this practice spread since the increase in the number of automobiles. Many persons seem not to realize that the products of the farm, including trees, are not common property.

Trees are private property, just as are other possessions. He who, without permission, goes on the land of another and helps himself to a tree is guilty of theft. That he often escapes punishment does not alter this fact. This sort of petty larceny cannot be condemned too strongly. It is all the more to be deplored because committed at a season which is universally dedicated to good will and the unselfish thought of others. Every home ought to have its Christmas tree, but that tree should be obtained honestly.

The only real problem that concerns the Christmas tree is

how to make it easier for each family to have its own tree. For in the home the Christmas tree will ever remain the center of the celebration of Christmas Day.

The natural setting of evergreens.—O. C. Simonds

In landscape work, nature is the best teacher in the use of evergreens as well as that of other growth. In visiting localities in which evergreens thrive, one is usually impressed with their beauty and wishes to have them about one's own home. The effects that should be studied are often found at the edges of a forest, or scattered along river-banks and margins of lakes and marshes. Here trees may range in size from less than a foot in height to those of large stature. The growth may include pines, spruces, cedars, balsams, hemlocks, junipers, and yews in the northern middle states, and, in the eastern states, broad-leaved evergreens as well. In the Middle West the more hardy conifers can generally be used with good effect where soil conditions are right and the air pure, but in the larger cities, with their smoky atmosphere, it is useless to plant any member of the pine family. Sometime in the future, when cities can be delivered from the pall of smoke that hangs over them, they may be able to raise evergreens with more satisfaction. At present, however, conifers planted in a smoky atmosphere are likely to look sickly and to excite feelings of pity rather than of pleasure.

Attention might be called to some attractive natural effects. At the edges of pine forests, or scattered about in open spaces near the edge, the pines and other evergreens often retain all their branches, the lower ones resting on the ground and reaching out farther than those above to secure light and air. These show the typical appearance which pines, spruces, firs, hemlocks, and cedars should have in one's home grounds or in other places where they are planted for ornament. Sometimes a belt of evergreen growth may be useful as well as ornamental by giving protection from cold winds, or shutting out of view unsightly objects. In such belts it is well to arrange the trees in colonies, pines being grouped with pines, and the more pointed and stiff-growing trees, like the spruces, with those of similar habit. It is said that evergreens should not be mixed or grouped with deciduous trees. To a certain extent this is true, but all will recall the beauty of autumn foliage, especially that of the maples, sumacs, birches, and blueberries, when this beauty is heightened by a background or a neighboring group of evergreens. A ground-covering of spreading junipers or yews frequently adds much to the artistic effect of the upright growth. Indeed, when the grounds are not very large, it may be well to fill nearly all of the open space with a low growth of this kind. Evergreens are beautiful throughout the entire year and especially so in winter when partly covered with snow and in spring when the new growth comes out and is contrasted in color with the old, and when the trees are thickly sprinkled with beautifully colored blossoms, the pistillate flowers often a rich red or purple, the staminate a bright yellow.

The principles of landscape-gardening which apply to the arrangement of plantations, the preservation of ample open space, and the natural irregular arrangement which gives such a charm to woods, apply to evergreens as well as to oaks, maples, and hawthorns. In using evergreens they should first be considered as objects of beauty in themselves; then as backgrounds for roses, elderberries, or other low growth that flourishes in the neighborhood, or as a foil to other plants. Yellow birches and hemlocks are often found growing near each other and seem to adjust their branches without much interference. A hillside covered with pines and bordered here and there at the bottom with Carolina roses, red-branched dogwoods, snowberries or viburnums, often gives a pleasing effect. A birch tree with its white bark shooting above the growth of roses or dogwoods may contribute to the charm of the whole composition.

Evergreens form an important part of that wealth of plant-life from which the landscaper must choose the material with which he makes his most effective compositions. They can be used with greatest safety for marginal planting, or as groups located near the margins of open spaces, near buildings, or on promontories or hillsides. When planted near the summit of a ridge or a hill, they emphasize more than other trees its effect of height.

Evergreens in the planted landscape.—S. F. Hamblin

In temperate regions, most of the evergreen trees are conifers, and also the greater number of ornamental evergreen shrubs of wide use in planting are dwarf conifers. The broad-leaved evergreens, as members of the heath and holly families, are of less universal use than the conifers.

Evergreens should be placed much more thoughtfully than deciduous trees and shrubs. The mere fact that they are more costly than deciduous woody plants, and more difficult to grow, puts them in a class by themselves. Yet even if they were cheap and easy to keep in good condition, they would still be very distinct and would need to be placed with care in regions in which the leaves fall from most plants in autumn. Evergreens are so very definite in their habit, texture, and color that each specimen counts very distinctly, and when planted carelessly in small areas give a very spotty appearance.

Evergreens are the same in the landscape at all seasons of the year. Although the common trees and shrubs run a yearly cycle from leafless twig to leaf, flower, and fruit, the evergreens, descendants from an earlier plant era, go through the seasons with little modification save the fresher green of the new shoots in May. The changes of growth and decay are theirs, but after they are planted their chief change is increase in size.

In winter months, contrasted with the white of snow and gray of leafless twigs, the dark greens of the conifers suggest warmth and cheer to man. Even beast and bird find shelter in spruce and pine in cold weather. This physical fact contributes greatly to our joy in their sight in winter. In summer, their heavier darker greens, against the broad paler leafage of deciduous trees, suggest shade and coolness. Under the hemlock branches in August it is cool and damp, and the sights and sounds of mid-summer are mostly absent. Their suggestions of physical comfort, at both extremes of the year, make evergreens particularly desirable near the dwellings of man. However, these factors do not render easier the problem of effective planting.

A study of the characteristics of coniferous evergreens from the point of view of art, the art of arranging them in landscape pictures, shows them full of contrasts. Although the foliage is small and narrow, it is so dense that the effect is not feathery, but heavy and solid. There is great difference between the texture effect of tamarix and cedar, yet the latter has the finer foliage. Only the pale greens of the deciduous conifers (larch and bald-cypress) and extreme forms of some chamæcyparis give a light touch to the picture. The density of the dark foliage is increased by the regular formal outline of most species and the regular structure in the placing of the branches. There is no more unrelated object on a peaceful lawn than a blue spruce, and two are twice as lonesome. The more irregular the outline and broken the branching, the easier the task of grouping, except for special effects. The dense tense attitude of most conifers makes them difficult subjects to handle. If only they could be dented inwards in places, and pulled out in others, they would be much more companionable among their fellows. Each specimen is so complete and perfect in itself that only when old age has robbed it of its symmetry does it become a subject for consideration as an object of art in the landscape.

In color, the normal dark shining green shows less range than do the greens of deciduous trees. Their color value to the camera is much the same in all species. Gray-greens in pine, blue-greens in spruce and fir, white lines on the under side of fir and hemlock leaves, give variety in detail that can be appreciated only at close hand. Unfortunately, freak colors are found in horticultural varieties in a range more than sufficient. Intense blue, bright yellow, pale silvery green, and bronzy purple are possible in many of the conifers, particularly in the smaller species. Pine and hemlock have mostly refused to depart from their normal foliage. In general, the farther the color of a conifer has ranged from a normal dark green, the less it should be planted in home pictures and the more care must be used in its disposition, when it is permitted, for it is always a special and striking object of all seasons.

By their density of twig and foliage throughout the year, evergreens offer ideal protection from wind and storm, as windbreak, shelter, and screen. A very effective shelter-belt can be made by a narrow strip of evergreens. Since conifers are a very heavy mass when grouped, this windbreak must also be a part of the landscape picture, and when used for a screen they will call attention in the direction toward which the view is to be shut off. Their double service of attracting as well as protecting must ever be borne in mind. The dividing planting must then be ornamental also. The best hedges are of evergreen conifers.

Evergreens of all kinds give a feeling of richness to the cultivated landscape, possibly in part because they are expensive and at times difficult to cultivate to perfection. As foliage plants they have come to be considered as the most beautiful and choice of woody plants. They may be sadly out of place, as seen in some small yard, or badly broken by insects and the elements because of lack of care, yet there is a special halo of inherent virtue around each one of them. The same is true in regard to a natural planting of conifers. Whatever the arrangement given them by nature, as a group they are pleasing and add tremendously to the beauty of that particular spot.

As nature puts out her spruces, firs, pines, and cedars, her pictures are always pleasing, and analysis of their arrangement shows how great advantage was taken of every change in soil and exposure. When man plants conifers to dress his scene, pictorial and nature-like compositions are rarely brought forth. A natural arbor-vitæ swamp has more to please the eye than the collections of conifers that wealth can put around its home. It is a far greater tax on the skill of the plantsman to set out a

97. The vegetable solids of topiary work.

dozen conifers, even all of a kind, than the same number of mixed deciduous trees. A good artificial staging of conifers is rare; it is too easy to secure an assorted effect instead of harmony of line and outline. The use of conifers in sections of the country in which some species are native and common seems more happy and related to the site than their use in regions of few native trees.

It must always be borne in mind that, except for a few species and irregular old-age individuals, conifers present a firm fixed outline against the sky. They make individuals, not masses, and are numbered off by the eye, except when on the large scale of a forest. Spruce and fir, arbor-vitæ and red-cedar are clear-cut tri-

angles and cones that will not lose their distinctive shapes unless planted together very closely. An array of various genera and species becomes a demonstration in solid geometry. This fact is made use of and heightened by clipping, and the vegetable solids of topiary work are the extreme of this idea. (See Fig. 97.) Many unclipped evergreens, however, have a very complacent well-groomed appearance. Most pines, hemlocks, and Douglas fir, and perhaps others, mingle their branches fairly well even in small groups. Even if their outline has a fairly close line relation, and although their foliage is similar to a marked degree in the genera, nevertheless their sharpness of outline and the individual characters of each make their mass formation a mixture and not a unified composition. It is advisable to have few species and fewer genera on display in any one section of a planting. The more numerous the species, the greater the diversity in skyline and composition.

The masses of conifers are darkest and densest of all vegetation; so also are their shadows very black on lawn or across structure or other vegetation. Coniferous evergreens are the deep tones in pictures out-of-doors. As contrast to structures, as background, low foreground, or horticultural adjunct, the shadows they cast have great pictorial value. Too many evergreens, because of depth of shadow, may make the picture too dark and dismal. Use of the lighter shades of green will help to offset this difficulty, as the selection of white pine instead of Norway spruce near a dwelling. Though the shadows may be as dark, they will be tempered by the lighter foliage color.

It is easy to see, therefore, that one evergreen in a planting may have more pictorial weight than any deciduous tree or several of them. Since its value in the picture is so great, its relation to the nearest vegetation is very important. In the grouping of the various conifers, avoiding the intense forms of color, any sorts that site and soil will allow to thrive may be placed together with fair effect. The lack of conformity in outline seems the greatest problem. However, spruce and fir look alike to the camera, the triangles are all triangular; juniper and arbor-vitæ are equally exclamation points; pine, hemlock, and yew at length spread out similar wide arms; and the low dwarfs, as Mugo pine, dwarf juniper, and the Tom Thumbs make vegetable mattresses. There are, then, these four groups, and a massing within each group gives similarities of outline and pleasing composition which is produced by the close relation of structure; a choice from any two or more of these groups gives distinct contrasts.

In small areas one conifer can dominate the scene; or a group of a few can be the central feature of the planting. This means that the evergreen plant material should be chosen and placed first (on paper) and the attendant other vegetation is chosen to set it off by contrast of outline, structure, texture, color, size, and position. An equal mixture of evergreens and deciduous trees and shrubs is rarely satisfying. There is too much equality in bulk and the contrast loses value. For best pictorial effects, it is safest to keep the two types of vegetation quite or nearly apart and separated, except when definite differences of vegetation are desirable, and then the differences are strengthened by inequality of bulk and quantity.

One evergreen tree is well set off by a background of other similar or contrasting evergreens, but it is too obvious to show off well in good composition or contrast in front of a mass of deciduous trees. A small group of related conifers, a small unit in themselves, looks much less lonesome against the larger area of deciduous background. They derive strength from one another and are less structurally unrelated to their contrasted vegetation.

Evergreens in mass formation make excellent backing to show off the special beauties of some tree—red maple in spring bloom or autumn leaf, crab-apple in flower or fruit, golden stems of willow—for the main mass of the picture is the changeless composition of the evergreens, enlightened by the gift of the seasons from the deciduous tree or trees. Special plantings of all kinds—azaleas, lilacs, lilies, peonies, irises—acquire double value when inclosed and framed by perpetual walls of dark green. A small planting thus set off may have a quantity and quality that a larger one unframed, or seen against sky, cannot possess. After the brief period of bloom, the glory goes back to the evergreens, and the spot is full of beauty.

By nature all evergreens, except cedar of Lebanon, Japanese umbrella-pine, Monterey cypress, and a few similar relics of older eras, are forest trees somewhere. Most of them, however, are seen as landscape specimens, in solitary grandeur upon a lawn. For this special use their many virtues decidedly fit them, and when placed so as to bear some relation to other objects their symmetrical sweep of branches renders them as complete in themselves as a Greek temple or statue. These conifers are, then, related to other objects, but not strictly grouped with anything, and when old age turns their symmetry into irregularity they have still a classic appeal.

Since their shape is so definite and permanent, coniferous evergreens are eminently suited to formal work of all kinds, and the size of material, from Tom Thumb arbor-vitæ to Austrian pine, can fit the scale of the design. The dignity and repose of a formal scheme is greatly increased by evergreen material, and the topiary art can assist nature. Here, again, the plants are not grouped, in the proper sense of the word, but are placed and spaced as the development of the design requires, living plants treated as geometrical forms, or solids for horticultural architecture. Since gardens were builded, evergreens have furnished the opaque solids.

In the relation of the tree shape to the topography, rather definite suggestions may be secured from nature. Most spiry-topped trees grow naturally in hilly and uneven lands. Spruce, fir, and juniper seem to reach upward and emphasize the irregularities of the ground surface. Much more use could be made of this relation of shape of tree and soil surface in planting, each to bring out the special character of the other. One cannot think of New England's rocky fields without juniper or balsam, and the slopes of the Rockies without fir or spruce. Conversely, the planting of stately firs or pyramidal cypresses in open flat land, unless, as in Norway spruce, there is great lateral spread of lower limbs, seems particularly unhappy and inappropriate. In narrow spaces, shut in and separated from the flat expanse by buildings, walls, hedges, and other high planting, the spiry evergreens seem in fairly permanent quarters, but only as special contrast to site and surroundings. The spiry kinds are related to structures of all sorts—house, barn, or bridge—only by intense contrast.

Pines, nearly all sorts, offer the other extreme. Their lines in maturity are mostly horizontal, and the species frequent flat lands and the plains. They are more picturesque in age; the pine is one of the few conifers that grows old gracefully. To this group of horizontal type, with grace in age, can be added yew, cedar of Lebanon, some junipers, hemlocks, and probably Douglas fir. These species are, thus, the most generally useful of large conifers. They fit all shapes of soil-surface, give level and regular lines against the sky, against structures and other solid masses, and mingle well in mass with one another, or with deciduous tree forms and foliage. More pines and cedars of Lebanon are needed in created landscapes, and not too many of the compact vegetable spires and cones, of which nature has created many in spruce and fir and juniper. The shapes of these are too similar to make them distinct to the average eye.

The larger evergreens have their particular place in the landscape. Another special field is filled by the low species and dwarf forms of the larger sorts. For formal and pattern beds of all kinds, the low junipers, yews, arbor-vitæ and retinisporas were apparently created. Lacking these, and some of the broad-leaved evergreens, as box and English ivy, the contrast of lawn and normal vegetation, with dark masses of three dimensions in set-designs, would not be possible, except as filled with herbaceous material. The plants are wholly restricted in their placing by the requirements of the design and the chief demand on them is that they live and thrive, yet increase in size but little lest they outgrow their allotted space and spoil the design. For the effect that Lord Bacon also observed in tarts, the regular ranging of this material has a decided place in certain styles of design. The chief requirement in the staging is a relation to some degree between the flat-topped, rounded, and pointed ones. To avoid monotony of forms or extreme diversity, securing harmony yet contrast in shapes, textures, and tones, requires an unusual degree of skill in placing plant materials.

The flat-topped and cushion-shaped forms of conifers, as dense varieties of spruce and arbor-vitæ, make very distinct groups in the landscape, so very distinct that they should be introduced with extreme caution in any except formal work. The spiry sorts, as Irish juniper or yew, are particularly useful as accents in the formal garden. The darkest forms, as savin and dwarf yew, give deep tones and shadows to this living painting; while the foliage tones of silver, gold, and blue add the high lights and sun touches. With such a wealth of material for this three-dimension sketching, the student of planting wonders why so little use is made of this field, and so assorted the results achieved. Good staging of dwarf evergreens will make happy the home-lover and the nurseryman. Weeping and irregular dwarf conifers give picturesque and Japanese effects when properly placed for a special touch, but most ungainly forms look crazier than ever because of poor placing.

Irregular dwarf conifers, as the many forms of juniper and chamæcyparis, are excellent ground-cover in poor soil in the sun. For good land and under trees, the many forms of yew of low habit, and for moist soils the dwarf loose varieties of arbor-vitæ, take the place of grass or low deciduous shrubs, hiding soil and slope through the year. One species at a time, in soil that suits it, with some broad-leaved evergreen shrubs and perennials of good foliage, gives carpets of undulating green that no other planting can duplicate. No soil is too dry and sunny, shaded or damp, or the space too narrow, in regions where homes are built, to prevent the use of this richest of soil concealments. Small areas of definite outline, covered with dwarf evergreens in definite plan, make evergreen gardens that satisfy the eye the year through.

Evergreen conifers, therefore, contribute in the landscape picture the dark masses, the contrasts, the solid lines against the sky, shelter in hedge, screen, and windbreak, the solitary specimen, accents and adjuncts to garden accessories, the best material for formal work, and permanent cover to hold and hide the soil. Except such types as the pine, they are weakest as parts of harmonious composition, for their chief purpose is individual contrast, except in large plantations.

A special use in modern plantings for conifers of low or medium size (no trees) is for foundation and entrance plantings. To connect house walls with lawn and topography, something more permanent in appearance than salvia or deutzia is often needed. The jumble of blue and Norway spruce, attended by golden juniper, which eventually die or become too big for the place, is seen from many a living-room window. Surely this kind of planting can be much better conceived, with a real unified relation to house and attendant objects. A few kinds, and not many of them, seem a safe rule for first attempts at this kind of planting. Plantings at entrances, doorways, street gate or portal of the garden, call for evergreen material. If the entrance is narrow, columnar junipers could be the main feature; when a feeling of space is desirable, Mugo pine and dwarf yew may mark the entrance. Good proportions in heights, diameters, textures, and colors suited to the type of gateway and their use seem to be the first requirement and often least considered.

Partly because of difficulties of cultivation and maintenance, but equally because an evergreen in northern lands cannot be so casually shoved into a planting as may deutzia and maple, sufficient use is not made of evergreens in plantings for their all-season wear. If more care is employed, not only in attending their physical wants, but in studying further their more effective staging as objects in the landscape picture, gardens will be built more finely. Enthusiasm for the artistic value of conifers, however, must be tempered by a thorough knowledge of their physical limitations. Too often the planting is made wholly with an eye to the present effects, with no thought of changes soon to be made by vigorous growth or early decay from unfavorable circumstances.

CHAPTER VIII

CULTIVATION AND PROPAGATION OF CONIFERS

THE requirements in soils and treatment for conifers are relatively simple, and yet good judgment and experience yield their rewards with these plants as with others. The first requisite is careful observation as to where and when conifers grow best. Every intending planter has occasion to see these plants somewhere, in nurseries, parks, home premises, or in the wild, and to note the particular conditions of soil, drainage and exposure under which they thrive. Other planters in the vicinity, nurserymen, landscape-gardeners, may be consulted; such relationships establish some of the best emotional satisfactions in the development of a property.

I. HOW CONIFERS ARE GROWN

Most of the conifers thrive on a wide variety of soils. Neutral and subacid soils probably suit the greater number, but some of them withstand considerable lime; this subject is in need of investigation and many positive statements can hardly be made as yet. Well-drained arable uplands, suitable for staple farm crops, are commonly chosen, yet many of the species, as redcedar and other junipers, grow well among rocks. Certain arborvitæ and the eastern native white-cedar (*Chamæcyparis thyoides*, which grows in an acid soil) thrive in moist places, even in swampy areas; but in general, water standing about the roots is fatal. It is singular that certain kinds, as bald-cypress, that naturally inhabit swamps often thrive under cultivation in well-drained even if moist lands. If particular soils or locations are demanded by any species, the fact is likely to appear in the comments in this volume.

The question of hardiness is, of course, all-important. It is not only the problem of temperature the given tree will stand, but also the exposure to winds, and, to a considerable extent, the source from which the tree is derived. Sometimes hemlocks and firs, for example, can be transplanted with safety from adjacent fields or woods, while the same species brought from a more southern or more protected region might not readily establish itself. This is particularly the case with species grown on the northern borders of their hardiness. If the plants are raised from seeds matured in similar or even more rigorous climates, they are usually more hardy.

In the way of actual tillage, little is required for the conifers, although they profit by it when young. The conifers are essentially lawn subjects, and sod is the natural setting. With scarcity of labor, however, tall grass and weeds are likely to get the start, making the place look untidy and to increase hazards of fire. The use of the mowing-machine will greatly help, when scythes and lawn-mowers are out of the question. Once well established, the evergreen plantation should require less care than many or even most other kinds of landscape plantings.

For hedges, special treatment is required. The ground should be deeply and uniformly prepared at the outset; kinds of conifers that stand clipping must be chosen; the plants should be uniform in size, vigor and shape. Unsheared tall hedges are properly wind-breaks or shelter-belts. Usually the fine-foliaged close-growing conifers are best for sheared hedges, as arbor-vitæ, the hemlocks, and the so-called retinisporas, although white pine lends itself well to shearing if planted when young; also Norway spruce if a tall rather coarse hedge is wanted. Old or large trees cannot be headed back satisfactorily for the making of trim hedges; they should be taken young and given consistent attention.

On the subject of pruning and renewing hedges, Frank A. Waugh writes recently as follows, the advice not being for conifers exclusively (Bulletin No. 272, Massachusetts Agricultural Experiment Station): In pruning "it is essential (1) to begin early. (a) The hedge plants should be rather closely cut back at planting time. (b) If they grow rampantly the new shoots should be headed back late in May or early in June of the first year. Certainly the plants should all be cut back again in early spring (February preferably) of the second year. The purpose of this early pruning is to force a thick growth at the base of the plants. (2) During all the formative years this severe pruning should be followed. In February the shoots of the previous year's growth should be shortened one inch to one foot (usually about five inches) of one-year-old wood; though obviously much will depend on the species being pruned and on the amount of annual growth. (3) Annual summer pruning is often desirable, in addition to spring (dormant) pruning, especially with rapid-growing deciduous species, such as privet, acanthopanax, etc. This summer shearing should be given immediately after the plants have made their first strong growth. The time will usually fall in late May and seldom later than the first week in June. (4) After a hedge has reached the stature prescribed for it, pruning aims to keep it within its limits and also to maintain the plants in a healthy growing condition. To accomplish these purposes it will be necessary to watch carefully the behavior of the plants and to remember that summer shearing tends to check growth and weaken the plants, whereas dormant pruning is more inclined to favor wood production. Summer pruning can thus be practiced on a hedge which is thrifty, but one which shows signs of debility should be cut back in winter and left to grow freely in summer. (5) Signs of decrepitude, decay, disease or advancing age are apt to appear in any old hedge. These may be due to drought, lack of fertilizers or attacks of insects; and all such cases will presumably receive appropriate remedy. From the standpoint of pruning, however, the practice should be to cut back rather heavily in February, perhaps cutting back into wood three or four years old, thus possibly marring the outline of the hedge for the time, the object being to stimulate a new growth in the old plants."

On the problem of renewal of hedges Waugh continues: "It may be well to remark further that no hedge should be regarded as quite immortal. The treatment which it receives is highly artificial and somewhat drastic, so that there need be no wonder if after 10 or 20 or 40 years the hedge becomes so ragged that it may better be abandoned. There are times when good sense would advise digging out an old hedge, root and stem, cleaning the ground, fallowing for a year or more, and making a new start with fresh young plants, perhaps of some other species.

"Even more frequently the emergency arises in which a section of a hedge requires replanting. A few plants are destroyed by insects or by a runaway automobile, or by fire or by winter-killing. These dead plants may be removed, the ground redug and freshened as much as possible, perhaps the old exhausted soil removed and replaced with fresh loam, new plants set in and forced to their best growth by special care. Under favorable conditions such repairs may achieve quite satisfactory results without more than two or three years' waiting."

For rock-gardens, some of the small conifers are very adaptable, adding a good accent and providing a wintergreen cover. No special treatment is necessary, the plants being chosen to fit the conditions. Some of the low and trailing junipers are specially useful for this work, with a few columnar, conical or mound-like dwarf pines and spruces (or similar things) for particular places in the lay-out.

Fertilizers, manures, and mulches

General fertilizing and bettering of the land is necessary to produce good results. In many cases it is desired to plant evergreens on barren outlying parts of the estate; the first consideration is to observe in the neighborhood or the region what species are most likely to thrive; usually it is not expected to obtain fine specimen trees quickly on such places, if at all; if possible the land should be first improved by good tillage, cover-cropping, and fertilizing. The practice of keeping the ground raked clean of natural leaf-fall and lawn-clippings to make it look "neat" causes the soil to become hard and "dead," lacking that soft springy feel to the feet that tokens good texture and aëration. Underground work, whether of ditches or service pipes, changes the natural drainage of the area and may seriously damage a plantation of conifers. As a class, the conifers do not withstand smoke and soot and dust; the fact that the foliage persists means that dirt may be carried over the year. They are not subjects for permanent planting in large cities.

Of experience with conifers in southern Connecticut, George P. Brett writes: "I have tried a mixture of fine bone dust, potash, and nitrate of soda for evergreens, but not with very satisfactory results, well-rotted cow-manure being the best solid fertilizer for these trees in my experience. For the tree not yet fully established and one that is ailing, nothing is so good as a liquid manure applied three or four times the first month or two after transplanting, trees apparently almost dead having come back to life again under this treatment. If the manure water is slightly warm, improvement comes more quickly. In the War when railroad freight was very badly delayed I had three large plants of *Pinus Thunbergii* lost on the rails for nearly four weeks and when they arrived they looked dead and I despaired of saving them. The trees were rather rare at that time and we made an effort by planting them and watering constantly at frequent intervals with manure water made from cow-manure. It was several weeks before the trees showed any real signs of life, but they are alive today and well-developed specimens of their species.

"All manures and fertilizers, unfortunately, greatly increase the growth of weeds and grass at the foot of the trees, choking and eventually destroying the beauty of the lower branches, and the removal of such growth in a large plantation is a serious matter when labor is difficult to obtain.

"I practice mulching in both winter and summer,—in summer for the purpose of conserving moisture and keeping the lower branches of the trees free from grass and weeds, and in winter to minimize the depth to which the ground will freeze. If heavy applications remain through the winter, this mulch should be taken off as soon as the ground begins to thaw out in the spring, as otherwise the area around the plant will remain frozen until long after the frost has come out of the surrounding earth, and in the hot spring suns, which we sometimes have, great losses will be caused by the inability of these plants to obtain water from the soil.

"Attention should be called to the use of nitrate as a tonic for the older trees where they show signs of needing food. The best plan is to dig it in not too near the roots or to put it in holes with crowbars around the tree, or to apply it as a solution and taking care not to spatter it on needles or bark."

The remaining advice on soils, manures, and mulches is by the late John Dunbar, verified by Arthur D. Slavin, both of the Rochester (New York) parks:

The greater number of conifers prefer a well-drained porous gravelly subsoil, overlaid with a light sandy loam. They seem to be particularly happy in a soil underlaid with a porous glacial drift. A few grow spontaneously in swampy grounds, such as tamarack, *Larix laricina;* cypress, *Taxodium distichum;* white-cedar, *Chamæcyparis thyoides;* and common arbor-vitæ, *Thuja occidentalis.* In cultivation, however, they succeed very well in ordinary well-drained soil. In fact, the common arbor-vitæ does well in dryish soils; specimens planted on knolls of light sandy loam underlaid with glacial drift are in excellent health. If conifers are set in clay land the soil should be thoroughly loosened by trenching or subsoil plowing, and well underdrained. Any available humus, wood-ashes, and well-rotted manure incorporated in the soil greatly aid in rendering it friable and porous for the roots.

All conifers respond well to cultivation, in growth and vigor. An area extending from the stem to one or two feet beyond the branches, stirred up with hoe and rake perhaps five or six times throughout the growing season, is very beneficial in conserving the moisture. Mulching with ordinary well-rotted barnyard manure in late autumn affords much stimulus to growth. By the following spring the manure will be in a desiccated condition and can be incorporated with the soil. William Falconer, who had charge of the Dana Arboretum many years ago, the best cultivator of conifers the writer ever knew, placed a heavy mulch of old straw, rotten hay, or any similar material over the roots of the conifers, and this was maintained throughout the entire growing season. In their remarkable health and vigor, the conifers showed a quick response to this treatment. Of course, this care mostly applies to conifers in a more or less juvenile condition. When they attain adult size, unless they show signs to the contrary, conifers are usually independent of such cultural attention.

Thirty-six years ago a street was extended through a hill on the east side of Highland Park, Rochester, New York. There was a cut of about one hundred feet. The slopes were graded to the angle of repose and on the steepest side a retaining wall was built at the base to prevent the sand from sliding. The material on the slopes was sand intermixed with varying glacial drift. About four years later, that is thirty-two years ago, the slopes were covered with Scotch, Austrian, white, and pitch pines, and red-cedar. Rotten hay, straw, decayed leaves, grass mowings, and the like were scattered amongst them. They have grown well and many of them are thirty to forty feet tall. These slopes now present a very dignified appearance at the entrance to the Pinetum.

At present we are mulching, with stock-yard manure, a number of conifers that show signs of enervation and indicate plainly they need food.

At one time we moved a number of conifers with frozen balls and these were very heavily mulched with manure. In summer they were soaked with water several times, to enable them to overcome the shock of root disturbance.

In many cases manure is not obtainable. In such event, newly moved conifers should be heavily mulched with rotten straw, rotten hay, or any similar material for a few years until they become established. The frequent stirring of the ground over the roots subsequently will conserve sufficient moisture.

We have never used artificial chemical manures on conifers and cannot say anything about them.

The transplanting of conifers

The differing advice as to the time of year in which conifers may be planted is indication that no one season is imperative.

98. A good ball of earth for transplanting.

Late summer and early autumn planting is now much advised, because the plant becomes well established and gains foothold for the earliest spring growth. The well-grown nursery stock now available, that has been twice or more transplanted, undoubtedly makes autumn planting more recommendable than formerly. Plants should be removed only with a good ball of earth. (Fig. 98.)

Experience in the transplanting of evergreens in the Rochester parks is written by John Dunbar: "We transplant conifers at all times of the year, excepting midsummer when they are in full growth. The best success is secured in spring when the buds begin to swell. From the end of August to the middle of September, if there have been abundant rains and the ground has been well soaked, is a very good time to move conifers. They may be planted late in autumn when circumstances compel it, but there is likely to be a considerable percentage of loss. Valuable conifers that stand in proximity to each other and require removal for better development, can be transplanted in winter successfully with large frozen balls on stone boats or tree-moving machines adapted to the purpose. The roots of conifers are very susceptible to injury from exposure to the air, and the utmost vigilance should be exercised to keep them covered and moist."

"With the exception of the hemlocks and some of the firs," writes George P. Brett from experience in southern Connecticut in exposed situation, "all the evergreens have proved easy to transplant with us. Some of them, indeed, can be moved at any season of the year, but we have usually found our losses less when the trees have been transplanted in the early spring months, this spring planting being superior to fall planting in this section of the country on account of the increasing winds of winter adversely affecting the fall-planted tree. Great care, however, must be taken to keep the roots constantly wet. They must never be allowed to get at all dry, and when transplanting from the wild, if a ball of earth cannot be obtained, some means must be adopted for keeping the roots wet until they are again planted. Wind is also a great enemy of the transplanted tree, especially of the evergreen, its masses of foliage catching the winds as would a sail, with the result that newly planted trees, unless firmly guyed, generally work a hole around the stem of the tree which will, if unfilled, eventually dry the roots. Most of the losses in my early plantings were due to this cause.

"Many trees are injured or killed, even after being established, by late winter conditions, when the ground is frozen; it is not alone the dry winds but the sunshine that cause damage. The needles are deprived of moisture by the combined action of the wind and sun, and the ground being frozen, none is available for the plant."

The treatment of evergreens that are balled and burlapped is described by Arthur D. Slavin: "Coniferous plants are generally sold by nurserymen with roots well packed in a ball of earth which in turn is firmly bound in burlap wrapping. The purpose of this practice is to conserve moisture and prevent the roots from drying out. When conifers are grown in a clay soil, it is easy to dig the plants with a ball of earth, but all conifers are not grown in clay and often when unpacking a shipment one will find that the ball has been built up about the roots after the plants have been dug. Often it will be found that the inner part of the mass is made up of light soil and the whole then packed in a layer or plastering of clay.

"Most often this ball of dirt, after the burlap packing has been removed, is planted with the tree. When this happens the roots are tightly enclosed in a soil medium perhaps not inducive to root growth and which acts as an insulating layer against the flow of soluble nourishment from the surrounding earth. The outside layer of the ball should be removed until the root ends are visible. This can easily be accomplished by means of a hand weeding tool or similar implement. If, after the outside layer of the ball has been removed, the soil about the roots is of poorer quality than where the plant is to be placed, then it will be advantageous to remove perhaps all the packing. In such cases, care must be taken, however, to see that the plant is firmly set with no air spaces about the roots and that there is sufficient moisture to prevent the root system from drying out.

"This writer does not use a ball of dirt for packing small conifers as the soil in the Rochester parks is light and it is almost impossible to lift a plant with the soil intact about the roots. Instead, the plants are packed in sphagnum moss immediately after digging. In this operation, the roots are carefully freed of soil, and sphagnum that has been previously soaked in water and then squeezed until it is only damp, is placed about the roots and the ball wrapped in strong waxed or water-proof paper. Such packing will keep the roots in good condition for several months. Also by this method there is a great saving in shipping expenses; often a dozen plants may be sent for the same price as one that goes with a large ball of earth."

The removal of large established evergreens should be managed by persons who are skilled in the operations and are equipped with the proper tools, machines and conveyances. It is a laborious and costly undertaking, if trees are large and must be transported long distances, and cheap or short-cut methods should not be undertaken. Under competent management the results should be satisfactory. The ball of earth should be ample (12 feet across for a pine tree 35 feet high), the roots well wrapped and the ball protected from spilling by canvas or burlap, the trunk must not be injured, and above all the roots must not be allowed to become dry. After the tree is placed, watering should be practiced until the plant has made new root connection and is able to make growth; and watering may have to be renewed even afterwards if drought overtakes the plantation.

The pruning of conifers

Whether one shall prune coniferous evergreens depends on the purpose in growing them. Some persons prefer that the plants take their natural course and develop the form characteristic of the particular species. Other persons desire to maintain symmetry and denseness as long as possible. Pines probably require less pruning than others, inasmuch as they are less formal; the scar is likely to last long before healing and it may not be hidden by the subsequent growth. Most of the other conifers profit by clipping, or the firs by disbudding. Of course, broken and injured branches should be removed or repaired.

The useful experience of John Dunbar may be appended: "The pruning of conifers is, perhaps, a little more difficult to explain than the pruning of any other woody plants. It seems needless to say that removal of the lower branches is a serious mistake, and, if healthy, they should be retained to the base. Pines, spruces, firs, and hemlocks have conical pyramidal outlines, some more so than others, and the elements of beauty consist in accentuating these attributes. Pruning or disbudding can be intelligently performed to add much to the natural symmetry. The extraction or removal, early in spring, of the central or terminal bud, will tend to compel the branches which start from the side buds to spread apart and form a much denser growth. Cutting back the previous year's terminal growth to a strong bud or branchlet on the main limbs over the tree, if the plant is inclined to be thin in its branching, always produces a much denser lateral growth. In the case of hemlocks, owing to the nature of their terminal growths, the removal of the central terminal bud cannot be accomplished very well, as the bud is very minute. The best method is to cut back the terminal branches to strong branchlets or buds, and a much denser growth will soon follow.

"Pyramidal junipers and arbor-vitæ, in which the object is to develop very dense pyramidal habits, are often clipped with shears in spring before growth starts to produce density of growth. In nurseries in which there are thousands of such plants, it may be a matter of business to treat them in this way, in order to facilitate the work. However, on private plantations it is better to use a sharp pruning-knife, or good standard pruning-shears, and cut the branches or projecting shoots back in 'shingling' fashion. When carefully pruned in this way, the trees present a more pleasing appearance and do not show such a stiff aspect as when shorn with the shears.

"When pruning is skilfully performed, the ordinary observer cannot detect what the pruner has done. Pruning or disbudding of conifers requires very intelligent observation, and one should have the desired results definitely in mind. Of course, there are different opinions about the pruning of conifers, some growers preferring to leave them entirely alone. However, a little pruning and disbudding in the juvenile state develops natural beauty. This applies to conifers from an ornamental standpoint, but from an economic or forestry point of view this kind of pruning has no application."

II. THE PROPAGATION OF CONIFERS

In this book it is not the intention to cover nursery practice or the propagation of coniferous evergreens in detail, or to prepare a text-book treatment. Enough may be said, however, to give the planter a general idea of the ways by which the plants are multiplied. The present account is partly that by Frederick

Ahrens in The Cultivated Evergreens, and additional paragraphs by Chester J. Hunn.

Conifers are increased by three general means, each of which may be discussed briefly: by seeds, by cuttings, by grafts. This account considers the growing of plants for ornamental planting only. The rearing of forest trees is quite another undertaking, on which there is a useful literature which the propagator may find by inquiring at the State College of Agriculture or the United States Forest Service; the discussion of that subject is not undertaken in this book.

Propagation by seed

The time of gathering the seed of evergreens is very important, when the cones begin to open near the tips being the proper season. The seed should be gathered at once, otherwise it will be lost. It should be kept in a cool place until sowing. Seed to be sown out-of-doors should be stored during winter in a cool dry room where the temperature does not fall below 36 degrees Fahrenheit. Extensive field propagation by seeds is not discussed in this account.

Further details of handling of seeds may be stated as follows: Store cones in shallow layers in trays with screened bottoms. Pile trays in series of one variety so that the loosened seed of all trays may fall below into a tight receptacle. Employ a circulation of heated air (like fruit evaporator) to further reflex the scales of the cones. Protect from rodents. When dried, flail the cones to release the remaining seed. Place loosely in bags and flail to rid seed of their wings; then winnow or run through a fanning mill to separate wings. Make sure that seeds are well dried and then store in glass carboys which may be sealed and placed in storage at 36 degrees Fahrenheit. Taxus, juniperus and certain others are two-year seeds, needing after-ripening by stratification at 41 degrees; ordinarily germination is delayed in the outdoor seed-bed.

Seeds should be sown in beds or frames, the small seed broadcast and large seed, like pinus, larix, and taxodium, in rows. The best soil is sandy loam, and for many conifers (tsuga, taxus and others) an acid reaction is desirable. One may use shredded Holland peat or acid woods earth to secure this condition. There are simple inexpensive soil testers that the propagator may find it advisable to use. Soils are sometimes treated prior to sowing with sulfuric acid as preventive of damping-off. If damping-off appears, applying a mixture of sand and sulphur is useful.

Seeds should be sown in moistened beds. Sand may be used to cover the seeds, although sand lightened with well-decayed humus is also good. Care must be taken as to depth of covering,—not so deep as to smother the seeds nor so shallow that they will dry out speedily. After covering the seed, firm the bed with a smooth plank. The bed may be covered with burlap that has been soaked in water, to prevent drying out; remove promptly, however, on first indication of germination. Take care that the plantlets are hardened off in late summer preparatory to the winter mulching.

Seed-beds should be protected from birds with cheese-cloth. When the seedlings have developed the first two leaves the cloth may be removed at night and replaced by day, and after they show the typical growth the cloth may be removed entirely. Careful watering is very necessary. This should be done in the morning with a fine rose, back and forth, to prevent the earth from forming a crust due to flooding.

The first winter, seedlings should be protected with a few dry leaves thrown over them and covered with evergreen boughs. The second winter, hardy evergreens do not need covering, with the exception of *Tsuga canadensis* and some tender abies. In early spring of the second year seedlings may be quickened by a dressing of dried blood at the rate of one pound for each 100 square feet of bed. Slatted shade-houses may be recommended for seed-beds if one undertakes the work extensively, and for the first few years of the life of tender species.

The hemlock, *Tsuga canadensis*, requires fall sowing outdoors in acid earth and protection from rodents and birds by complete screening above and below the soil. The seed germinates in late winter and early spring when there occurs alternation of day thawing and night freezing. Hemlock should be kept two or three years in the seed-bed. It requires more shade than most species. The seedlings should be kept two or more years in shaded plant-beds and protected by winter mulches. It is not ready for open field planting until six or seven years old.

Taxus is grown in large quantities from seed in the attempt to secure upright growing seedlings. The pulp should be removed immediately. Sand as an abrasive is used to cut the gelatinous and resinous pulp. The seed should be sterilized.

Seeds of *Juniperus virginiana* should be examined and those that show large infection by larvæ rejected.

When seedlings are two or three years old it is time to transplant; larix and taxodium transplant better when two years old. Transplanting should be performed before the seedlings start new growth, puddled in a garden soil filled with humus; the humus soon takes up moisture and falls off, root contact being quickly established. To cause the formation of a good root system, these seedlings should be transplanted every two years until they are ready to be set permanently. Evergreens transplanted often will keep a good shape and ball and may be moved any time in spring or fall, when those not transplanted will be a total failure.

Older plants that become bare around the base may be given new life by digging around the tree two feet deep, keeping out far enough to prevent the cutting of any roots and filling the hole with good fertile soil.

Tender evergreens should be sown in flats or pans in the greenhouse. A drainage of broken pots of about three-fourths of an inch should be placed at the bottom, and the flat then filled with a mixture of good leaf-mold and potting soil, with enough sand to make it mellow. After the seed is sown, it should be covered according to size, the small seed liberally, and large seed with more covering. The flats are kept in a greenhouse or frame with temperature of about 50 to 60 degrees Fahrenheit. One should always water in the morning. Careless watering often spoils all the seedlings during the summer. The seed-flats should be protected from the hot sun. When winter comes the flats may be placed in a cool frame against a greenhouse, preferably being supplied with a line of hot-water pipes to keep out the frost; if this cannot be provided, a good cellar will answer. In moderate weather, plenty of fresh air should be furnished. The plants must not be kept too wet, but care should be taken that they do not dry out entirely. The second year, about the middle of September, the strong plants may be placed in pots, and planted out in spring; the smaller ones may be transplanted in flats and kept for another year, potting in September to be set out in spring. After two years the transplanting should be repeated.

Propagation by means of cuttings

Propagation of the forest type of conifers is seldom undertaken by means of cuttings both because of the difficulty of obtaining a good callus and the slowness of rooting. The dwarf and ornamental conifers are capable of cutting-propagation for the most part, as dwarf piceas, taxus, thuja, prostrate tsugas.

Late in the season is a practicable time to begin propagating by cuttings in flats or beds. The flats may be eighteen inches long, fourteen inches wide, and five inches deep. Three-fourths of an inch of broken pots should be placed on the bottom, then three-fourths inch of potting soil, and the remainder of the flat filled with sand, which must be tramped in with the feet to make it very solid. Loosely packed flats are not satisfactory. The sand for propagating should always be covered, to preserve the natural moisture and to avoid the necessity of much watering. Good lake sand, not too fine, is the best; when this cannot be obtained, other good sand can be used, but it must be clean and not mixed with clay or other binding material.

Mid-September is frequently recommended as a proper season

for starting conifer cuttings, but of course something depends on the latitude. Acceptable time is when the slowing of growth takes place. In central New York this period is about the middle of August, applying to both hotbed work and the flat method just mentioned. On the other hand, the work may be delayed until the rest period is well advanced, October to February, with November and December probably the best months; wood is then in good condition for cutting-propagation.

Good vigorous cuttings should be taken from one-year growth a few inches long, and trimmed for one and one-fourth inches. They should be set in the rows two inches apart, using a dibble with a blunt point, placing with the cut directly on the sand. They should then be pressed and firmed, for cuttings put in loosely will not root well. After a moderate watering, the flats should be put in an air-tight shaded frame.

When the cuttings are beginning to heal, the flats may be placed on the sand in the propagating bench. Starting with a moderate bottom heat of about 65 degrees, after a month the temperature may be raised to 70 degrees, care being taken not to dry the flats from the bottom. To prevent this, a funnel is put between the flats and sufficient water poured through to keep the sand on the bench moist.

At the end of May well-rooted cuttings may be planted from the flats in the free ground. The rows should be about eight inches apart, and the plants set at the same depth as they stood before, packing the soil firmly. During the summer the soil should be loosened frequently with the garden hoe or a similar tool.

Some of the more slowly rooting evergreens, such as retinispora or chamæcyparis, some junipers, *Thuja orientalis*, *Cedrus libanitica*, and all picea, should be left in the flats in a half shady place during summer and potted in September. Taxus cuttings, even if well rooted, should not be planted out in spring, but should be potted in September and kept over winter in a frost-free frame or a cool greenhouse.

On winter propagation by cuttings Hunn notes as follows: Make cuttings as long as possible with the base near to or including a bit of two-year-old wood. Remove basal leaves to a height so that the cuttings may be inserted in the rooting medium; cut off with the tip of a knife unless stripping causes no damage. When making the cuttings one should begin to form the new top, as pyramidal or globe-shaped. Nip back tip of prostrate cuttings to cause the first break. Trimming should be reduced, as more foliage under proper turgid conditions means better rooting. Grade cuttings according to size and bench in groups to have about equal rooting and removal. Insert in firmed bed, using a large knife to make a deep cut in the earth. Keep a straight-edge marking-stick at the left of the row. Set the cuttings in rows 2 inches apart and from $\frac{1}{2}$–1 inch in the row, and about $1\frac{1}{2}$–2 inches deep. Face the fan sprays with the row so as to keep open space for air movement between the rows. Press the soil about the base of the cuttings, then give the straight-edge several sharp taps with a mallet and move the stick out carefully and tap against the other side of the row of inserted cuttings. The straight-edge should be in place to guide the opening of the next furrow. When the setting is completed, water the bed to moisten the medium and to even and firm it. Watch the moisture content of the sand medium to avoid drying or an excess which will cause rotting of the base of the cuttings. Shade for a few days and maintain the humidity by syringing the tops of the cuttings, and water the walks frequently. Bottom heat should range from 65° to 72° Fahrenheit with the air temperature 5° to 8° cooler. Plenty of light should be allowed but no extreme top heat; whitewash the glass as winter days lengthen. Syringe according to the weather from one morning application to two or three a day. After most of the cuttings are rooted, begin potting in $2\frac{1}{4}$-inch rose-pots, using a sandy loam with some humus but no manure. Reset strong but unrooted cuttings in another part of the bed and carry until a fair proportion is rooted. Under proper climatic conditions, the rooted plants may go to beds outdoors in June. In western New York, the spring-potted plants are carried in pots throughout the summer. In autumn, the plants are knocked out of the pots and placed in flats, filling the spaces with soil which is pressed firmly and watered. The flats may be wintered in protected frames or in a pit greenhouse. The plants are ready for lining-out, preferably under irrigation, the following late May or early June. Train into shape by shearing and move to wider spacing in the nursery after two years. Move quickly with a fair amount of soil, and prevent injury to the roots by drying. If convenient, settle them by watering and then give normal nursery culture. The general plan of moving every two years should be adopted.

Perhaps the outstanding recent advance in the propagation of conifers from cuttings is in careful choice of rooting medium and in the use of permanganate of potash for treating the cutting. The time of rooting taxus cuttings can be reduced from 160 to 110–120 days. Acidity of bed is important. A method adopted at Edinburgh Botanic Garden is to water occasionally with "vinegar," made of 1 cc. glacial acetic acid in 2,000 cc. water (¼ oz. to 15 qts.). Sand is made acid "just over the line" from neutral, and kept so. Holland peat has proved to be a good medium for some conifers, particularly taxus. The permanganate of potash method of hastening rooting in conifers is to soak base of cutting 12–18 hours in 4¼ quarts of water in which 1 ounce of permanganate is dissolved. Sometimes the cutting-beds are drenched with a gallon of water in which 1 ounce of permanganate is placed, applied to each square foot 48 hours before bedding the cuttings. Edinburgh method uses 1 ounce to 1 pint of water diluted at rate of 1 fluid ounce to the quart for each square foot of bed. For summer and softwood cuttings the bed is drenched with 1 ounce permanganate to 1 gallon of water for each 2 square feet; useful for difficult plants. Use of permanganate of potash lessens rooting time of cuttings, reduces the exuberant callus so often formed in conifers, sterilizes the propagating medium, and induces acid reaction.

Propagation by means of grafting (Figs. 99, 100)

When seeds are not available and when the rooting of cuttings is impossible or impracticable, both species and varieties may be multiplied by grafts. In this case, the operator must know not only how to perform the manual operation of grafting (which it is not intended to discuss here) but also the kind and condition of stocks on which the grafts or cions are to be set.

The first consideration in the choice of stocks is to obtain those of close botanical relationship to the cion. Thus, all the varieties of red-cedar are to be grafted, if possible, on *Juniperus virginiana* itself; *Thuja occidentalis* is a good general stock for other thuja. Piceas may go on *P. Abies;* abies with long needles on *A. concolor*, and with short needles on *A. alba (pectinata)* or *A. balsamea.* For *Pinus Jeffreyi, P. attenuata, P. ponderosa* var. *pendula*, and all other forms, *P. ponderosa* stock should be used. All pines resembling *P. nigra* should be grafted on that stock. *Pinus Strobus* varieties should be grafted on that species, as well as *P. cembroides, monophylla* and *edulis, P. Bungeana, P. flexilis*, and *P. aristata.* For *P. Mugo* and its varieties, *P. rigida*, and varieties of *P. sylvestris*, the latter should be employed. *Pinus resinosa* must be used for its varieties as they will not grow on any other stock. Varieties of tsuga should be grafted on *T. canadensis*, and forms of pseudotsuga on *P. Douglasii.*

The stocks (or understocks) should be secured well in advance; they should be two or three years in seed-bed, or one to two years in the lining-out area. The essentials of a suitable stock are (1) close affinity, (2) sufficient diameter so that it is larger than the cion, (3) root vigor. The preparation of understocks should start in late April or early May for the latitude of central New York; this preliminary care is essential to vigor and the best results.

Some of the operations on stocks are: clean up base of stock so that all wounds are healed; keep the bottom free for grafting low; cut back roots to induce new shoots and renewed vigor; pot firmly in center of pot; water, and plunge into plant-bed or shade-house; push the plants to keep up vigorous growth. Harden off in autumn to hasten rest period; mulch as winter approaches. Bring stocks out of rest period sometime before grafting is to begin, usually about midwinter in the North; keep them slow in cool greenhouse and on the dry side; syringe top of plant but keep down new growth, aiming at root-action; water heavily 24 hours before grafting.

The styles of grafting in conifers are side-graft, veneer-graft, inarching, and sometimes root-grafting. It is essential that all joints be perfect and tight, good carpenter joints; see that there is perfect contact of cambium on stock and cion. The newly grafted plants are kept in a frame; lay plants in furrows in peat at an angle so that outer face of cion is partly exposed to light; shade a few days, but open for slight drying off in forenoon; see that the thread with which the grafts are tied does not bind. In about the fourth week, remove about one third of top of stock to force more growth to cion; eighth week remove second third of stock; twelfth week cut stock back to stub, and set plants on protected greenhouse bench; gradually harden, preparatory to removal to shade-house or shaded plant-bed in June or July, sometimes in May.

Inarching is a good practice for particular things that are rather difficult to propagate, as *Picea pungens* var. *argentea* (erroneously called Koster's). It has the advantage that both stock and cion are on their own roots until after the union has been established; the cion may heal if it fails to unite with the stock and then remain as a regular branch of its parent plant. Inarching is facilitated when the cion plants are large and bushy with a number of good branches near the ground. The stock plants are usually kept one year in pots and then plunged in the soil around the base of the cion plant (which remains out-of-doors). The stock should be of good size to take a large cion. It may be necessary to secure the parts on a framework to prevent injury. The operation is performed ordinarily in early summer. Bind very firmly at the union and also at one or two other points to prevent movement. Wax the union thoroughly or else use wax bandage. To hasten union, the stock may be notched successively above and away from the cion; the cion may be similarly notched below and away from the stock. The plants are staked and mulched for winter. Disconnect from cion parent and remove when one year old and treat like a greenhouse grafted plant.

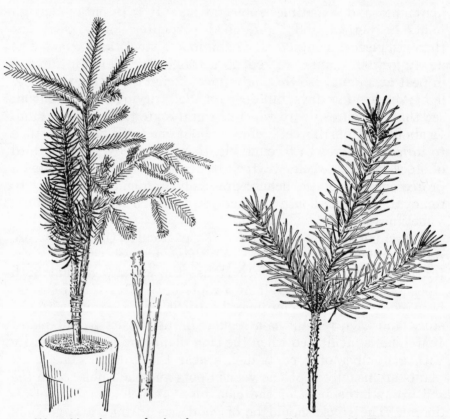

99. Side-grafting of spruce, showing also method of insertion.

100. Cion employed in Fig. 99.

XXXIV. Columnar Italian cypress, *Cupressus sempervirens* var. *stricta*; California.

XXXV. Monterey cypress, *Cupressus macrocarpa*; California.

XXXVI. Lawson cypress, as a planted tree, *Chamæcyparis Lawsoniana*.

XXXVII. Cypress and arbor-vitæ. Left, *Chamæcyparis nootkatensis*; New York. Center, *Thuja orientalis*; New York. Right, *Thuja Standishii*; Massachusetts.

XXXVIII. Arbor-vitæ in fruit. Left, *Thuja plicata*, nearly full size; New York. Right, *Thuja occidentalis* var. *filiformis*, nearly natural size; Massachusetts.

XXXIX. Pasture juniper of the Northeast, *Juniperus communis* var. *depressa*, Massachusetts.

XL. Above, Korean arbor-vitæ, *Thuja koraiensis;* New York. Below, Utah juniper or cedar, *Juniperus utahensis;* Fishlake National Forest, Utah.

XLI. Dwarf or ground conifers. Above, *Tsuga canadensis* var. *pendula* young; Massachusetts. Below, *Juniperus chinensis* var. *Pfitzeriana;* New York.

XLII. Cedars of Wakefield, *Juniperus virginiana;* Virginia.

XLIII. Ground-cover junipers. Above, *Juniperus chinensis* var. *Sargentii;* Massachusetts. Below, *Juniperus horizontalis* var. *alpina;* New York.

XLIV. Natural park of conifers. *Picea Engelmanni* with tree of *Abies lasiocarpa* at left; Montana.

XLV. Native groves of Lodge-pole pine, *Pinus contorta* var. *latifolia;* Inyo National Forest, California.

XLVI. Hillside planting in Durand-Eastman Park, Rochester, New York, comprising Pseudotsuga in the background. *Tsuga canadensis, Pinus resinosa, Picea glauca* and *P. pungens*; and *Juniperus virginiana* in foreground.

XLVII. Well-grown spruces. Left, Picea Abies var. conica; New York. Right, Picea orientalis; Massachusetts.

XLVIII. Back-yard planting of tall and dwarf conifers; A. H. Hill, Illinois.

CHAPTER IX

EXPERIENCES WITH CONIFERS

SPECIES of conifers at the command of planters in North America are so many and represent such diverse regions of the earth that no one person is likely to have experience with all of them. Moreover, the conifers have not yet been the subject of sufficiently careful planting tests, in great variety, except in a few localities. The full utilization of them is still an undeveloped branch of horticulture, considering the country as a whole, notwithstanding the fact that many of them are widely planted and that certain kinds are now deservedly popular for home and park planting.

The keynote to success with conifers is adaptation; and of course the adaptation is really a local problem, differing with each separate place. A few wide-spread and prevalent species, as white pine, Austrian pine, Norway spruce, arbor-vitæ, can be made to thrive under diverse conditions, but, for the most part, each species is peculiar unto itself and the intending grower must read all the notes he can find on the adaptation to his region, closely observe successes and failures where the plant has been tried; and often he must set more plants than he needs, with the expectation that some of them will succeed.

Outstanding non-commercial growing collections of conifers in the East are the Hunnewell estate at Wellesley, Massachusetts, where many kinds have now arrived at age and maturity; the arboretum of the Central Experimental Farms at Ottawa, Ontario, Canada; the unsurpassed plantings at the Arnold Arboretum of Harvard University, Jamaica Plain, Massachusetts, experiences in which are incorporated in the systematic account originally written by Alfred Rehder; the parks of Rochester, New York; and two notable estates in southwestern Connecticut, one of George P. Brett, Chairman of the Board of

Trustees of The Macmillan Company, and the recent rapidly enlarging collection of Robert H. Montgomery at Greenwich.

This chapter is devoted to experiences of competent persons with conifers in several parts of the northern and eastern regions of the continent. They are sufficient to give the intending planter a good view of the subject. The discussion may well begin with the experiences of the lamented John Dunbar of the Rochester parks, and who was long associated with the late Charles S. Sargent in the study of trees and shrubs. He contributed his observations to The Cultivated Evergreens published ten years ago; and that contribution has now been reviewed in the light of subsequent experience by Arthur D. Slavin, active Horticulturist of the Rochester parks and who was reared in them and had the advantage of working under Dunbar as well as under his father Bernard Slavin, present Superintendent of the Parks and long a recognized authority. This article may well be accepted as a general introduction to the handling of conifers. The younger Slavin speaks of Dunbar as "A man of brilliance and great energy who accomplished work of value; his death in 1926 was mourned by all who knew him, from the common laborer who toiled under his direction to the highest minds in horticultural endeavor. That he died before he saw the fruits of his labors appears almost to be a characteristic of plant men. Last year it was my pleasure to spend a short time in the neighborhood of his younger days in Scotland about that wonderful country of braes and lochs where appears such a paradise of woody plants. It is easy to understand why, having received his early training in that country, he became such a student of his profession."

"The climate of eastern North America" writes Dunbar, "is not adapted to the successful growth of many beautiful conifers, and very few of the species native toward the Pacific Coast succeed in the East. This is due not so much to the cold as to the fierce sweeping dry winds of late winters. The precipitation of moisture is much more abundant on the Pacific Coast, west of the Cascade Range, than it is in the northeastern states."

Experiences in the Rochester parks—Dunbar and Slavin

Among public collections, the most recent conetum of noteworthy size is in Durand-Eastman Park at Rochester, New York. This collection was begun in 1912 with plantings of many thousand native conifers. About 1916, after the original planting had attained sufficient size to constitute at least a partial protection, the setting out of more specialized materials was begun. Since that time additional planting has been an annual occurrence. The pinetum at Highland Park in the same city was started in 1896 and until a few years ago was the largest public collection exclusive of that at the Arnold Arboretum; it is now exceeded in size by the newer collection at Durand-Eastman Park.

When planting conifers in this area, two vital points are to be remembered. (1) The material must not be so placed that it is openly exposed to the south: in late winter there is sufficient sun heat to thaw out exposed vegetation, and at night a sufficiently low temperature to freeze the plant again. It requires little of this quick alternate thawing and freezing to kill the buds and other tender parts and thus destroy the potential growth for the coming season. (2) Conifers placed where they are in a sweep or exposed to prevailing winds usually have their foliage browned in cold seasons, and again in the summer if there is hot drying wind and only minimum moisture in the soil.

The two collections of conifers in the Rochester parks have demonstrated two important factors regarding growth. It has shown (1) that conifers grow best in a light sandy well-drained loam and (2) that increased humidity improves the texture and color of the leaves. In the pinetum at Durand-Eastman Park which is directly on the shore of Lake Ontario, the soil is a light sandy silt loam. Here many of the pines, spruces, and firs make an average growth of eighteen inches a year. Highland Park, about ten miles from the Lake, has a greatly decreased humidity and a heavy gravelly loam; the collection in this park shows an average annual growth of less than eight inches, and the foliage does not present the vigorous appearance of that observed in the other area.

In this discussion of the Rochester experiences, the statements as to size and relative hardiness are definite, but this cannot be said in respect to suggested uses. Only the general employment of a plant can be indicated in writing. Its actual position in beautifying the landscape must be left to the creative instinct of the planter. Often this instinct is not well developed and the vogue is likely to be followed arbitrarily. The result is often a stereotyped expression in the landscape. A vivid example of this condition is in the planting of two conifers, placed one on either side at the entrance to the house or other building. Often some form of the Colorado spruce is chosen; and frequently one sees this form of planting in almost every dwelling the length of a city block or street. There is nothing intrinsically wrong about such a treatment and certainly there is no more vigorous grower than the Colorado spruce; the objection lies in the fact that the idea has been overdone.

Another common fault is the ill-chosen material so often seen in foundation plantings. Such plantings commonly cross the front of the house which, in addition to the entrance, is usually open with windows. Low-growing material is necessary for this work, else as it grows it will exceed the height of the windows and shut out the light. It then becomes necessary either to remove the plants or cut off their tops, the latter operation always resulting in an ungraceful appearance and in most cases fatal injury to the plant. When choosing material for such planting, one should always determine, before any purchase is made, the ultimate height of the plant when it is full grown. Plants to be placed in front of windows should not exceed the height of the window-sill. It is not safe to use material for such plantings merely because it looks well in the nursery. In a few years those same plants may reach to the windows of the top floor.

Yews.

The yews stand today as one of the most valuable groups of ornamental evergreens. Arborescent or shrub-like in habit, they seldom attain a height of more than twenty feet. The requirements are not difficult to meet as they appear to do well in either light or heavy soils. Wind and sun are the worst enemies and may cause a browning of the foliage in both winter and summer. The many forms of yew make it possible to obtain material to fulfill almost any requirement.

The English yew, *Taxus baccata*, was at one time the leading member of the genus in North America for ornamental purposes. However, in recent years the Japanese species has, to a large extent, taken its place due to greater hardiness. The English yew makes a beautiful specimen with lustrous dark green leaves and may be expected to thrive if given the protection of other plantings. It should be placed in a situation where there is no open exposure to the south as the buds and foliage are easily damaged by the late winter sun. Among the color forms of this species are var. *lutea* with yellow fruit and var. *fastigiata variegata* which has an erect habit of growth and foliage with yellow margins. The latter is one of the most striking and colorful forms of the species.

The Irish yew, *Taxus baccata* var. *fastigiata*, is the most outstanding of the upright growing forms. A beautiful small tree, it is difficult to deal with in this area because its height often prevents its proper protection in the winter. Its form of growth is distinctly upright with fastigiate branching. In England, where it grows under ideal conditions, it makes a beautiful column often more than thirty feet tall. Var. *erecta* is an upright bushy form which becomes broad with age. It is made up of many erect or ascending branches and with foliage which is narrower, shorter, and not as striking as that of the Irish yew.

The spreading forms are the most successful representatives of *T. baccata*, their low character of growth permitting them to be covered with a protective blanket of snow during the winter months. Var. *Dovastoni* has an erect slow-growing leader and many long spreading branches. A plant in the collection at Highland Park now measures about five feet in height and more than eight feet across. Var. *repandens* is a prostrate grower and the only plant of such character in the species. It seldom reaches a height of more than two feet and will often cover an area more than six feet in diameter. It is the hardiest form and is commonly used for low plantings.

The more or less shrubby forms are represented by several varieties. Var. *adpressa* is an odd form of shrubby habit with leaves which are short, rounded or almost square and notched at the apex. The fruit generally protrudes from the fleshy cup which surrounds it. Var. *glauca* is large and bushy with slightly glaucous leaves which impart a grayish appearance to the foliage. Var. *aurea* is a golden-leaved form of shrubby habit although it is said sometimes to assume a tree-like habit. Var. *Washingtoni* is of massive bushy habit in old age. The leaves are tipped with yellow when the new growth appears. Towards the end of the season this aureation fades and during the winter often disappears.

The Canadian yew, *Taxus canadensis*, native as an under-growth shrub from Newfoundland to Virginia, is often known commonly as ground-hemlock. In damp woods it produces a charming effect with its spreading branches covered with the rich dark green leaves. It does remarkably well in cultivation in open exposures, provided the roots are thoroughly mulched and kept cool. The leaves, however, assume a very different appearance, becoming somewhat smaller and shorter and not having the dark green color they show in native shady conditions. When located in a southern exposure the late winter sun will invariably brown the foliage as will a cold north wind. As it is a forest plant these conditions are to be expected if it does not have partial shade.

The Japanese yew, *Taxus cuspidata*, is much hardier in North America than the English yew. It stands open exposure without damage and, although the leaves may become somewhat browned by severe exposure to the sun or wind, the plant seldom succumbs to such damage. Like most evergreens it prefers a light soil for maximum growth and when placed where the soil is fertile and well-drained there is little danger of failure. It is more robust in appearance than *T. baccata* and has larger, more lustrous, and better colored foliage. Seedlings to the extent of several thousand have been planted out for game cover in Durand-Eastman Park at Rochester. After thirteen years these plants, set out about twelve feet apart, are in many cases touching each other. They range from three to eight feet in height. This species is used extensively for border work and mass planting. It is not to be recommended for foundation work unless the area to be planted is large. In var. *aurescens* the young leaves are brilliant yellow. After the first year they generally fade to green.

There are several dwarf forms of the Japanese species which are more valuable for design than the type because they are regular in habit of growth whereas the species is often variable. Var. *nana* is the commonest form and is a beautiful plant. It is low, dense, and diffuse in habit with long spreading horizontal branches which become ascending at the ends. The foliage is large, broad, and a beautiful dark green. Specimens of this variety measuring five feet in height and sixteen feet in diameter are not uncommon in older plantings. Var. *densa* is a compact form with ascending branches which often affect an almost globose appearance. It is a delightful shrub for use in the rock-garden or in formal planting. Var. *Thayeræ* is a low vase-shaped form with horizontal or ascending branches extending from the center and turning gracefully upwards towards the ends. Var. *minima* is a true dwarf. After more than fifteen years the type has attained a height of only nine inches. This form was discovered by Bernard H. Slavin in Durand-Eastman Park where he had planted it out some years previous amongst a group of seedlings. The branching is irregular, ramified, and generally ascending. An irregular roundish plant best describes its habit. The leaves are the same in character as those of the type but are much smaller and measure only about five-eighths of an inch in length. Although not yet in general cultivation, it is an excellent specimen to use as a representative of the taxad group in the small rock-garden. It is also adaptable for use as a dwarf border in formal planting.

Taxus media represents a rare condition in the Taxaceæ. It is a supposed hybrid, result of a cross between *T. cuspidata* and *T. baccata*. It is intermediate between the parents in its botanical aspect and, in this area, enjoys about the hardiness of the Japanese species. Var. *Hatfieldii*, named for the discoverer of the hybrid, is conical in outline and is made up of many branches of erect habit. The Hicks yew, *Taxus media* var. *Hicksii*, is a most valuable plant and will undoubtedly become the American representative of the Irish yew. It is columnar in habit with closely set erect branches. The foliage is like that of *T. cuspidata*. For formal effect it is best to keep this shrub sheared on the sides and occasionally to clip the top so as to strengthen the branches and thus remove, in so far as possible, the danger of heavy snow spreading or breaking them. It has become popular for use in planting where the effect of height is desired. It is also in demand as a hedge plant. Cuttings of this form taken in 1920 have produced plants which now measure eight feet in height and three feet in cross-section. They have never been touched by the pruning knife. Had they been so treated, they would now be at least two feet taller than their present height.

Taxus Hunnewelliana is another hybrid having as its parents *T. cuspidata* and *T. canadensis*. This cross shows much of the character of the Canadian yew. It has narrower foliage than the Japanese parent and is more slender. The foliage turns brown during the winter, a common habit of *T. canadensis*.

Cephalotaxus.

The plum-yew, *Cephalotaxus drupacea*, from Japan, is the only species hardy in this area. It is shrub-like and seldom more than twelve feet tall with a loosely branched sprawling habit.

The foliage is somewhat like the yew but larger, more sharply pointed, and stiffer. It is an interesting plant and finds favor in group plantings where the more hardy materials surrounding it may act as a protective barrier against cold winds and southern exposures. Var. *nana* is dwarf, of somewhat spreading habit formed by suckers from which arise ascending or erect branches. Var. *sinensis*, with narrower leaves than the type, differs little in ornamental appearance and enjoys about the same hardiness.

Torreya.

Torreya nucifera is a very distinct yew-like plant from Japan. There are several species of Torreya but *nucifera* is the only one fairly hardy at Rochester, New York, and it must be planted in a situation well protected from the sweep of cold winds. The habit is spreading and bushy, and the two-ranked deep green lance-shaped leaves are very ornamental. It does not bear a cone but rather a drupe-like fruit somewhat like a pear in shape, purplish when ripe, and about one inch long.

Pines.

The bristle-cone or hickory pine, *Pinus aristata*, is a shrub or at the most a low bushy tree. It presents a unique appearance with loose ascending branches which are densely clothed with short dark green leaves from which there are many minute exudations of resin. This latter condition gives the foliage the appearance of being covered with many small silver dots. It is a most decorative plant and may be used in any dwarf or low planting.

The Chinese white or Armand pine, *Pinus Armandi*, is a Chinese and Korean species and when once established is a beautiful tree. It is similar in habit to the Himalayan pine but more spreading. The leaves are long, light green, and droop from the branchlets. The cones assume the shape of an almost perfect cylinder and measure seven to eight inches in length. This pine is somewhat tender and requires all the protection possible from cold winds.

The jack pine, *Pinus Banksiana,* has no ornamental value, but to some persons it presents a picturesque appearance. It is very hardy, as it grows as far north as Hudson Bay. It does well on sandy slopes. The slender branches are spreading and occasionally much divergent.

The lacebark pine, *Pinus Bungeana,* from China, has slender curving branches and forms a dense tree. When it passes the juvenile state, the bark of the main bole begins to assume a peculiar flaky light gray aspect. It grows slowly and has a bushy appearance for a number of years. It is quite hardy. The bark on the stems of adult trees in China is said to be white.

The Swiss stone pine, *Pinus Cembra,* from central Europe, is of remarkable beauty and quite hardy, as the foliage is not browned by the coldest winters. In its juvenile state it forms a dense pyramid and is of very slow growth. This pine is well adapted to situations in which space is much restricted. It requires moist good soil.

The Japanese red pine, *Pinus densiflora,* is a small spreading flat-topped tree with orange-brown bark and branchlets of a lighter color covered with a bloom. It is a valuable ornamental tree of normal hardiness provided it does not receive the sweep of cold winds. Specimens in the Rochester parks are about twenty feet tall. The var. *umbraculifera* is better known than the type, and forms a low flat-topped bushy plant. It is used in formal gardening. Var. *globosa* is a dwarf form, roundish in habit and with light green foliage. Var. *pendula* is also dwarf with pendulous branches. Specimens in the Durand-Eastman Park pinetum are doing nicely but as yet are not sufficiently developed to present much of an ornamental appearance.

The limber pine, *Pinus flexilis,* from the mountains of California and eastward, has usually horizontal and pendulous branches, forming a very beautiful outline. Its leaves are short and rigid and look quite different from other white pines. It is hardy, of slow growth, and seems to thrive best at the base of a slope where moisture is abundant, but well drained.

Jeffrey pine, *Pinus Jeffreyi*, from southern Oregon to California, is much rarer in cultivation than the bull pine. It forms a narrow pyramidal outline. The leaves are dense and bluish-green, and it is hardy. It has attained a height of forty feet in the Highland Park pinetum over a period of thirty-four years.

The Korean pine, *Pinus koraiensis*, is not a common conifer in American parks or gardens, although it was introduced many years ago. The branches spread horizontally, but are somewhat divergent and are inclined in some individuals to be rather thin. It is very hardy and of slow growth, and is well adapted to restricted situations. Occasional removal of the central buds in spring to produce a dense lateral growth is beneficial.

The oneleaf pine, *Pinus monophylla*, is a native of dry regions from Utah, Nevada, and Arizona. The habit is dense broad pyramidal with foliage bluish-green. When young it makes slow growth and is sometimes difficult to establish. However, once started it grows well and makes a beautiful addition to the landscape. A large specimen in Highland Park is now seventeen feet tall.

The western white pine, *Pinus monticola*, native from British Columbia to northern California and Montana, bears a strong resemblance to the eastern white pine. The leaves are a little stiffer and shorter than in the latter. It is not difficult to identify, however, its cones being longer than *P. Strobus* and its habit more compact and pyramidal. Although it is a western species, it grows with a vigor equal to the white pine. Specimens in Highland Park measure fifty feet in height. Because of its extreme hardiness and compact pyramidal habit, it is of great value in ornamental work.

The Swiss mountain pine, *Pinus Mugo*, from the mountains of central Europe, has an ascending shrub-like habit, from a wide base, and grows to twenty feet or more in height. It is very hardy and does not brown in the coldest winter. Sometimes it is seriously attacked by pine-leaf scale. It is very important for small gardens. This species is exceedingly variable. Occasionally it forms a low mat on the ground not over three feet high and twenty feet across and again it will grow to a height of fifteen feet and form a broad rounded mound. A low variety is sold under the name of *compacta*, and is a most desirable plant for many situations. The Mugo pine in its many forms is one of the most important low pines for parks and gardens, as it is well suited to different soils and exposures. It is not injured in the bleakest exposures. A spreading dwarf form was found a few years ago by Bernard H. Slavin, Superintendent of Parks at Rochester, New York. It has since been named *Pinus Mugo* var. *Slavinii*. It is low, dense and spreading with erect branches. The leaves are shorter than in the other forms. The type plant now measures more than six feet across and is not more than two feet high.

The Himalayan white pine, *Pinus nepalensis (excelsa)*, has handsome long leaves frequently eight inches in length. The branches are horizontal, drooping, and occasionally divergent. A well-developed individual on the border of a lawn is an object of much beauty. The cones on older trees add to their beauty in autumn. They are slender, often more than nine inches long, and hang gracefully from the branches. In this area trees more than forty feet tall are not uncommon. In some places it is subject to insect attack.

The Austrian pine, *Pinus nigra*, is native in Europe and western Asia. Some trees grown from seed, collected by the late Henry J. Elwes in Bosnia, are standing in the collections of the Rochester parks. Their habit is pyramidal with slightly ascending branches. The branchlets are light brown and the foliage light green. The typical form is planted as extensively as the Scots pine. With its stout spreading branches and large dark green leaves, a well-developed Austrian pine is an object of much beauty. It is perfectly hardy in the coldest exposures, and makes an excellent windbreak as it grows rapidly. It maintains itself well in this country for at least sixty to seventy years. The Crimean pine, *Pinus nigra* var. *caramanica*, with thin branching habit and dark green prominent leaves, is now thirty-four feet tall in the Highland Park pinetum. The Cevennes Pyrenean pine, *Pinus nigra* var. *cebennensis*, is a low-growing tree with a broad base, orange-colored branchlets, and grayish-green leaves. The Corsican pine, *Pinus nigra* var. *calabrica*, comes from southern Europe and is more pyramidal than the other geographical forms. Its branches are somewhat ascending and the branchlets light brown in color. The leaves are a lighter green than in the other forms. Var. *pyramidalis* is an upright form of the Corsican pine. The branching is almost fastigiate and the habit symmetrical. It is useful for planting in small areas. *Pinus nigra* var. *Hornibrookiana* is one of the few dwarfs of this species (Plate IX). It is the result of propagating material found on a "witches-broom" growing on an Austrian pine in Seneca Park at Rochester, New York. It is a small irregularly branched shrubby plant densely covered with stiff lustrous dark green foliage. The leaves are shorter than any of the other forms of the Austrian pine and seldom measure more than two and a half inches in length. It is an excellent addition to the present material which may be used for foundation and rock-garden work.

The Japanese white pine, *Pinus parviflora*, has a very characteristic aspect. The short leaves give a tufted crowded appearance. The branches are usually horizontal and occasionally somewhat divergent, and the habit picturesque. There are fine specimens of this species in the Arnold Arboretum. It is not particular about soil conditions. Var. *glauca* has foliage of light bluish-green with a silver cast. The latter is caused by the stomata on the under side of the leaves. Neither the type nor form are large trees in cultivation, usually about twenty feet tall.

The Macedonian white pine, *Pinus Peuce*, from the mountains of southeastern Europe, bears a general resemblance to the Swiss stone pine in its pyramidal habit. It is slow-growing and quite hardy and well adapted to small ornamental grounds. Specimens in the pinetum at Highland Park at Rochester are a little more than seventeen feet tall. Due to its slow growth and dense habit, it is often attacked by the white pine scale. However, it is not more susceptible to this pest than many of the other pines.

Amongst the three-leaved pines the most useful species is the bull pine, *Pinus ponderosa*, native from British Columbia to western Texas. There are individuals of this handsome pine in Rochester, New York, fifty to sixty years old and sixty to seventy feet tall, in perfect health. It passes through the severest winters without injury. The branches are spreading and variously curving. The long handsome leaves are thickly disposed on the branches, and the whole aspect when well developed is very dignified. The bull pine seems most at home in a well-drained moist soil at the base of a slope or in a ravine. The variety *pendula* has very long drooping leaves, with the branches slightly pendulous, and is very distinctive. There is an excellent example of this pendulous variety on the grounds of the late W. C. Barry, forty feet tall. Var. *scopulorum* is a geographical variety found in the Rocky Mountains. It is smaller in all its details and is more pyramidal with shorter branches than the type. Plants in the pinetum at Durand-Eastman Park have reached a height of twenty-one feet in eighteen years. It is a valuable ornamental tree especially where a bold effect is desired in a minimum amount of space.

The table-mountain pine, *Pinus pungens*, native from New Jersey to North Carolina, has a decidedly flat-topped picturesque appearance, quite distinct from any other pine. It is hardy. The cones are very persistent, clinging tenaciously to the branches for ten or fifteen years, and are difficult to remove.

Amongst the two-leaved species, the red or Norway pine, *Pinus resinosa*, native throughout the northeastern states to Newfoundland, is perhaps the most useful for ornamental planting. It is very hardy and adapts itself to many situations and soils. It appears to do remarkably well in clay soil. When isolated it forms a broad round head towards adult age. The foliage is abundant and massive. For the landscape-gardener this is a most important pine for bold effects.

The pitch pine, *Pinus rigida*, native throughout the northeastern states, is likely to be despised by some planters, but it adds a picturesque appearance in adult age to the landscape. It will grow and look happy in pure sand. It is, therefore, recommended for sandy areas and slopes.

It is fortunate that the white pine, *Pinus Strobus*, one of the most beautiful of all conifers native as far north as Newfoundland, is so well adapted to cultural conditions. In very exposed situations the white pine may become partly browned from the sweep of cold penetrating winds. Nevertheless, it makes a noble windbreak when planted rather closely as the trees give mutual support to each other. The plants may be set seven to eight feet apart and when they begin to crowd they should be thinned out and planted elsewhere. The white pine is a beautiful object standing alone on the edge of a lawn. It is highly ornamental under varying conditions and with its horizontal branches, slightly curving upwards, succeeds well in light sandy soils. The pyramidal white pine, var. *fastigiata*, is a noble plant in formal gardening. It has not been in cultivation many years and specimens are not known over twenty-five feet tall. The dwarf white pine, var. *nana*, forms a low round bush that seldom attains a height of more than four feet. This is a most important variety in a situation where a low conifer is required.

It should be said that in some regions the white pine is subject to several enemies and diseases, and this possibility should be considered in advance.

The Scots pine, *Pinus sylvestris*, has been planted extensively in this country and various opinions are expressed about its utility. It maintains a good appearance from fifty to seventy years in most cases, other conditions being equal. It grows rapidly and is absolutely hardy. The branches are usually spreading and sometimes pendulous, and when well grown it is ornamental. Adult trees are characterized by yellowish-brown bark which is ornamental in a winter landscape. There is a form, var. *argentea*, with silvery-blue leaves, which is very distinctive. Two dwarf varieties, *nana* and *Watereri*, are excellent for small places and useful in rock-gardening. The former is rather broad and erect in habit with irregular branching and blue-green foliage. The latter is a larger plant of upright symmetrical form with steel-blue foliage. Five feet is the usual size of an adult specimen. Var. *fastigiata*, the upright form of the Scots pine, is a most interesting tree. The habit is strictly narrow pyramidal with an erect main stem and erect or ascending branches. One of the original specimens in North America, and perhaps the largest, is at Durand-Eastman Park at Rochester. It is twelve years old and measures ten feet in height with a maximum cross-section of twenty-three inches.

The Chinese pine, *Pinus tabulæformis*, is not commonly known in this area. It is a good grower and plants set out seventeen years ago have reached a height of twenty feet. Although the specimens are yet too young to determine the habit of the adult tree, at the present time the branching is open and foliage dense and light or grayish-green. It is unlikely that this tree will stand much cold wind and, therefore, it should be provided with some protection. The group at Durand-Eastman Park in Rochester is located at the base of a hill facing the east and larger trees are placed to the front to prevent an over-abundance of sun.

The Japanese black pine, *Pinus Thunbergii*, is a small tree of picturesque appearance. The branches are set some distance apart and, towards the base of the tree, are long, often spreading close to the ground and becoming erect at the ends. Towards the upper half of the tree they are short. This species does well in light soils and appears to succeed even in sand. It is not injured by open exposures and is often used for windbreaks and seashore plantings where a tall tree is not required.

Firs.

The firs are notable objects in parks and gardens, particularly in juvenile conditions. The thick characteristic leaves, thickly disposed on the generally horizontal branches, are very attractive. They do not, perhaps, exhibit the graceful appearance of spruces, but in the decoration of parks and gardens they supply a most important part, from a different standpoint. The development of several dwarf varieties has fulfilled a much needed requirement for material in the small garden and rockery. Firs must have fertile well-drained soil and, if possible, a moist atmosphere, to be in vigorous health.

The silver fir, *Abies alba* (*A. Picea*), from the mountains of central and southern Europe, is distinguished by the leaves lying very flat on the branches. It is a very beautiful species and fast-growing where it is perfectly hardy. In the northeastern states it is a little hardier than *A. cephalonica*. There are several silver firs growing in the vicinity of Rochester, at least sixty-five feet tall and perhaps seventy or more years of age. All are examples of what a tender tree may do when planted in well-protected favorable conditions. Var. *pendula*, with pendulous branches, often makes a picturesque appearance when grown to good size. Var. *tortuosa* is a bushy compact dwarf with crowded branches and short lustrous dark green leaves. A plant at Rochester measures about two feet in height and four feet in diameter. It is especially useful for rock-gardens.

The balsam fir, *Abies balsamea*, which always looks so attractive in native conditions in northern woods, soon assumes a most unhappy appearance in cultivation and cannot be recommended. Undoubtedly, one of the few places where it is enjoying success under cultivated conditions is at Durand-Eastman Park at Rochester. The specimens are in mass plantings where they are completely surrounded by other trees and, after nineteen years, have attained an average height of twenty-five feet. Doubtless the soil, atmosphere, and protection satisfy their requirements. The dwarf variety *hudsonia* is successful in cultivation and is in demand as a rock-garden plant.

The Greek or Cephalonian fir, *Abies cephalonica*, with its sharp-pointed leaves and dense habit of branching, is one of the most beautiful firs where it proves hardy. It is very likely to be badly scorched by the winter's sun in February after a low night temperature. In the winter of 1916 and 1917, some of the largest plants were severely injured, but it can be grown by carefully studying conditions of exposure that may suit it. It is a beautiful tree in the middle states. Var. *Apollinis*, with yellowish branchlets and longer more acute leaves, is perhaps more hardy than the type. A specimen received from the Arnold Arboretum, twenty-seven years ago, is now thirty-six feet tall.

The Cilician fir, *Abies cilicica,* from Asia Minor, is a handsome species. Invariably, the lower branches die after the tree has attained some height. Nevertheless, it still makes a beautiful specimen when the bare trunk can be hidden by a surrounding planting of other low-growing or shrub-like evergreens. The largest trees in this area are now nearly forty feet tall.

The white fir, *Abies concolor*, is one of the best in cultivation in northeastern America. The interior form from Colorado is best adapted to planting. In twenty-six years it attains a height of thirty-nine feet, with a distinctly pyramidal outline and branched to the base. The large flat leaves, thickly disposed on the branches, are very noticeable and give it a good dignified appearance. Seedlings vary considerably and frequently show a glaucous-bluish tinge in the leaves. The white fir should be planted in moist good soil, preferably at the base of a slope where abundance of moisture can be supplied, or in a situation in which the soil is porous and moist and well drained.

Farges fir, *Abies Fargesii*, from central China, appears to be hardy and a good grower when once established. It requires protection against sun and wind and might, during a severe winter, be seriously injured. Although it shows promise, it has not been grown a sufficient length of time to state its reaction to all possible conditions. It is a beautiful small tree at the present time with chocolate-brown branchlets and dark green foliage.

The Momi fir, *Abies firma*, from Japan, has rigid large dark green leaves which are bifid or split at the apex into two minute sharp points. The branches are horizontal and give a massive or heavy effect to the tree. Until several years ago, there was an excellent specimen about thirty feet tall in the pinetum at Highland Park. Unfortunately, it became injured and was removed.

The Nikko fir, *Abies homolepis*, from Japan, is one of the most important exotic species introduced into North America. The largest individuals are at least fifty-five feet in height and in perfect health in some gardens in this country, and densely branched to the base. The tree forms a handsome pyramid, resting on a very broad base. The leaves are large and deep green. This fir has been planted considerably around New York and New Jersey. *A. homolepis* var. *umbellata* is equally hardy and has about the same habit of growth, but the cones are green, whereas in the former they are violet-purple.

The Alpine fir, *Abies lasiocarpa*, does not thrive in the eastern states. Its variety *arizonica* is, however, of sufficient hardiness to permit its use in ornamental work. It is generally seen as a bush or small tree, narrow pyramidal in habit with cork-like cream-colored bark and bluish-green leaves which are pale blue on the new growth. It is this latter feature that makes it so much in demand for landscape work.

Abies nobilis is perhaps one of the noblest of all firs as it grows in a wild state on the Pacific Coast. After twenty-nine years in western New York, it is only a dense bush six to eleven feet tall and does not seem inclined to form a leader and become tree-like. It seems, however, to be quite hardy. Var. *glauca*, with silver-gray leaves especially on the new growth, is a beautiful specimen in the garden. It is a slow-growing form and seldom reaches a height of more than eight feet. It is hardy in the eastern states and, given good well-drained soil, will always prove a valuable addition to the garden or large rockery.

Nordmann fir, *Abies Nordmanniana*, native of the regions southeast of the Black Sea, presents a remarkably noble appearance when in good health. The large very flat leaves are densely crowded on the horizontal branches. The cones are of good size and cylindric in shape. On specimens of fair size they add to the beauty of tree in late summer and early autumn when they stand, perched in erect position, on the uppermost branches. Occasionally the leaves on the south side will be a little browned from the winter sun after the middle of February. It is a very important fir in the middle states. In the New England states this species should be planted in well-protected situations.

Abies recurvata, an introduction of the late E. H. Wilson from western China, has so far shown a hardiness equal to any of the firs with the possible exception of *A. concolor*. It is pyramidal in habit with closely arranged horizontal branches. The leaves are long, stiff, sharp-pointed, and lustrous dark green. This species receives its name from the character of the leaves which are recurved and point back toward the base of the branch. This feature is particularly noticeable on the young growth towards the top of tree. Specimens at Rochester have never shown signs of injury due to cold or dryness and after seventeen years are more than fourteen feet tall.

The Siberian fir, *Abies sibirica*, at the age of twenty-nine years is a tree twenty-five feet tall. Although it appears hardy, it requires the utmost protection and even then is likely to become scraggy in appearance. It cannot be considered an ornamental plant in the northeastern states.

The Himalayan fir, *Abies spectabilis*, is not known as a hardy tree in the northern states. A dwarf variety, var. *brevifolia*, is, however, grown in this area. It is a compact small bush-like plant with dense horizontal branches and lustrous dark green foliage. A plant at Rochester, which must be covered in the winter to prevent frozen buds, is now about a foot high.

Veitch fir, *Abies Veitchii*, from Japan, is very hardy and has never shown the slightest signs of winter-injury. In a juvenile condition this fir is very handsome, but when it approaches adult size, it becomes thin in habit. This tendency can be very much obviated by disbudding or removal of the central buds of the branches and occasional stopping of the leader to induce a denser lateral growth. Var. *olivacea*, a form with cones green when young and grayish-brown at maturity, coned for the first time in 1930 at the Durand-Eastman Park pinetum. The tree is more than seventeen feet tall.

Douglas fir.

The so-called Douglas fir, or red fir of lumbermen, *Pseudo-tsuga Douglasii*, is another of the few conifers from the western side of the continent that does excellently well in northern and northeastern states. It is, however, the form from the interior, known as var. *glauca*, that is perfectly hardy in the East. The beauty of the Douglas fir is difficult to exaggerate. Typical color of the foliage is dark yellow-green, but seedlings often appear with glaucous-bluish foliage. It forms a handsome pyramidal outline. The branches are very irregularly whorled or circled on the stem and it differs very much from a spruce or fir in this respect. Branches are also horizontal, with a slight curve downward in the center, and turn up gracefully at the ends. Occasionally they are slightly divergent. In moist well-drained soil it grows rapidly and attains a height of thirty-five feet in twenty-six years. Douglas fir planted on porous sandy slopes does not grow as rapidly as in more congenial conditions, but it forms a sturdy dense growth and presents an excellent appearance. A well-developed individual on the edge of a lawn, with plenty of room for spread of branches, is a beautiful object. Var. *globosa* is a low-growing bushy form well adapted to gardening in restricted situations. Var. *pendula*, with the branches drooping at the ends, is highly ornamental. Var. *pyramidata* is a semi-dwarf form. It is distinctly formal and conical in habit with closely set horizontal branches which decrease regularly in length from the base to the apex of the tree. The leaves are noticeably smaller than those of the species. The type is growing at Cobbs Hill in Rochester. It is about nineteen years old and twelve feet tall.

Spruces.

The spruces are remarkably beautiful trees in parks and gardens when well grown and healthy. Their pyramidal outlines, with the branches commonly arranged in circles or whorls, present a graceful appearance. The spruces, as a rule, are not as well adapted to dry sandy soils as are pines. Mostly they do not thrive in cold wet soils, but prefer a sandy loam thoroughly well drained. In native conditions spruces appear to be at home on hill and mountain slopes where moisture is abundant but never stagnant.

The Norway spruce, *Picea Abies* (*P. excelsa*), is perhaps planted more extensively than any other spruce in the northern and northeastern states. It is much to be regretted that experience after many years shows it to be unfitted for this locality. The greater number of the Norway spruces in this region after twenty-five to thirty-five years begin to go backward. The tree is fully hardy, but the climatic conditions do not seem to suit it. In dry sandy soil it invariably is attacked by red-spider. Occasionally it is seen in adult age in healthy condition in valleys or on slopes in deep, cool, moist, well-drained soil. It is a magnificent forest tree in central Europe. When a quick effective evergreen windbreak is desired, provided the soil is well drained, it serves this purpose very well for many years. In adult individuals the branches are stout and spreading, with frequently long slender branchlets suspended from the main branches, and in a healthy tree this habit appears highly ornamental. There are a number of pendulous, columnar, and dwarf varieties of the Norway spruce. The dwarf varieties appear to show more virility than the type. The vars. *Maxwellii, Ellwangeriana, microsperma, inversa, cupressina,* and *nana* have variously formed low bushy and conical habits. They are excellent plants for many situations in ornamental gardening where low evergreens are required. In twenty-five years some of these very slow-growing dwarf forms do not attain over three feet in height. There are two distinct tree forms, var. *pendula* with drooping branches and var. *viminalis* with hanging branchlets. Both are good trees when properly developed, especially the latter which presents a very graceful appearance when arranged in group plantings with other conifers or deciduous trees.

The Iramomi spruce, *Picea bicolor*, from Japan, is decidedly promising, but it is rare in cultivation. There are individuals in the Hunnewell pinetum fifty feet in height and branched to the base, in perfect health and very handsome.

Picea Breweriana, from the Siskiyou Mountains of northern California, does not do well in the East. Like the Serbian spruce, it has broad leaves and under suitable conditions is a most graceful tree. In this area, it is too tender for successful cultivation and only those plants which have a maximum amount of protection survive.

Engelmann spruce, *Picea Engelmanni*, native from British Columbia to New Mexico, is a tree of singular beauty. The strictly pyramidal outline, with the branches closely arranged in circles and maintained to the base, renders it particularly desirable for ornamental grounds. The lower branches are maintained under average conditions from forty to fifty years, and it will probably compare favorably with any other spruce in this respect. As far as the writer's observations are concerned, it is very rare for any spruce to maintain all of the lower branches during its entire life, that is, for one hundred years or more in cultivation in the northeastern states. Var. *glauca*, with glaucous or light bluish-green foliage, is a color form.

The white spruce, *Picea glauca* (*P. canadensis*), most decidedly requires a cool moist well-drained soil to be happy. Under such conditions it forms a dense pyramidal habit. It usually has light green-bluish foliage. The branches are ascending and horizontal, and often the branchlets are pendulous. White spruce is largely planted and often placed in dry sandy conditions where it is attacked by red-spider, and it then presents an unattractive appearance. It is often seen in northern Ontario, in groves and isolated, sixty to seventy feet in height, the individuals standing alone densely branched to the base, in perfect symmetry, and no spruce could appear more ornamental. Var. *cærulea* is a color form with glaucous foliage. Var. *nana* is a dwarf compact rounded bush. Var. *tabuliformis* is also a dwarf form with spreading horizontal branches. A specimen in the Rochester parks is about two feet high and almost four feet across.

A remarkably interesting dwarf form of *Picea glauca* (or perhaps of *albertiana*) is var. *conica*. It was discovered by J. G. Jack, of the Arnold Arboretum, near Loggan in Alberta in 1904. It is distinctly conical in habit with small fine bright green foliage. The largest specimens observed measure fifty-two inches in height. It is used commonly in formal gardening.

The Saghalin spruce, *Picea Glehnii*, from Japan, is hardy and very desirable for situations where a small tree is desired. It is narrow pyramidal in habit with small lustrous dark green leaves. It is slow-growing, specimens of some age in Highland Park being only seventeen feet tall.

Picea heterolepis was identified in 1931 when a plant in Durand-Eastman Park coned for the first time. The determination was made principally from the cone which has distinctly emarginate scales. The general appearance of the tree is somewhat similar to the white spruce, *P. glauca*. The specimen is now more than eleven feet tall.

The Yezo spruce, *Picea jezoensis*, from Japan, is not hardy under all conditions and must be afforded maximum protection for success. It requires fertile well-drained soil and a moist atmosphere. Attempts to grow this plant at Highland Park have failed although specimens at Durand-Eastman Park are now more than seventeen feet tall and in a healthy condition. Var. *hondoensis* with light colored branchlets and smaller bluish-green leaves, is supposed to be more hardy than the type. This feature appears to be true as specimens at Durand-Eastman Park have reached a height of more than ten feet in twelve years.

Picea Koyamai is an interesting Japanese species. It was

introduced into this country in 1914 and, thus far, shows promise of doing well. Specimens appear to be hardy and the growth is excellent. It suggests in many ways the Norway spruce except that it is more openly branched and has distinct reddish-brown branchlets which are noticeable from some distance. A group of this species in Durand-Eastman Park averages about thirteen feet tall.

The black spruce, *Picea mariana*, native from Canada to Virginia, and often abundant in swampy or wet grounds, does not succeed well in cultivation in western New York. After ten to fifteen years it presents an unattractive appearance. Var. *Doumetii*, unlike the type, is an excellent ornamental form. It is a semi-dwarf or slow-growing tree of conical habit and dense bluish-green foliage. A plant in the Highland Park collection is seventeen feet tall.

Picea Maximowiczii, from Japan, is a very rare spruce in cultivation. It has short stout leaves and slender branches spreading and ascending, and inclined to be slightly divergent. It is a slow grower and in twenty-four years does not exceed thirty feet in height.

The Serbian spruce, *Picea Omorika*, from the Balkan region, belongs botanically to a small group of spruces in which the leaves are flat or flattish, and it is the only one in this group that is cultivated to any extent in this area. The habit is narrow pyramidal, with the branches ascending and spreading. The branchlets are often slightly upturned, disclosing the dark green under side of the leaves in contrast with the silvery lines on the upper surface. This spruce requires well-drained, moist, deep, rich soil to be in perfect health. It is quite hardy. Specimens in the pinetum at Highland Park now measure thirty-five feet in height.

The oriental spruce, *Picea orientalis*, native from the Caucasus west into Asia, is a tree of remarkable beauty. The small dark green leaves, very much crowded and appressed on the branches, give it a charming appearance. Branches are spreading and ascending, especially towards the ends, and when in perfect health and vigor are thickly disposed from base to apex. It retains its lower branches as well as any spruce in cultivation in the northeastern states. Near the entrance of Riverside Cemetery, Rochester, New York, are two beautiful groups of the oriental spruce planted thirty-nine years ago. The leader is sometimes attacked by the white-pine borer. Var. *nana*, a dwarf form of shrubby appearance and irregular branching, is useful for small gardens. The leaves are smaller than the type.

The tigertail spruce, *Picea polita*, from Japan, is one of the most distinct species, with its rigid leaves and stout branches. It requires a moist rich soil and a well-protected situation, and under such conditions it is quite hardy. In some parts of the country it is alleged to lose the lower branches early, but trees in the northeastern states after thirty-four years are retaining the lower limbs.

The Colorado spruce, *Picea pungens*, native throughout parts of Colorado, Utah, Wyoming, and New Mexico, is perhaps one of the most popularly planted conifers. The spruce gall-aphis is a common pest on this tree and unless properly cared for, once an infestation begins, may seriously affect the appearance or even destroy the specimen. Trees growing in the shade or where they are under-nourished generally lose many of their lower branches when they reach an appreciable age. Amongst the various forms with glaucous, bluish, and silver foliage, perhaps the var. *argentea* with silvery-bluish foliage is most distinct. Var. *glauca* has bluish-green foliage, and var. *viridis* leaves which are dark green. The latter is seldom seen in ornamental work. Var. *Kosteriana* has bluish-green foliage and pendulous branches. This form is so very pendulous that it requires a stout stake to prevent it from tumbling over. This form is the true Koster's blue spruce, the form offered by nurserymen being either *argentea* or *glauca*. The var. *compacta*, a low bush form, is an excellent plant for decorative gardening in formal conditions.

The red spruce, *Picea rubens*, native from Canada, northern New York to Pennsylvania and North Carolina, is a handsome tree in native conditions, and of great economic importance. It does not thrive in cultivation and cannot be recommended for ornamental conditions in parks and gardens.

Picea Schrenkiana, from central Asia, is a slow grower. The largest specimen in the Rochester parks is now four feet high and five feet broad at the base after twelve years. It appears to be perfectly hardy. Whether it will develop into a tree in this area seems improbable from present observations. It is now irregularly conical and bush-like in habit. The branching is horizontal and the leaves stiff, sharp-pointed, and gray-green in color.

Picea Wilsoni is quite different from the other Chinese spruces and very distinct. When young it appears hardy but of slow growth. Later, as it becomes better established, it shows excellent development. It is pyramidal in habit with horizontal branches. The branchlets are almost white making it easy to identify. Specimens in Durand-Eastman Park are now almost eight feet tall.

Hemlocks.

The hemlock, *Tsuga canadensis*, is native from New Brunswick and Wisconsin south to northern Georgia. Although the species grows far north, when it is planted in situations fully open to the sweep of cold and dry winds, it is likely to be badly browned on the exposed sides. The plant is usually gregarious in a wild state in gulches, valleys, and river-gorges where moisture is abundant and naturally well drained, and depends on mutual support by growing in masses. The hemlock is one of the most graceful conifers, and it is indeed fortunate that such a lovely subject can be cultivated in the parks and gardens of the northeastern United States. The slender branchlets droop gracefully, and in a well-developed individual the lights and shadows are displayed with fine effect. The late Josiah Hoopes, a great admirer of conifers, declared that if he were restricted to one evergreen, he would surely choose the hemlock. In a well-protected situation on the lawn, the tree retains the lower branches for many years. It is a mistake to plant the hemlock in a dry poor soil. The tree makes a very beautiful protective screen or belt, other cultural conditions being equal. When skilfully managed it produces a most beautiful hedge and stands the shears well. The var. *pendula* is one of the most graceful pendulous conifers, and forms a flat broad low top, with branchlets drooping at the ends of the branches. Fortunately, this handsome plant is sold in many American nurseries. Var. *globosa* is a low bushy form, well adapted to restricted situations in the garden. Var. *atrovirens* is dense and compact, forming a low broad pyramid. It attains a height of twenty feet and perhaps much higher.

The Carolina hemlock, *Tsuga caroliniana*, native from the Blue Ridge Mountains to northern Georgia, is very distinct in its character from the common hemlock. It is essentially a smaller tree and has a more compact habit of growth. The foliage is very dark green. The largest specimens at Highland Park are twenty-two feet tall. Its cones are much larger than those of the common hemlock. In the autumn, when the branches are loaded with the yellowish-brown cones with the scales fully opened, it is an object of singular beauty. It is perfectly hardy, and requires a cool moist well-drained soil.

The Japanese hemlock, *Tsuga diversifolia*, forms a bushy habit in cultivation, with a number of stems. Wilson says it makes a tree eighty feet tall in Japan. It does not attain anything like that height in this region. The conspicuous white lines on the under side of the leaves contrast very markedly with the dark green on the upper surfaces.

The Siebold hemlock, *Tsuga Sieboldii*, from Japan, is more difficult to establish than *T. diversifolia* and is not considered as hardy as that species, although an opposite result is reported in another region. It forms a bushy tree and does not exceed twelve feet in height in nineteen years. It must be planted in a sheltered situation. It is said to attain about the same height as *T. diversifolia* in its native state.

Cedrus.

The Atlas cedar, *Cedrus atlantica*, and the var. *glauca* failed in western New York in severe winters. In Long Island and New Jersey, however, they succeed remarkably well, and healthy specimens can be seen on various estates.

The Deodar cedar, *Cedrus Deodara*, is more hardy than the Atlas cedar. It is a most beautiful tree and is occasionally planted in this area. It cannot, however, be considered as hardy and only those specimens placed in the most protected locations prove successful.

The cedar of Lebanon, *Cedrus libanitica*, native on the Lebanon Mountains and in northern Africa, is one of the noblest conifers. The geographical form that has been commonly cultivated in Europe and in some parts of this country is not hardy in western New York or in any part of New England. Many years ago C. S. Sargent had seeds collected on the highest mountains in Asia Minor, where the species occurs. This race, fortunately, has proved quite hardy at the Arnold Arboretum, and the young trees are now of considerable size. It is very satisfactory at Rochester. The stout horizontal branches, radiating very irregularly and forming a broad head, present a picturesque appearance. It requires a warm rich well-drained soil.

Larix.

The larches are deciduous conifers, but all are beautiful ornamental trees. The European larch, *Larix decidua*, commonly distributed throughout central and northern Europe, is a valuable tree for parks and private estates. The habit is pyramidal and often forms a long spire-like top in adult trees. The branches have a yellowish-straw color. The fine deep green leaves, which when unfolding in spring have a yellowish-coppery tinge and in autumn assume a yellowish-bronze color, are very attractive. The European larch does very well in light sandy soil and grows rapidly. A pyramidal form, var. *pyramidalis*, is distinct. It is formal in habit with ascending to almost erect branches and is a valuable ornamental tree for formal work. The type is now growing in Highland Park and in a period of about twenty-nine years has attained a height of thirty-four feet with a maximum spread, near the base, of eighteen feet.

A hybrid between *Larix decidua* and *L. Kaempferi* (*L. eurolepis*) which appeared in Scotland, is growing rapidly in the pinetum. Specimens received seventeen years ago are now eighteen feet tall. These trees are true intermediates between the parents. It is said by foresters in the British Isles to combine the hardiness of both parents and to be free from disease.

The Dahurian larch, *Larix Gmelini* (*L. dahurica*), has not yet been distinguished from its variety, *Principis Rupprechtii*, in the collections at Rochester. As the only difference lies in the character of the cones, the trees must bear fruit before exact determinations can be made. According to E. H. Wilson, the true Dahurian larch is seldom in cultivation, in which case all the material at Rochester may be the variety. Specimens labeled under both names in the pinetum at Durand-Eastman Park show a broad pyramidal habit and dark green leaves which are pale or glaucous on the under side. They are about sixteen feet tall. Var. *japonica*, a form native to Japan, has been in cultivation for almost half a century. It is known by its ascending branches and dark red hairy branchlets. A tree in Highland Park is now thirty feet tall.

The Japanese larch, *Larix Kaempferi* (*L. leptolepis*), has very broad horizontal branches, which curve upward and form a very broad pyramid. The leaves have a bluish-gray tinge. The branchlets are characterized by a reddish-brown color. In the autumn the leaves turn deep yellow. Japanese larch does excellently well in cultivation, and is a most desirable ornamental.

The American larch or tamarack, *Larix laricina*, native from Manitoba to Pennsylvania, is usually found in swamps and very damp soil. It forms a narrow pyramidal head when young, but in old age it is often very irregular in outline, and the branches, particularly in adult trees, are arranged very irregularly. The tamarack, when isolated and well developed, is a very ornamental tree. Although usually native in wet soils, it is not a success in cultivation unless placed in well-drained land.

The western larch, *Larix occidentalis*, comes from British Columbia and Oregon. It has much longer leaves than the eastern *L. laricina* and does well in this area although not widely represented.

The Chinese larch, *Larix Potaninii*, is an introduction of the present century. It should prove a valuable ornamental tree. The habit is broad pyramidal with spreading branches. The leaves are rectangular in cross-section, making it easy to determine. Specimens in Durand-Eastman Park are twenty-one feet tall.

The Siberian larch, *Larix sibirica*, is considered by some authorities merely a northern form of the European larch. It has, however, longer leaves than that species and more ascending branches. It is hardy here but does not show sufficient character to supplant the European larch in ornamental work.

Pseudolarix.

The Chinese golden-larch, *Pseudolarix amabilis*, is an elegant ornamental tree. The branches are long and spreading and very irregularly whorled, with the lower ones horizontal and the upper ascending. The branchlets are yellowish-brown. The leaves are deciduous, light pale green, two to three inches long, in dense spire-like clusters. The foliage turns to a clear deep yellow in the autumn. It requires a light sandy moist loamy soil to be in good condition. It is hardy, and the oldest trees in this country show no signs of failing. The largest trees at Highland Park are thirty-two feet tall, twenty-seven years planted.

Taxodium.

Taxodium, although not evergreen, is a true conifer. It is represented by three species, two of which are hardy in this area. They are beautiful trees with different foliage color for each of the three seasons during which it appears. Found in swamps or in wet land, they must, when grown in cultivation, be afforded situations where the soil is well-drained and fertile. With rare exception, that is their one requirement for success.

The bald-cypress, *Taxodium distichum*, native from Delaware to Florida, is a beautiful narrow tree with horizontal branches and fine plume-like foliage. When the leaves first appear they are a light green becoming a soft green during the summer. With the coming of frost in early autumn they turn a light orange-brown before falling from the tree. Specimens fifty feet tall are not uncommon. A pendulous form, var. *pendulum,* is somewhat broader than the type with branches which droop gracefully toward the ends and whose branchlets are pendulous. There are two specimens of this form at Highland Park which have attained a height of about forty-five feet in thirty-eight years.

The pond-cypress, *Taxodium ascendens*, is seen in lakes and ponds from Virginia to Florida. It is not so ornamental a tree as *T. distichum* and is seldom seen in the northern states although it appears to be hardy. It is slim and gaunt in habit with short branches and erect lateral branchlets. The leaves which appear on these branchlets are scale-like and often unnoticeable. Var. *nutans* is a form with the lateral branchlets pendent rather than erect.

Sequoia.

The big tree, *Sequoia gigantea*, is one of the noblest vegetable organisms on the earth. The largest trees in cultivation on the eastern side of the continent were in the Ellwanger grounds on Mt. Hope Avenue, Rochester, New York. The seeds were brought from California by "Pony Express" in 1854 by Ellwanger & Barry. They raised about three thousand seedlings and most of them were sold in England. Ellwanger & Barry planted a small group near their office and they did remarkably well. The largest individual in 1916 was seven and nine-tenths feet in circumference and fifty-five feet in height. The severe winter of 1916 and 1917 so injured them that two years later they died. If they were planted out when quite small, which is probable, they therefore were growing exposed to a series of winters extending to about sixty years. There is a large tree growing at Aurora, New York (see Sequoia, page 141). Sequoia is, however, not to be recommended for ornamental grounds in the northeastern United States.

Cryptomeria.

Cryptomeria japonica is the only species of the genus and is native in Japan. It is not hardy in this area although in the vicinity of New York City there are some excellent specimens about forty feet tall. It is narrow pyramidal in habit with short branches and bright green foliage. It is successfully employed as an ornamental tree on the Pacific Coast. Var. *Lobbii* is much hardier than the type. Trees in Highland Park now measure more than twenty feet in height. It differs a little from the species, being narrower in habit with denser branching and lighter green foliage.

Umbrella-pine.

The umbrella-pine, *Sciadopitys verticillata*, a native of Japan, presents a most singular appearance amongst conifers. There are two kinds of leaves: those on the shoot small and scale-like, but at the end of the branch much longer and linear and forming an umbrella-like circle. The habit of young trees is narrowly pyramidal. Wilson states that in forest conditions in Japan the habit is gaunt and thin, and is very different from the dense pyramids to be seen in American parks and gardens. The umbrella-pine should be planted in deep moist well-drained soil to appear at its best. It has not been injured in the Northeast in severe winters.

Cypress.

The Lawson cypress, *Chamæcyparis Lawsoniana,* is native along the Pacific Coast from southern Oregon to northern California. Without doubt the most beautiful member of the genus, it unfortunately enjoys a moisture-laden atmosphere and does not thrive in dry climates. It is a narrow pyramidal tree and, on occasion, attains a height of fifty feet in this area. In good specimens the foliage which ranges from a light to glaucous-green, spreads a beautiful color over the tree. Var. *glauca* has light bluish-green foliage. Var. *Allumii* is a semi-dwarf of almost formal pyramidal habit and with ascending branches which are covered with light silvery-green foliage. This form appears to be able to withstand dryer situations than the type. Var. *Fletcheri* is also a good grower in dry localities but will not stand much cold. There is a specimen in the pinetum at Durand-Eastman Park more than two and a half feet tall. It is a dwarf columnar plant with juvenile foliage which is glaucous or light bluish-green. Where there is no severe exposure it should find much favor for use in dwarf borders, rock work, and foundation planting.

The Nootka cypress, sometimes known as the yellow-cedar, *Chamæcyparis nootkatensis,* is native from Alaska to Oregon. It is a handsome tree for ornamental purposes with a broad pyramidal habit and dense dark green foliage which completely covers the tree. In its natural state, it grows under conditions of great humidity and, therefore, does not do well in dry places. For best results it should be situated in partially shaded or protected areas where evaporation is at a minimum. A tree in Highland Park measures thirty-one feet in height after thirty-four years. Var. *glauca* is a form with glaucous or light bluish-green foliage.

The Hinoki cypress, *Chamæcyparis obtusa,* from Japan, is now as well known in cultivation as *C. pisifera.* It forms a very handsome tree with horizontal branches and the branchlets somewhat pendulous. The foliage is a lustrous dark green. Trees, sixty feet high, have been known in the northeastern states. In the local collections specimens are more than twenty feet tall. This tree must have rich well-drained soil for success. There are a number of varieties of the Hinoki cypress, as: *aurea*, a slow-growing form with foliage which is tipped with yellow; *aurea Youngii*, with golden-tipped foliage and somewhat drooping branchlets; *Crippsii*, a semi-dwarf of conical habit with pale yellow foliage; *gracilis*, also a semi-dwarf or slow grower of compact pyramidal habit with slightly pendulous branchlets; *gracilis aurea*, similar to the preceding but with golden-tipped foliage; this color feature of the leaves is very distinct in the spring but as the season advances it fades and in autumn the color is almost entirely green. An interesting dwarf, var. *Tsatsumi*, was received from the Elm City Nurseries of New Haven, Connecticut, in 1919. It is a low spreading compact evergreen with dark green thread-like foliage. It appears to be the hardiest form of the species and makes excellent growth. At the present time it is in great demand as a rock-garden plant. Var. *nana* is a dwarf, long in cultivation. The habit is very dense and the branches are much crowded together, somewhat in layers.

The Sawara cypress, *Chamæcyparis (Retinispora) pisifera*, from Japan, is a very popular evergreen in American gardens. The typical form is a beautiful ornamental tree when grown to one stem. The type should be much more widely grown, for as an ornamental it is not surpassed by any of the seminal or vegetative forms that have been produced from it. The Sawara cypress, or any of its varieties, should always be planted in positions well protected from the sweep of the prevailing cold winds in well-drained soil. The variety *filifera*, with long slender branches, becomes in time a broad round dome and very decorative. Var. *filifera aurea* is a color form of the preceding with golden-yellow foliage. Var. *plumosa* has a very distinct pyramidal outline and, with the plumose branches and branchlets, is very ornamental. Var. *squarrosa*, in which all the leaves are acicular and bluish silvery-green, is a most distinct form and always attracts attention. It is indeed difficult to connect it with the type from superficial observation. Var. *squarrosa intermedia* is a dwarf form, with foliage the same as the preceding variety. It is a low bush-like plant with rounded sides and a more or less flattened top. As it seldom attains a height of more than two feet, it is generally listed as a plant for the rock-garden or as a filler in foundation planting.

The white-cedar, *Chamæcyparis thyoides*, cannot be recommended as an ornamental plant in this region. Native from Maine to Florida and generally found in cold swamps, its appearance does not seem to improve when it is placed in fertile well-drained soil in cultivation. It is the hardiest of all the members of the genus.

Arbor-vitæ.

The Korean arbor-vitæ, *Thuja koraiensis*, is a low spreading shrub with more or less trailing branches which become upright towards the ends. The foliage is distinct from the other species. It is soft bright green on the surface and glaucous, appearing almost white, on the under side. Although introduced into this country only fourteen years ago, it is much sought for rock-gardens and low miscellaneous plantings.

The common arbor-vitæ, *Thuja occidentalis*, which in a natural state extends into northern Canada, is known as one of the hardiest coniferous evergreens and the most abundantly planted. It is employed extensively as a protective hedge. Many of the market-gardeners in Irondequoit, New York, use arbor-vitæ in hedges on the western, northwestern, and northern sides of areas in which they raise early spring vegetables. When this species attains sufficient size it serves a protective purpose admirably and is used in this way in many parts of the country. The common arbor-vitæ in a wild state is variable in its habit, often forming a dense upright pyramid, and frequently with partly spreading branches. There are at least fifty or more varieties of the common arbor-vitæ in cultivation. Some of the larger pyramidal forms are var. *robusta* (var. *Wareana*) with a broad pyramidal habit and deep green foliage which is well retained throughout the winter. Var. *Vervæneana*, with its pyramidal habit and slender branches, is very graceful. The foliage has a faint tinge of yellow, but not conspicuous enough to be disagreeable. Var. *Douglasii pyramidalis* has a narrow pyramidal habit, with short dense crowded branches, and is an excellent form in decorative gardening. Var. *Boothii* is of compact pyramidal habit with bright green foliage especially toward the tips of the leaves. Var. *Buchanani* is pyramidal with loose ascending branches. Var. *Douglasii aurea* is pyramidal in habit with yellow foliage. Observations tend to show that this color form, although hardy and growing well, will not attain the height of the Douglas arbor-vitæ. Var. *cristata* is pyramidal in habit with the branchlets twisted and crowded in tuft-like arrangements on the branches. Var. *Columbia* is similar to the type but with foliage which is dotted with silver. Only plants enjoying good growth and vigor show this color characteristic. Var. *lutea* is the yellow-leaved form. It is pyramidal in habit with yellow foliage which sometimes turns a pale green toward the end of the season. This tree often attains a height of more than eighteen feet. Amongst some of the best low forms are var. *globosa*, low, roundish and bushy; var. *Ellwangeriana*, a low dense sort which with age becomes slightly pyramidal, and characterized by typical and acicular leaves; var. *Hoveyi* becomes a pyramidal-shaped bush in which the branches have the appearance of being folded together in layers; var. *pumila* (Little Gem), an admirable low form which in thirty-five years does not exceed two and a half feet in height and forms a spreading low cushion, retaining a dark green color; var. *Reidii*, a spreading large bushy form with smallish leaves, but likely in time to become a little thin; var. *Rosenthali*, a slow-growing compact pyramidal form with coarse lustrous dark green foliage arranged in more or less vertical planes on short stiff branches; specimens of this variety, set out nine years ago are now scarcely more than three feet tall. Var. *spiralis* is a fairly small tree of narrow pyramidal habit with short branches at the ends of which the foliage is arranged in peculiar whorl-like fashion. Var. *Woodwardii* is a dwarf globose form with a somewhat flattened top and ascending or erect branches. The foliage is dark green and not as dense as that of the other dwarf forms. It is used in foundation work and formal planting. Var. *plicata* is a semi-dwarf form with short branches and lustrous green foliage. A pendulous form, var. *pendula*, is somewhat irregular in habit with drooping branches. The main stem is seldom self-supporting and must be tied up, otherwise it will develop as a more or less spreading plant. When properly cared for, this plant makes a graceful appearance in the garden. Probably it can be used in rock work where it can be left to develop for itself and act as a covering.

The oriental arbor-vitæ, *Thuja orientalis*, from eastern Asia, has usually a strictly pyramidal habit. Branches present the appearance of being densely folded together. The foliage is a bright olive-green color which it retains well throughout the winter. Many named varieties are in cultivation, with dwarf, densely columnar, and pendulous habits. Unfortunately, in the past it was difficult to keep the foliage from browning when planted in the colder localities of the northeastern states. In 1909, the Rochester Park Bureau received from the Arnold Arboretum a packet of seed of this tree. Although complete records are not available, it is thought that the seed was sent from China by E. H. Wilson. Several hundred seedlings were grown and eventually planted out. None has shown the least signs of tenderness and they do not brown during the cold season. One plant of this hardy strain was left in the nursery row for observation. It is now a tree more than seventeen feet tall and almost nine feet through near the base. Var. *aurea* is a dwarf form similar in habit to the type and with golden-yellow leaves which become greenish-yellow as the season advances. Var. *bonita* is also a dwarf of broad conical habit and slow growth.

Var. *nana compacta* is a small rather columnar plant with foliage similar to the species. It does not appear to grow more than two or three feet tall. Var. *conspicua* is a compact columnar form of medium size with short dense light green foliage tipped with yellow. Var. *Sieboldii* is rather oval and compact in habit with erect branches. Specimens of this form average about three feet in height and two feet in diameter. Var. "Rosedale" is a most interesting and beautiful dwarf form. It is an irregularly roundish bush, densely covered with light bluish-green acicular foliage. It seldom attains an average diameter of more than three feet.

The western arbor-vitæ, *Thuja plicata*, native from Alaska to Montana, is, very fortunately, one of the few conifers from the western side of the continent that is promising in the East. The largest individuals in Highland Park are thirty feet tall and branched to the base, and the foliage retains a deep green color throughout the year. In the collection at Durand-Eastman Park, cuttings taken from plants mentioned above were grown and set out in 1916. Due to better soil conditions, these plants grew exceedingly well and are now four feet taller than those in Highland Park. There is no indication at the present time that they have reached their maximum height and it is not improbable that they will eventually become as tall as many of the native conifers. This tree assumes a very graceful pyramidal outline. It should be planted in good well-drained soil. It is one of the most beautiful conifers in cultivation.

The Japanese arbor-vitæ, *Thuja Standishii*, is a very beautiful decorative plant. It has a somewhat broadly pyramidal habit, and the foliage, with a pale green aspect, does not change throughout the year, or only very slightly in winter. The tree requires a fertile well-drained soil and some protection from the open sun to appear at its best. A specimen in Highland Park now measures about eighteen feet in height and is twelve feet through at the base.

Thujopsis.

The Hiba arbor-vitæ, *Thujopsis dolabrata,* is a monotypic genus from Japan and, while hardy in this area, it requires some protection against sun and wind. Although described as a tree in its native habitat, it seldom attains a height of more than ten feet in this country. It is broad pyramidal in habit with foliage similar to the arbor-vitæ but much larger and of lustrous green color. A specimen at Durand-Eastman Park is about four feet tall and six feet across at the base. Var. *nana* is a dwarf, approaching a globose habit with leaves which are smaller and a lighter green than the type. Var. *Hondai* has smaller leaves and is supposed to be hardier than the type.

Libocedrus.

The incense-cedar, *Libocedrus decurrens,* native on the Pacific Coast where it is said to attain a height of ninety feet, is only semi-hardy in this area. For successful cultivation it requires protection from the late winter sun and cold prevailing winds. It does best in a light well-drained soil. A beautiful tree of slender pyramidal habit with lustrous dark green foliage and cinnamon-colored bark, it is a valuable addition to any landscape. There are several specimens at Rochester which appear happy and are more than seventeen feet tall. Due to exposure, the trunks are nude of branches within five feet of the base.

Junipers.

The junipers are very important in ornamental culture. There are numerous decorative forms amongst them, nearly all of which are suited to light dryish soils.

The Chinese juniper, *Juniperus chinensis,* native of northeastern Asia, in the typical form does remarkably well in cultivation. The habits of the pistillate and staminate forms are quite distinct; the staminate is more robust and faster growing, with a pyramidal habit; the pistillate or fruit-bearing form has a looser habit and evidently does not grow so large. The brownish-yellow fruit is very attractive throughout the winter months. Many species of junipers have two types of leaves—scale-like and acicular (needle-shaped). This is marked in the Chinese juniper. Var. *Pfitzeriana* is one of the most important decorative junipers in cultivation at the present time. It is one of the best low conifers to plant close to the walls of a house, and, if given room to develop, adds much dignity to a home. The branches spread out almost horizontally and in time form a large irregular bushy head six to eight feet tall. The branchlets at the tips of the branches are pendulous and the foliage is light olive-green. Var. *pyramidalis* is a form introduced to cultivation by the United States Department of Agriculture, through the late F. N. Meyer. It forms a distinct narrow pyramid and all the leaves are acicular. The foliage is light bluish-green and is remarkably decorative. Var. *pyramidalis glauca* is a form of the preceding with lighter colored foliage. Var. *japonica* is a spreading form with decumbent branches and short erect branchlets. The foliage is light green and mostly acicular. It grows about eight inches tall and in time will cover an area of ground more than seven feet in diameter. Var. *Sargentii* is a low spreading shrub which does not exceed one foot in height and forms dense mats ten to twelve feet in diameter. Amongst the low spreading junipers, this is one of the most important for covering banks and slopes, and is useful in rock-gardening. It does remarkably well in poor sandy soil, by cultivating and mulching for two to three years to get the roots well established. Var. *variegata* forms a low dense pyramid with the tips of the branches silvery-white. The white coloring is not sufficiently prominent to be disagreeable.

The common juniper, *Juniperus communis*, widely native throughout northern parts of the northern hemisphere, is rare in cultivation in this country. Its typical tree form, with branches forming an irregular open head and ten to twenty feet tall, is said by Sargent to be occasionally found in New England, eastern Pennsylvania, and on the high mountains of North

Carolina. Var. *aurea* is a color form with yellow leaves which turn to green as the season advances. The Polish juniper, var. *cracovia*, is a pyramidal form. It is somewhat bushy in appearance with gracefully drooping branchlets. The Irish juniper, var. *hibernica*, and the Swedish juniper, var. *suecica*, suffer in severe winters. The former has a strict narrow columnar habit. The Swedish juniper is also narrowly upright, but the ends of the branchlets droop slightly. Both of these junipers are likely to be pulled apart and their prim stiff forms much injured by heavy snowstorms. It is necessary to support them with stout iron posts driven deeply in the ground and kept out of sight in the interior of the mass. When tied securely outside the branches they resist the destructive tendencies of heavy snowstorms, and the posts are left undisturbed throughout the year. A dwarf form known as var. *suecica nana* is also columnar in habit but seldom attains a height of more than two to three feet. It is like the Swedish juniper, having the reflexed branchlets as in that form. Var. *oblongo-pendula* is another pyramidal form with ascending or erect branches and pendulous branchlets. When growing well the branches often become overladen with growth and bend out. The same condition occurs in the winter when there is heavy snow. Var. *depressa* is the common low form sold in nurseries and is abundant in rocky ground and poor soil in the St. Lawrence Valley, New England, and northern Ontario and Quebec. In several forms this juniper is rather commonly cultivated and is valuable for rocky banks and slopes. Planted three to four feet apart in a massed border, it forms an excellent frontage to a group of larger conifers. The habit is low branching, and in time it forms stout recumbent stems. It seldom exceeds three feet in height and usually it is not over two feet. Var. *aureo-spica* is a color form of *depressa* with the young leaves yellow becoming green later in the season. Var. *nipponica*, a geographical form found by E. H. Wilson in the mountains of Japan, is a procumbent shrub. In this area it grows slowly and must be afforded fertile well-drained soil and a maximum of protection against southern exposures and cold winds. As it is only four to six inches in height, it should prove useful in the rock-garden.

Juniperus conferta, introduced by Wilson from Japan in 1915, is a littoral species and forms dense mats on sandy shores. The deep green leaves are densely crowded, straight, and pale green beneath. Experience has shown it to be quite hardy. Specimens now measure about twelve inches high and cover an area more than six feet in diameter. Because it does best in light soils, it finds favor for covering slopes. It is also commonly used for rock falls in rock-gardens.

The creeping or horizontal juniper, *Juniperus horizontalis*, is widely distributed in North America in native conditions. It is often found on sand-dunes, and in western New York, in Genesee County, it grows abundantly in Bergen Swamp with its roots in the water. The horizontal juniper has long prostrate stems which cling closely to the ground and is one of the best for banks, rocky slopes, and rock-gardening. Var. *Douglasii* is a very low trailing form with bluish foliage which assumes a purplish tinge in the autumn. This is often sold in the nurseries as Waukegan juniper. In twenty years it will form a low mat twelve to fifteen feet across. Var. *alpina* appears as an upright grower when young, but in a short time develops procumbent branches which measure to fifteen inches in height. The foliage is steel-gray in color. With age this plant will cover an area more than seven feet in diameter. When bedded out in mass it presents a sight of great beauty especially if surrounded by a green lawn. Var. *plumosa* is a low spreading shrub with a flat top formed by spreading branches and horizontal plume-like branchlets. The foliage is green and turns purple towards the tips in the autumn. After seventeen years, plants in Highland Park measure six feet in diameter and less than two feet high. Var. *procumbens* is a particularly interesting plant. It is entirely prostrate with branches which run along the ground and with branchlets which seldom measure more than two inches in length. The foliage is acicular, soft green, and more or less appressed to the branchlets. It never attains a height of more than five inches and covers an area of about nine square feet. It is excellent covering for slopes and sandy banks and is useful for rock falls in the rock-garden. Var. *variegata* is a procumbent plant with erect or ascending branchlets which are covered with slightly bluish-green foliage tipped with white. This form is now growing in Durand-Eastman Park and covers an area more than six and a half feet in diameter. It is about sixteen inches high. It is entirely hardy but must have a well-drained soil to insure its success.

Juniperus procumbens, from Japan, is closely allied to *J. squamata* in general appearance. It is a low spreading shrub with ascending branchlets and short spiny bluish-green leaves. It seldom reaches a height of more than two feet and covers an area often more than four feet in diameter. It is quite hardy and is often used as a ground-cover.

The needle juniper, *Juniperus rigida*, is a native in Japan, Korea, and northern China. When planted in good well-drained soil it is a successful grower and a valuable ornamental tree. The habit is pyramidal with horizontal or slightly ascending branches and pendulous branchlets. Although it may be classed as a hardy species, it is best planted within the confines of other material where it will receive protection until it becomes established. Plants in the Rochester parks range from twelve to seventeen feet in height.

The savin juniper, *Juniperus Sabina*, which is native in many parts of the eastern northern hemisphere, has a low erect habit of growth, and will in time attain a height of six to eight feet. The usually imbricated leaves are dark green. Planted four to five feet apart, it forms an excellent border to larger evergreens in the background. It is also valuable for planting at the angles and corners of cement steps winding up steep slopes. It is not fastidious about soil conditions and does well in light sandy poor soils. Var. *tamariscifolia*, a geographical form from southern Europe, has a spreading or procumbent habit and is quite different from the type. It is an excellent prostrate juniper and has a most agreeable bright green color. The leaves commonly are needle-shaped. It is excellent on banks and slopes. Var. *fastigiata* is a columnar form. It is erect and narrow in habit with closely arranged branches and branchlets which are erect or ascending. The foliage is dark green and generally scale-like. It does not attain a great height; plants in the pinetum at Durand-Eastman Park are seven feet tall. It is an excellent small tree for corner plantings and semi-formal gardening.

The western red-cedar, *Juniperus scopulorum*, native to that section of the Rocky Mountains where the climate is dry, is hardy in this area. Were it not for the fact that its fruit requires two seasons to mature, whereas *J. virginiana* requires only one, it would undoubtedly be classed as a geographical variety of that species. It is pyramidal in habit with slender ascending branches and gracefully drooping branchlets. The leaves are fine, scale-like, and grayish-green, although specimens have been found with entirely green foliage. It is a graceful tree and an object of great beauty when planted among other conifers in the landscape.

Juniperus squamata, from western China and the Himalayas, is a low form with prostrate stems and scale-like linear much-crowded leaves, grayish-green, with two white bands above. This juniper is likely to suffer in a very cold winter, unless it is buried in snow. It is often used for borders or planted in mass to cover slopes. Fortunately, the varieties of this species enjoy greater hardiness in this area. Var. *Fargesii* is an upright form with ascending and somewhat spreading branches. The foliage is pale green. Although described as a tree where it is native in western China, it is doubtful whether it will ever assume more than a bushy proportion in this section of the country. Its slightly irregular form of growth makes it a valuable plant for foundation work and border planting. Specimens measure about three feet in height at the present time. Var. *Wilsonii*, also from western China, is a bushy columnar form with almost erect branches and branchlets which are reflected at the apex. The foliage is dark bluish-green. Plants at Durand-Eastman Park are now five feet high after sixteen years. It is hardy and presents an excellent appearance when used in group or border plantings. Var. *Meyeri* is known as one of the aristocrats of the conifers, its beauty being such that it was grown by the trade almost immediately after its introduction into this country. It is an irregularly branched shrub about three feet tall. The leaves are glaucous on the under side and bluish-green above, combining to give the foliage a steel-blue color. It offers a picturesque appearance when planted in groups and also makes an excellent specimen plant where there is not sufficient room for a larger tree.

The red-cedar, *Juniperus virginiana*, is native from Nova Scotia to Georgia and eastern Texas and is widely distributed between these points. It often grows naturally in sandy gravelly hillsides and is excellent for planting in poor open soils. The red-cedar is variable in its habit, as it often forms a narrow pyramidal tree with the branches erect, or the branches are horizontal and the ends ascending, the general outline being conical. It is extremely hardy and suitable for planting in cold exposures. The red-cedar is said to attain a height of one hundred feet in some native conditions, but it does not exceed forty to fifty feet in cultivation.

There are numerous varieties of the red-cedar and many are excellent decorative garden plants. Var. *glauca* is perhaps one of the most popular forms in gardens. The habit is somewhat loosely pyramidal and the foliage has a delicate bluish cast. Var. *tripartita* is a spreading bushy form with an irregular head which in thirty years does not exceed eight feet in height. It looks very different from the typical red-cedar. Var. *Schottii* forms a low dense pyramid with foliage of a light olive-green color. Var. *Canaertii* is of low compact pyramidal habit, with foliage of a dark grass-green color, and is quite distinct from all other varieties in this respect. It has very distinct bluish berries. Var. *venusta* forms a narrow pyramidal column and in twenty years attains a height of twenty-five feet. It has light green scale-like foliage. This is a rare plant in cultivation, and on account of its distinct habit is very desirable for garden decoration. Var. *Burkii* is a narrow fastigiate form with bluish-green coarse scale-like and acicular foliage which is arranged in dense fashion on the branchlets. Var. *elegantissima* is a loose openly branched form of pyramidal habit. The leaves are of both types and are golden-yellow at the tips. This is without doubt the best variegated form of the species. Two pyramidal types growing in Highland Park appear to be lost to cultivation although they were at one time carried by the trade. Var. *pyramidalis glauca* is narrow pyramidal in habit with erect branches and bluish-green mostly scale-like foliage. Var. *pyramidalis viridis* differs from the preceding only in the color of its foliage which is lustrous dark green. The great value of these forms lies in their apparent hardiness under open exposure to sun and wind. Var. *pendula* is the most graceful variety for the garden. The habit is somewhat spreading and the branchlets pendulous. There is an excellent specimen in the Arnold Arboretum. Var. *Kosteri* forms a wide-spreading bush and bears a strong resemblance to the variety of the Chinese juniper known as *Pfitzeriana*, the general branching habit of both forms being much alike; in time this variety will probably not exceed five feet in height, and with its graceful spreading branches it is a most important decorative plant for gardens. Var. *globosa*, a dwarf form, is well adapted for use in the rockery or in foundation planting. It is a dense shrub-like bush with many irregular branches and dark green scale-like leaves. It seldom attains a height of more than four feet.

Conifers in the Middle Country

In the region from Indiana to Kansas and northward the choice of dependable conifers (unless near the Great Lakes) is reduced because of climatic limitations. Yet there are enough reliable conifers for this great expanse to meet all essential needs. These kinds are largely in the genera Pinus, Picea, Pseudotsuga, Juniperus, Thuja, although other groups yield adaptable species for particular places and uses.

The utilization of native conifers should be stressed in severe climates and newly settled regions. Thus N. E. Hansen writes for South Dakota (Bulletin 254): "With proper care as to methods and varieties, South Dakota planters can grow evergreens with success upon our most exposed prairies. Some of our hardiest and best native American evergreens have been greatly neglected for European varieties less desirable for prairie conditions. . . . Much depends on the original source of the seed. Attempting to acclimate a mild-climate evergreen to northwestern prairies is useless, as acclimating is a work that nature takes thousands of years to complete. It is best to take advantage of nature's work by selecting varieties already adapted to prairie conditions."

Reliable conifers for general and trying conditions of the Middle West are white fir (*Abies concolor*), Douglas fir, Mugo pine, red-cedar, Rocky Mountain cedar (*Juniperus scopulorum*), with Japanese yews for smaller effects.

The remaining discussion of conifers for the Middle West is the reprinted article contributed to The Cultivated Evergreens by the late E. Bollinger together with suggestions by A. H. Hill of Dundee, Illinois.

Taxus.

The yews afford useful ornamental subjects. Various forms of the English yew, *Taxus baccata*, may be grown. *T. baccata* var. *repandens* is a low spreading form with luxuriant dark green foliage not unlike *T. cuspidata*, but of lower growth and more spreading. For planting in front of other evergreens it is one of the most desirable. It stands the winter well when planted in a sandy loam with perfect drainage. It is well to shade the plant somewhat when exposed to full sun in late winter as it is somewhat subject to sunburn, and, therefore, does best on a northern exposure. Var. *aurea* is a golden form. Var. *fastigiata* and *fastigiata aurea* can be grown in the Northwest with protection and planted in a protected spot among other evergreens. All varieties of English yew are propagated from cuttings or by grafting.

Western yew, *Taxus brevifolia*, is of dwarf compact growth. It is the darkest of all evergreen trees and is of irregular and picturesque outline, about five to six feet high and with a spread of four to five feet. It is very popular on account of its extreme hardiness and beautiful dark green color. It requires a rich clay loam and perfect drainage and is propagated from cuttings and by grafting on *T. canadensis*.

Canada yew, *Taxus canadensis*, is a valuable dwarf evergreen seldom more than three feet high, with dense dark green foliage. It is particularly attractive in autumn when loaded with its scarlet fruits. It thrives best in shady situations and well-drained silt loam and is hardy in the Northwest and Canada. This yew is useful for nature planting as well as for hedges and formal gardens. It can be pruned to any desired shape. The foliage assumes a reddish tint in winter. It is propagated from cuttings in lath frames with gentle bottom heat or in hothouses.

Japanese yew, *Taxus cuspidata*, grows forty to fifty feet high in Japan, but under cultivation does not attain this height. It is one of the hardiest yews and withstands extreme heat and cold in America. It is of close upright compact habit. This beautiful yew is valuable on account of its dark luxurious foliage and irregular form of growth. The tree grows in any rich garden soil with perfect drainage. It is propagated from cuttings and grafting on *T. canadensis*.

Pines.

Pines are very easy to cultivate. So various are the soils and situations in which the different species are found in their native countries that there is scarcely a spot for which one or another kind is not suitable. Some species grow on the bleakest hills and flourish in shallow sands near the Great Lakes and the seashores.

The gray pine, *Pinus Banksiana*, is native farther northward than any other American pine. It has no commercial value and is planted only on account of its peculiar stunted growth.

The Swiss stone pine, *Pinus Cembra*, has been a favorite for ornamental planting. Its leaves are dark green and the tree of very compact pyramidal form. The branches are short and when the tree is older it becomes often very picturesque, having an open round-topped head. It is somewhat difficult to raise from seed as they are slow to germinate and the seedlings are likely to damp off unless closely watched on hot sultry days.

Japanese red pine, *Pinus densiflora*, is perfectly hardy, of compact habit, but exceedingly slow in growth. Its density of foliage and drooping habit make it a valuable ornamental tree for formal effect. The foliage is a bright green. The var. *globosa* forms a perfectly flat top. It is quite hardy and valuable for ornamental planting, and is a promising asset to the newly introduced conifers.

The limber pine, *Pinus flexilis*, resembles somewhat the white pine, but is of more compact habit and the foliage is a darker green. It is perfectly hardy in the Northwest and grows in any kind of soil, but prefers a sandy loam. The branches are flexible and the tree of bushy habit. It is employed in ornamental planting for barren bluffs and ravines where natural effects are desired.

The dwarf *Pinus Mugo* is one of the best of the pine family for low and compact growth. In form it varies from a prostrate shrub to a pyramidal tree twenty-five to forty feet in height. This pine is perfectly hardy in any part of the United States and Canada and grows in any kind of soil except in low muck and undrained marsh-land; it will do well even in sandy gravelly soil.

Austrian pine, *Pinus nigra*, is grown for its wood and for

ornamental purposes. Its form is a regular symmetrical pyramid, and when older its flat top becomes picturesque. It is valuable for bold natural effects and windbreaks. Given ample space it will maintain its lower branches and become a source of beauty for thirty to forty years. Its dark green foliage and stiff branches will withstand wind and heavy snow.

For dry windy and exposed places, *Pinus ponderosa*, or bull pine, is well adapted. It thrives in pure clay, and also does remarkably well in sandy soils. Its broad coarse twisted flexible leaves of deep grayish-green, set firmly in a strong sheath, stand stormy sweeping winds well. The tree may be used for screens, windbreaks, or as a background for other trees.

Table mountain pine, *Pinus pungens*, is a most interesting irregular tree and when young resembles *P. Mugo* in habit but not in color. Its foliage is of a pale yellowish-green. This tree will grow thirty to forty feet high. The branches are spreading, forming a broad often flat-topped head. It is hardy in the Northwest and Canada. The tree grows in moist soil but prefers a gravelly subsoil.

The red or Norway pine, *Pinus resinosa*, grows in almost any kind of land, except a heavy clay, but thrives best in a sandy soil. It is perfectly hardy, even in northern Canada, and is often planted in places where no other pine will grow. Its luxuriant dark green foliage and uniform size add to the landscape.

Pitch pine, *Pinus rigida*, is an open irregular pyramidal tree to about seventy-five to eighty feet high. It is planted on rocky slopes on account of its picturesque habit when older. Plants are easily raised from seeds.

Common white pine, *Pinus Strobus*, grows in very different situations and soil, except in pure sand or submerged, but thrives best in a sandy loam. It is extensively planted for forest purposes, not only in America but in Europe, on account of its fast growth and the commercial value of its wood, and is also widely used for ornamental planting on large estates for natural or for woodland effects. It is very pleasing as a background for other pines and conifers on account of its rapid stately growth. White pines transplant easily and require less care after transplanting than any other pines.

In America the Scots pine, *Pinus sylvestris*, is cultivated largely for windbreaks and when quick growth is desired. It grows in most kinds of soil, from a heavy clay to a pure sand. This species bears transplanting better than other pines.

Firs.

A few firs are generally recommendable for the Middle Country. *Abies balsamea*, balsam fir, rarely exceeds fifty feet in height. As an ornamental it has no special permanent value, as it retains its beauty only for the first fifteen years; during this period, when in health and vigor, it is extremely beautiful, both in color and form. Balsam fir should be employed in ornamental planting rather as a filler and not as a permanent tree for later years, as it loses its lower branches, has a sickly appearance, and should then be removed. The balsam fir is easily propagated from seed, which germinates freely.

White fir, *Abies concolor*, is grown extensively for ornamental purposes. It is perfectly hardy in all parts of the United States. It grows in any kind of soil, but thrives best in a well-drained clay or loam with a gravelly subsoil; it will not do well in low or water-soaked undrained ground. The color of the foliage varies from a soft sea-green to a deep blue. Its stately, erect, and spreading branches give this tree a strikingly noble character. The white fir withstands heat and drought well in the Middle West. It grows from one hundred fifty to two hundred fifty feet high and its trunk from three to six feet in diameter. The seeds taken from the Colorado type are more likely to germinate than those grown at the Pacific Coast.

Nordmann fir, with its dark green foliage, silvery-white below, does well when planted with other evergreens in groups, when it is partially if not wholly shaded and protected from the winter sun. Most firs are subject to sun-scorch, but especially

Abies Nordmanniana and *A. Veitchii*. Both are perfectly hardy and should be planted on a northern exposure, in medium clay loam. They will do well on undrained land or in a gravelly hard-pan soil.

Douglas fir.

Douglas fir, *Pseudotsuga Douglasii* (often called *P. taxifolia*), is valuable for landscape planting on account of its easy propagation from seeds, easy transplanting and fast growth, hardiness and adaptation to any soil except low undrained swampy land. The tree is of tall symmetrical habit. The foliage varies in color from a dark green to a light bluish-silvery hue. It withstands the wind remarkably well and can stand considerable shade, maintaining its branches to the ground when given ample room, and making excellent lawn specimens.

Spruces.

The spruces are natives of the cold climates and should not be planted extensively in the South. In northern Illinois and southern Wisconsin the white, black, blue, and green Colorado spruces are very often badly damaged by the red-spider. When a good force of water is convenient, they are easily eradicated; if not, the trees will gradually die. Like the pines, spruces are easily propagated from seeds sown in the spring.

The Norway spruce, *Picea Abies* (better known as *P. excelsa*), is probably the best known and most extensively cultivated spruce in the United States and Europe. It has a straight trunk from one hundred to one hundred and fifty feet in height and from five to six feet in diameter. None is better adapted for planting in narrow strips for shelter or seclusion, because of its rapid growth; it makes excellent hedges for shelter in nursery-gardens, windbreaks for fruit-gardens and farm buildings. In the great prairie country of America this beautiful and useful tree should be planted for protection. It grows in any kind of soil except gravelly and sour or water-soaked undrained ground.

It maintains its branches well to the ground if given ample room to grow, and is, therefore, valuable for single specimens on lawns as well as for a background to other evergreens. The foliage is dark green and when older the branches are drooping, melancholy yet graceful, and beautiful for the open stretch of landscape as well as for woodland effects.

Some of the variegated forms of Norway spruce are interesting when young. The young growth of var. *argenteo-spica* is whitish, gradually turning a pale green. Var. *aurea* has leaves of a golden-yellow on the exposed side and the remainder dark green, giving the tree a peculiar aspect. Both varieties are beautiful when the sun plays on the branches, which on young trees are erect, but when older become pendulous. Trees do not grow quite so fast as the Norway spruce, but are just as hardy, and grow well in any kind of soil, even in a heavy clay. They do especially well in partially shaded places and in the open lawn; on account of the dense growth are well adapted for single specimens. These forms should be grafted on the Norway spruce when dormant, as they do not come true from seed like most variegated conifers.

Engelmann spruce, *Picea Engelmanni*, somewhat resembles the white spruce, only it is more beautiful in color and texture of foliage, a silvery-bluish hue. The habit of the tree resembles *P. pungens*. It is just as valuable for ornamental planting, but should be placed on northern exposures. It is unable to stand the hot dry winds in the open prairies, but is perfectly hardy in the other northern and western states. The tree grows well in a clay loam, but not in a gravelly or sandy soil.

The white spruce, *Picea glauca* (often known as *P. canadensis*), is perfectly hardy in the extreme North. It grows in any kind of soil and can stand low situations better than any other spruce. Its height is about fifty to sixty feet. The trees are planted very extensively for ornamental purposes on account of the pleasing whitish-green color. The Black Hills spruce, var. *densata*, is particularly good.

Black spruce, *Picea mariana* (formerly called *P. nigra*), grows in nearly the same situations as the white spruce. Its habit is a regular pyramid, its foliage bluish-green, and the bark lighter colored. The wood is inferior in quality and snaps frequently in burning. It is a beautiful tree while young and is valuable for parks and gardens on account of its close compact growth, color of foliage, and the retaining of its branches close to the ground even when old.

Another interesting spruce is *Picea orientalis*, native of Asia. It does well only in partially shaded situations and it does not grow rapidly. It holds its branches well to the ground and thrives best in a rich black loam. This species is subject to winter sunburn, and should be planted on northern exposures or where it is partially shaded during the winter months by other trees.

Colorado spruce, *Picea pungens*, grows in all soils, seems perfectly hardy in most northern climates and is easily raised from seeds. It is a strong symmetrical upright tree. The color of foliage varies from light silvery to dull green, and from a dark blue to light purple. Color and form make it a valuable tree for the landscape-gardener. It is of very slow growth until about a foot high, then it seems to shoot up very fast, keeping its lower branches well to the ground. This spruce is not so easily transplanted as some other piceas. It should be root-pruned or transplanted at intervals. It develops fibrous roots. Transplanting on cloudy days and a liberal overhead watering for several consecutive days will benefit the plants. Red-spider is a common enemy of this beautiful spruce; a good force of water applied once or twice a week in the growing season usually controls this pest. Prominent forms of the Colorado spruce are var. *argentea* (sometimes called Koster's) and var. *glauca*, both with bluish-white foliage.

Hemlock.

The hemlock spruce, *Tsuga canadensis*, likes moist ground and will grow to a height of seventy-five to eighty feet, with a circumference of six to nine feet, and uniform for two-thirds of its length. When young and planted in a favorable soil, the hemlock is very ornamental, owing to the symmetrical arrangement of its branches and to its tufted foliage. At this age it is used for hedges, owing to its density of growth and ease of shearing. It is very valuable for single specimens and if pruned occasionally will maintain its branches well to the ground. If planted with erect-growing conifers the hemlock will relieve their stiff effect with its graceful drooping branches. It will adapt itself well in shady places for undergrowth for other trees and will grow in such situations better than any other evergreen. For planting on northern exposures of bluffs and ravines, the hemlock is most valuable.

Chamæcyparis.

Several forms of Chamæcyparis are among the important conifers for home grounds and parks. These plants are frequently known as *Retinospora* (or *Retinispora*), a name once applied to certain juvenile forms of Chamæcyparis and Thuja. *Chamæcyparis pisifera* is an open grower of upright form, the branches somewhat pendulous toward the end. The foliage is light green, glaucous beneath, very graceful and feathery. Var. *filifera* is a medium-sized pyramidal tree of unusually graceful outlines, the ends of the branches drooping in long filaments. This variety seems to be perfectly hardy in the most extreme exposures, either to heat or cold. It does best when planted in a damp but well-drained clay loam. Var. *plumosa* and its variants are not hardy in the extreme North, but in the Middle West they are planted extensively on account of the beautiful soft foliage and pleasing form. These are perfectly hardy without protection even in the northern parts of America. Both varieties are propagated from cuttings and grafting. They require a silt loam soil with perfect drainage.

The plant called *Retinispora plumosa argentea* is a form of *Chamæcyparis pisifera;* it has light green foliage and white-tipped branches. *Plumosa aurea* is a golden form. Both varieties require some protection in winter, especially from the sun. *Squarrosa* (*C. pisifera* var. *squarrosa*) is a densely branched bushy tree with spreading feathery branchlets. It is not a strong grower and should be planted in front of taller trees. All the retinisporas are propagated from cuttings or grafted. They require care when young, gentle bottom heat for the cuttings in lath frames as well as in the greenhouse, and copious watering overhead.

Another species is *Chamæcyparis obtusa*, a bushy grower of solid or compact form. It is one of the strongest growers of its class. The foliage is firm, of a clear green color and graceful drooping habit. Var. *nana*, with very dense short foliage of an extremely dark green, is well adapted for rock-garden planting.

Arbor-vitæ.

American arbor-vitæ, *Thuja occidentalis*, is one of the hardiest and best evergreens for shelter-belts and timber planting. The American arbor-vitæ is the original from which many types have been developed. When planted with ample space, it maintains its branches from the bottom up. It is, therefore, very attractive for lawns and windbreaks. This tree is very hardy and dependable in almost any situation, but moist location is preferred. The foliage is soft and flexible and of fine deep green color. The tree is easily grown from seeds sown in early spring in lath frames or brush-shades. Var. *Douglasii aurea* is a type with deep yellow foliage, of medium height, forming a broad bushy specimen. In planting it is grouped with other evergreens and adds contrast with its unusual bright golden color, being especially attractive when planted with the darker shades of green as a background. It grows on any ordinary good land, but does especially well in a damp cool clay loam. It does not always come true from seed and is usually propagated from cuttings taken in early fall, with gentle bottom heat in frames or greenhouse. The cuttings should be kept cool until callousing takes place, when heat both in bottom and top can gradually be increased. Cuttings should be shaded from the direct sun, watered freely overhead, and given plenty of air. Var. *Douglasii pyramidalis* has feathery lace-like crested foliage of a dark green color. The habit is pyramidal. It is of slow growth, to about eighteen to twenty feet high, and is perfectly hardy and grows well in moist clay loam.

Many other *Thuja occidentalis* forms are desirable. Var. *lutea*, Peabody Golden arbor-vitæ, is a distinct bright golden type. It is of rather slender growth, twelve to fifteen feet high. It grows best in clay loam. On account of its brilliant golden hue, it is useful where color effect is desired. Var. *alba* has silvery white-tipped foliage, forming a pleasing contrast to the otherwise dark green leaves. It varies in habit from a low compact growth to a loose feathery pyramidal bush, and is hardy and easily propagated from cuttings or by grafting. Var. *robusta*, Siberian arbor-vitæ, is a very beautiful dark green conical type. Its habit is distinct and its branches short and stiff. The foliage is a dark sea-green. It is of rugged constitution and perfectly hardy, but of slow growth. It is propagated from cuttings. Var. *Woodwardii* is one of the best globe-shaped arbor-vitæs. It maintains its shape without artificial means. The color of foliage is a pleasing sea-green. It grows about three feet high and is as hardy as the species. Var. *Hoveyi* is a very pretty dwarf compact form, with yellowish-green foliage. The habit is globose. It is hardy in southern Wisconsin, Minnesota, and other western states and is useful for low planting in front of other taller-growing plants. It is propagated from cuttings. The soil requirement is a moist well-drained silt loam, but it also does well in moist black mucky soil. This plant is subject to winter sun-scorch and should be planted where the rays of the sun will not fully reach it in the middle of the day. Var. *Smithiana* is a beautiful low-growing compact form. The very dark green soft foliage, gradually changing to almost purple in the fall, gives this plant a special merit where low growth in formal and rock-gardens is required, also for grouping in front of taller varieties. It will maintain its low-growing tendencies, but will spread, unlike any other arbor-vitæ. It grows best in a well-drained clay loam and is easily propagated from cuttings, the wood being rather soft. It is perfectly hardy and does well in partial shade as well as in the full sun. It is not subject to sunburn in late winter, and is easily transplanted. Var. Tom Thumb is the smallest of its class known, being a tufted little plant of very low compact growth, rarely exceeding nine inches. It is valuable for rock and Japanese gardens and edgings of walks. The plant is propagated from cuttings; it is perfectly hardy in the Northwest.

Junipers.

Some of the junipers are outstanding subjects for planting in the Middle Country, and the use of them is increasing as the various kinds become better known. They supply the need for low evergreens in home grounds, for border planting, banks and rock-gardens, and may now be obtained in quantity.

Forms of the Chinese juniper supply many needs. *Juniperus chinensis* var. *variegata* is a white-tipped form of columnar growth, reaching a height of twenty feet or more. The foliage is a dark bluish-green with white tips at the end of twigs and branches. It requires a damp but well-drained soil and is useful for planting in formal gardens and lawns. Var. *aureo-globosa* forms a perfectly round globe, is very dense in growth, with light green foliage having a yellowish hue. It is valuable where low planting is desired in rock-gardens, Japanese and flower-gardens. It requires a rich sandy loam, is propagated from cuttings and grafting on allied stock and is hardy if planted on well-drained soil. Var. *japonica* is a very dwarf form seldom growing over twelve inches high. It is a rapid grower, producing long branches that cling to the ground. It is useful for terraces, hillsides, and edging of rock-gardens and is perfectly hardy. Propagation is by cuttings and layers. Var. *Pfitzeriana* forms a low broad pyramid. The branches grow horizontally from the stem, forming a flat spreading top. It is not a rapid grower, attaining a height of six to ten feet, and is perfectly hardy. This variety is valued for its graceful plumosa-like foliage and good lively color. Propagation is by cuttings and grafting. Var. *columnaris* is attractive and useful, as also var. *Sargentii*.

The low native juniper, *Juniperus communis* var. *depressa*, has many upright branches and seldom exceeds five feet in height. It thrives best in a sandy or gravelly soil and is extremely hardy and a rapid vigorous grower. The foliage is grayish-green, light silvery-green beneath. It is propagated from seeds and cuttings. Landscape planters make use of it to cover unsightly spots and as an edging to taller trees. Fruit of this variety matures the third year when it is used for medicinal purposes and manufacturing of spirits. Var. *aurea* is a golden form. It is hardy, and useful for color effect with other junipers. Some of the stock listed as *J. communis* is really *Juniperus horizontalis*.

Another well-known race of *J. communis* is the Irish juniper, var. *hibernica*, a compact pyramidal or columnar form. It does best in damp but perfectly drained soil and is hardy in the Middle West. It requires copious and frequent watering during the summer months. It is valuable for formal planting in gardens and lawns. Propagation is by cuttings or grafting. Swedish juniper, var. *suecica*, is similar to var. *hibernica*, but grows higher and is of a lighter and more bluish color and the branches do not grow quite as stiff and compact. In general the form is pleasing and useful when formal effects are desired. It is propagated from seeds, cuttings, and grafting.

The trailing or creeping *Juniperus horizontalis* is adaptable for ground-cover and edging garden walks. It is propagated from cuttings and layers. The Waukegan juniper, var. *Douglasii*, is an interesting prostrate form. It seems to love the sand and gravelly soil, yet it will do equally well in rich garden soil or on rocky slopes, banks and terraces. The color of the foliage is a soft blue in spring, changing to a rich purple color in the fall. This form is very useful for wall-covering, rock-gardens, and edging of walks. It is a rapid grower and easily propagated from layers taken in early October and planted in lath frames in a sharp sand. The plant thrives on sunny slopes and does equally well in partially shady situations. Var. *plumosa*, Andorra juniper, is attractive in habit and in its rich bronzy winter color.

The Eurasian *Juniperus Sabina* is very hardy, of erect habit, with numerous spreading branches. It is useful for a foundation for other trees. The plant does best in a dry gravelly sunny situation. Propagation is from layers and cuttings. Var. *tamaris-cifolia* is an excellent dwarf creeping variety, suitable for rock-gardens, edging, and ground-cover. It is hardy in the Northwest and is one of the best of the low type of junipers. The native American juniper formerly known as *J. Sabina* var. *prostrata* and also as var. *procumbens* is *J. horizontalis*.

The Rocky Mountain or Colorado juniper, *Juniperus scopulorum*, is very hardy and rugged and is available in interesting forms. It makes a narrow compact and symmetrical subject with a single stem. It is valuable for landscape effect because of its good erect habit and beautiful silvery foliage. Propagation is by means of cuttings or by grafting on allied stock.

Of late years the red-cedar, *Juniperus virginiana*, has been extensively employed for ornamental planting, especially in the Northwest and Canada. Its extreme hardiness and stately upright compact habit make it very useful for windbreaks, especially for exposed windy positions. It grows well in any soil except in a sour alkali, but does best on a gravelly or sandy subsoil. The color of foliage varies from a dark green to a steel-blue. Junipers vary in habit from a tall pyramidal tree to a low prostrate or trailing shrub. *J. virginiana* and its allies are mostly propagated from seeds, cuttings, and layers. The seed is hard to sprout and requires two to three years for germination. When propagated from cuttings, a gentle bottom heat is required. It is best done under glass, taking the cutting from nearly ripened wood in the early fall. Stool cuttings are preferable for those varieties with scale-like leaves. These are also increased by side grafting in the winter on previously potted plants of allied species. Copious watering overhead is essential until the graft is set. The plants propagated by layers in early fall require gentle bottom heat.

Several varieties are deserving. *Juniperus virginiana* var. *glauca* is a distinct blue type of pyramidal habit. The young growth is almost silvery-white, changing to a beautiful bluish-green in winter. For landscape effect it is excellent. It is perfectly hardy, of compact growth, and thrives in a rich clay loam. Propagation is by grafting on *J. virginiana*. Var. *Schottii* is planted for its pyramidal compact growth and extreme hardiness. It is propagated from cuttings. Var. *Canaertii* is a pyramidal compact form attaining a height of fifteen to eighteen feet. The foliage is dark green. The plant is useful for planting in formal and natural gardens and its silver-colored fruit is attractive. It does well in any ordinary garden soil and is propagated from cuttings and grafting. The Hill and Dundee junipers, var. *pyramidiformis* and *pyramidiformis Hillii* are good pyramidal and columnar forms.

Evergreen conifers in Canada.—*Macoun*

Vast areas in Canada were at one time covered with an evergreen coniferous forest, and over other very large tracts there was a mixture of evergreen and deciduous trees in which conifers were still a very important part of the forest. In addition, in the more southerly parts of the province of Ontario, the hardwoods were the prevailing trees, with a comparatively small proportion of evergreens. While the lumberman's axe and the forest fires have destroyed thousands of square miles of fine evergreens, yet there are still great coniferous forests in Canada, fine woodlands of mixed timber, as well as those other districts in which there are just enough evergreens to make a pleasing variety in the landscape. Canada is looked on by many as the land of the pine and the hemlock, whereas, in reality, it possesses many kinds of trees. The evergreen is, however, a great asset because of its value for lumber and pulpwood, but it means much to the average citizen apart from this. As a shelter from the winds of winter, a windbreak of evergreens is most desirable and is particularly appreciated in parts of Canada where high winds are frequent, and especially on the prairies, where the cold is so intense. A windbreak of conifers is a veritable haven of shelter for the farmer and for his flocks and herds. Not only do evergreens afford this shelter from the wind, but their very greenness in winter makes the landscape much more cheery during the months of frost and snow. When used as specimens or in groups on the lawn, conifers are very effective in beautifying the landscape. As hedges, evergreen conifers are among the best trees and should be much more widely used for this purpose.

The yews.

Owing to the many persons of British origin living in Canada who have a certain reverence for the yew, of which there are such old specimens in Great Britain, there is considerable interest in the yew in the Dominion. In the coast regions of British Columbia, where *Taxus brevifolia* becomes a fair-sized tree, one's affection for the yew is readily satisfied, but in eastern Canada the wild species, *T. canadensis,* is so unlike the British yew that it is scarcely taken into consideration. The Japanese yew, *T. cuspidata,* has filled the want there.

While the common yew, *Taxus baccata,* succeeds well near the west coast of British Columbia, it is not satisfactory in eastern Canada, although it will sometimes grow well for a time. No doubt, if plants were obtained from the coldest part of its range in Europe, the yew would succeed better than it usually does. A specimen of var. *variegata,* after thirty-three years' growth, is still in good condition at Ottawa and is now about eight feet high.

The western yew, *Taxus brevifolia,* reaches a height of twenty to twenty-five feet or more along the west coast of British Columbia where it is native. It is not grown much under cultivation there, although it is a fairly ornamental tree. It is not hardy in eastern Canada above the snow-line.

Canada yew, *Taxus canadensis*, is a native of Canada from the extreme east to the province of Manitoba. It has been under cultivation at Ottawa for forty years and has reached a height of about five feet, but is so open in habit that it is not particularly ornamental.

The Japanese yew, *Taxus cuspidata*, has been under test at Ottawa for thirty-six years and has proved quite hardy. The best specimen, planted in 1896, is now about twelve feet in height. The foliage is a rich deep green in color, and, as the tree or bush is of a compact habit, it is ornamental and makes a good substitute for *T. baccata*. The var. *nana* or *compacta* is also hardy, but specimens planted in 1896 are but four feet high, though compact in habit.

The pines.

The pine is closely associated with the name of Canada. It is one of the most important timber trees, and many million feet of Canadian pine lumber have been sent to other lands. In this connection, however, the pines are given in order of their usefulness as ornamental trees in Canada, the native species being dealt with first.

While there are nine native species, the white pine, *Pinus Strobus*, is the most important commercially and also the best for ornamental purposes. It is wild in the provinces of Manitoba, Ontario, Quebec, Nova Scotia, New Brunswick, and Prince Edward Island, and has done well when introduced in British Columbia, but is not hardy on the prairies. It is the most attractive pine grown in Canada, the graceful outline of the tree, the soft leaves and their lively color helping to make it a very ornamental species. This pine has made an excellent hedge plant at Ottawa, a hedge planted forty years ago still being in excellent condition.

The western white pine, *Pinus monticola*, makes a fine large tree. It is a native of southern British Columbia and grows there at an elevation of about 6,000 feet. While not so graceful as the white pine, being a closer or more upright grower, it makes a good ornamental, and is succeeding very well at Ottawa, Ontario.

The red pine, *Pinus resinosa*, is found in the same provinces of Canada as the white, but is not nearly so common. As an ornamental tree it has proved somewhat disappointing in places, because of its tendency to become rather ragged in appearance after the first fifteen or twenty years. Its foliage, also, is somewhat dull in color. It is not as attractive as the Austrian pine, which it resembles somewhat, although it is hardier than that species.

Western yellow pine, *Pinus ponderosa*, is a native of the drier districts of British Columbia, and is a magnificent tree when growing either under forest conditions or as single specimens in that province. It does well when planted in Ontario and makes a fine ornamental and lawn tree, its massive appearance giving it a distinct character. The bark of the trunk is also striking. It bears some resemblance in a general way to the Austrian pine, but can be readily distinguished by its having leaves in clusters of three. When obtained from the coldest part of its range, this tree proves hardy in places on the prairies.

The lodge-pole pine, *Pinus contorta* var. *latifolia* (*P. Murrayana*), is a very useful ornamental species for the prairie provinces because of its hardiness. It resembles the Banksian pine very closely, but is more ornamental, the tree having the appearance of being better clothed with foliage. The cones are also persistent as in that species. It is a native of the foothills and mountains from Alberta in the east, to the west coast, and varies much in different parts of its range. It does well when planted in eastern Canada, where, however, it is little used because of more ornamental species hardy there.

Banksian pine, *Pinus Banksiana*, commonly called the jack pine, is wild on poor light soils in Canada from the Atlantic west to the Rocky Mountains. It has little value as an ornamental tree, as it has the appearance of lacking foliage, but is useful to the prairies as being one of the few species that can be grown there.

Pitch pine, *Pinus rigida*, is a native of eastern Canada, although not a common tree there, and is one of the few three-leaved pines in this country. It is not of particular value as an ornamental, not being very attractive in outline.

The limber pine, *Pinus flexilis*, is a small not very ornamental tree, native of the foothills and Rocky Mountains of southern Alberta and British Columbia. It helps to make a greater variety of evergreens on the prairies where it is hardy, but apart from this would seem to have little value for ornamental purposes.

Whitebark pine, *Pinus albicaulis*, is a native of the timber limits of Alberta and British Columbia, where it is a small scrubby tree. So far as known, it has not been tested on low elevations for ornamental purposes.

While not having as wide an adaptability as some species, the Austrian pine, *Pinus nigra*, is, perhaps, the most ornamental exotic pine which thrives in Canada. It can be grown successfully in the provinces of Ontario, Quebec, New Brunswick, Nova Scotia, Prince Edward Island, and in British Columbia. It is a handsome tree and makes a good lawn specimen, though not as graceful as the white pine.

Scots pine, *Pinus sylvestris*, is hardier than most exotic species and trees twenty-five to thirty years of age may be found on the Canadian prairies, and here it is proving more useful than in eastern Canada where the tree does not become so shapely as some other species. The Scots pine varies much in growth and shape, depending on the source of the seed from which the trees are grown.

Mountain pine, *Pinus Mugo*, makes a very attractive bushy tree and is always much admired. It succeeds well in eastern Canada and can be grown in some places on the prairies.

Swiss stone pine, *Pinus Cembra*, although one of the slowest

growing of all pines hardy in Canada, is one of the most ornamental. It is suggestive of a columnar-shaped white pine, being
very upright in growth, which makes it suitable for situations
in which a tree is desired that will not take up too much space.
It is very hardy and succeeds in all the provinces of Canada.

While the Korean pine, *Pinus koraiensis*, has been little
planted in Canada as yet, and is a rather slow grower, it is a
very promising species for ornamental purposes. At Ottawa, a
tree planted in 1896 is about thirty feet in height, and next to the
white pine is, perhaps, the most ornamental species in the
Arboretum. It is a five-leaved pine, heavier in appearance and
darker in foliage than the white pine, and is strongly recommended for trial in eastern Canada.

Few trees of *Pinus Peuce* are to be found in Canada. It is
proving hardy at Ottawa, and, planted in 1896, has made a
compact attractive tree about twenty-three feet in height. It is
a rather slow-growing five-leaved pine, rather upright in habit
and of bluish-green appearance, and, while not as ornamental
as *P. Strobus*, *P. Cembra*, or *P. koraiensis*, the best three five-
leaved pines for eastern Canada, it is a useful species.

Additional species doing well, at least when young, in the
coast region of southern British Columbia, including Vancouver
Island, where the winters are very mild, are: *Pinus Ayacahuite, P.
Coulteri,P.densiflora,P.Jeffreyi,P.Massoniana (P.tabulæformis?),
P. quadrifolia, P. radiata, P. Sabiniana, P. Torreyana*. No doubt
other species not yet thoroughly tested will be found hardy.

The firs.

The firs are not so valuable as the spruces for ornamental
purposes, for although attractive in eastern Canada when young,
they lose many branches and become ragged-looking later on.
In the coast regions of British Columbia, however, they succeed
particularly well and make fine ornamental specimens for
many years.

The balsam fir, *Abies balsamea*, is a rapid-growing tree which is attractive when young, with its deep green glossy foliage, and is useful for temporary effects in the landscape. When grown in the open, however, it becomes rather unsightly after being planted twenty to twenty-five years, and at Ottawa many specimens have died about this age.

While some specimens of alpine fir, *Abies lasiocarpa*, have killed back at Ottawa, most have proved hardy. Much depends on the source of the plants or seed from which they are grown. It has a denser habit of growth than *A. balsamea* and promises to remain well clothed with foliage for a longer period. It is wild in the Canadian Rocky and Selkirk mountains, and east of the mountains in the Peace River district.

Lowland fir, *Abies grandis*, is a native of the west coast of Canada and grows to be very large there. When given abundance of room it makes a fine ornamental tree. It does not succeed in eastern Canada.

White or amabilis fir, *Abies amabilis*, is native in the coast regions of British Columbia and is not hardy in eastern Canada. Its habit is more pendulous than that of most species.

White or silver fir, *Abies concolor*, is the best ornamental species in eastern Canada. Some forms are almost or quite as blue as the Colorado spruce and, because of its more graceful or less stiff outline, is more attractive than that spruce. It is one of the most beautiful evergreens hardy in eastern Canada.

Nordmann fir, *Abies Nordmanniana*, is a useful ornamental tree for the west coast. The dark green glossy leaves with the silvery-white of the under side give it a very striking appearance. Specimens from coldest districts are worth trying in eastern Canada.

Siberian fir, *Abies sibirica*, is hardy at Ottawa but looks best when young. The foliage is of a lighter green than that of most other firs. It is more useful for temporary than for more permanent planting.

Like the other firs, Veitch fir, *Abies Veitchii*, looks best when young. The foliage is attractive, being deep green above and silvery below, making a fine contrast. This is comparatively hardy at Ottawa, but loses some of its branches from winter-injury. It also is more suitable for the west coast.

Additional species succeeding in the coast region of southern British Columbia, including Vancouver Island, are: *Abies cephalonica* and var. *Apollonis, A. homolepis, A. cilica, A. nobilis, A. alba.*

The Douglas fir.

Douglas fir, *Pseudotsuga Douglasii,* is one of the most valuable Canadian trees. It reaches a great size in British Columbia, where it is native, and it grows also in Alberta in the Rocky Mountains. Its use as a timber tree is well known, but where it is native it is not prized as an ornamental, except that huge specimens are admired in the parks or native woodlands. In eastern Canada, however, where it has been planted for ornament, it has proved very desirable. After forty years it is better clothed with foliage and branches at Ottawa than almost any other conifer, and from this experience it is highly recommended. Trees are now over fifty feet in height. It is important when growing this tree in eastern Canada to obtain seed or plants from the colder or interior parts of its range. If obtained from the west coast, it will not do well. The color of the foliage varies considerably.

The spruces.

The spruce is a very important tree in Canada, as a large proportion of the great quantities of pulpwood cut in this country is spruce, and much lumber is manufactured from it. It is valuable for ornamental purposes also. There are five species in Canada, the white, black, and red in the east, and the Engelmann and Sitka spruces, and also the white, in western Canada. Of these, the most ornamental are the white and the Engelmann. The following species are given in order of their relative value as ornamental trees, beginning with the most useful.

White spruce, *Picea glauca,* is wild in every province in

Canada, and is particularly useful in the prairie provinces where so few evergreens are hardy. It is a rapid-growing tree of attractive form. The foliage of the bluest specimens almost rivals that of the bluest forms of the Colorado spruce and, if it were not for the serious insect pests which attack it in eastern Canada, it would be the best spruce to plant for ornamental purposes, but it is frequently rendered very unsightly by attacks of the spruce gall-louse and budworm.

Black spruce, *Picea mariana,* is a much slower grower than the white and is more upright. It is wild mainly in the swampy lands of eastern Canada and in the prairie provinces northward. Though not nearly as attractive as an ornamental tree as the white spruce, its characteristic form and persistent cones give variety and, being very hardy, it is also useful in the coldest parts of Canada. The var. *Doumetii* is a pyramidal sort of striking color.

Red spruce, *Picea rubens,* is seldom met with as an ornamental tree, as it is not nearly so attractive as the white spruce with which it grows in eastern Canada. The leaves have none of the bluish tinge which makes the white spruce so attractive and it resembles the Norway spruce in color, although not so graceful a tree as that species.

For nearly thirty years the Engelmann spruce, *Picea Engelmanni,* succeeded well at Ottawa and has now reached a height of about thirty feet, but the leaves and branches are dying from the base up and the trees are becoming very unsightly. This species is a native of the mountains and particularly the mountain valleys of Alberta and eastern British Columbia and, though enduring severe winters there, is evidently not suited to the climatic conditions of the low altitudes in eastern Canada. It is of a fine pyramidal form, and, when young, the trees are very attractive. As with the Colorado blue spruce and the native white spruce, the color varies from greenish- to steely-blue.

Sitka spruce, *Picea sitchensis,* is a fine tree, native to the western coast regions of Canada where it reaches a large size and is very valuable for timber. It makes a good ornamental subject also, the foliage being particularly attractive, but, in a part of Canada where so many ornamental evergreens succeed, it is not prized as much as a lawn tree as it otherwise would be. It is not hardy in eastern Canada.

The Norway spruce, *Picea Abies*, is the most generally planted for ornament and for windbreaks in eastern Canada. It is a very rapid grower and soon becomes an attractive object on the lawn or quickly makes protection from wind. It is useful for hedges also. While the stock usually supplied by nurseries is not hardy on the Canadian prairies, it does fairly well when seed is obtained from the coldest districts in which this spruce is native. At Ottawa, most trees of Norway spruce planted forty years ago are still fine specimens, well clothed with foliage, though some are now becoming ragged. In other places in the province of Ontario good trees considerably older than this may be found. There are many horticultural varieties of this spruce, most of those listed by nurserymen having been tested at Ottawa. The best of the larger growing forms is var. *pyramidata*, which makes a handsome pyramidal-shaped tree, closer in habit than the type. Some of the pendulous forms are attractive for a time, but are likely to become ragged. There are many dwarf or semi-dwarf varieties which are attractive. Among the best of these are *compacta*, *Remontii*, *Clanbrasiliana*, and *pygmæa*.

Next to the Norway, the Colorado spruce, *Picea pungens*, is the most planted in Canada of the species not native. It is hardy in all the provinces, succeeding very well on the prairies. The variety with steely-blue leaves, known as *glauca*, is the most popular, and this is, as a rule, the only tree thought of when this species is mentioned, unless it be the form known as *argentea*, which is of a particularly fine bluish color. This variety, which is usually grafted, needs to be watched when young and a leader trained, as it often takes a sprawling habit for a time unless this is done. While the Colorado spruce makes a handsome though rather rigid-looking specimen when young, in eastern Canada when it is twenty-five to thirty years old the foliage and branches die from the bottom up, and in a few years they become so unsightly that they have to be removed. However, they are well worth growing for the first twenty years or more, and some specimens at Ottawa over forty years old are still in fine condition.

While *Picea Omorika* is not well known in Canada as yet, it promises to be a very useful ornamental species, at least in the eastern provinces. It is hardy at Ottawa and makes a handsome though rather slow-growing tree. There is a pleasing contrast in the leaves, which are glossy and dark green on one side and with lines of white on the other.

Picea jezoensis, often sold under the name of *Abies Alcockiana*, while hardy so far as the terminal growth is concerned, usually has many dead branches in eastern Canada, which prevents it from being as attractive as it otherwise would be. There is a marked contrast between the deep green of the lower side of the leaf and the silvery-white of the upper. It should be more satisfactory on the west coast. The var. *hondoensis* has made a better specimen tree, being much more clothed with foliage than the species.

Picea Schrenkiana is an attractive looking spruce of pyramidal habit and quite hardy at Ottawa. The foliage, while rather dull in color, is distinct from other species. It is uncommon in Canada as yet, but is well worth having where one has room for a number of species.

Picea obovata is much like the many small-leaved and slow-growing varieties of Norway spruce and has been called a variety of it. The cones are, however, much smaller than those of the Norway spruce. It is hardy at Ottawa.

Some specimens of the small-foliaged *Picea orientalis* have proved hardier than others at Ottawa. In most cases it has killed back considerably and is not satisfactory on the whole.

The hemlocks.

The common hemlock, *Tsuga canadensis*, is one of the most beautiful North American trees. It is graceful in habit and its small foliage is of a distinct, characteristic, and pleasing shade of green. It grows to large size, but is a relatively slow grower, and for this reason makes a good lawn specimen for many years, as the branches usually are held to near the ground. One is fortunate in having large specimens of hemlock in a landscape where there are clumps of trees or woodland and it makes a very attractive feature. When used for hedge purposes, hemlock proves very satisfactory and makes one of the best low-growing evergreen hedges, as it is a slow grower and can be readily kept in shape. Moreover, it stands shade better than some other trees. Var. *gracilis* has smaller leaves than the type and is even slower growing. It is an ornamental variety. The common hemlock is not hardy on the prairies, but does well both in eastern Canada and in British Columbia.

Western hemlock, *Tsuga heterophylla*, makes a fine large tree in British Columbia, where it is native in the mountains and along the western coast. It is an important timber tree, the wood being better than *T. canadensis* in the East. While it has not been used much as an ornamental, it is attractive in appearance and very graceful in outline and should be planted more. It is not known under cultivation in eastern Canada. From most sources it would prove too tender, but if obtained from the coldest districts where it grows wild it might succeed. This was long listed as *T. Mertensiana* in Canadian lists of plants.

Black hemlock, *Tsuga Mertensiana*, is a native of the mountainous and western coast regions of British Columbia. It is a rather small tree as it grows in Canada, with bluish-green foliage, and is quite ornamental, but has been little cultivated as yet. This may be grown successfully in eastern Canada if specimens are obtained from the coldest part of its range.

The cedars.

The three well-known species of cedar succeed near the Pacific Coast in British Columbia, namely, *Cedrus atlantica, C. Deodara,* and *C. libanitica.* The Deodar cedar is, perhaps, the most popular. They are striking-looking trees and are used with good effect.

The sequoias.

The sequoias, or big trees of California, of which there are two species, *Sequoia sempervirens* and *S. gigantea,* grow well near the southwest coast of British Columbia, including the southern part of Vancouver Island. The California big tree, *S. gigantea,* succeeds, perhaps, better than the other species, and is making a fine evergreen tree there.

The cryptomeria.

These beautiful Asiatic trees do not succeed in eastern Canada, but do well near the Pacific Coast and especially on the southern part of Vancouver Island. There is only one species, *Cryptomeria japonica,* of which there are a number of horticultural varieties, the best being var. *elegans.* The attractive foliage and form of the cryptomerias make them very popular where they grow well.

Cunninghamia.

Cunninghamia lanceolata, which is closely related to the pines, has been under test on Vancouver Island for several years and is doing fairly well.

The cypresses.

The true cypress is too tender for Canada, but there are other trees known as cypress which are hardier. Few species succeed in eastern Canada, however, but on the lower mainland of British Columbia and on Vancouver Island they do well, the fine Lawson cypress being one of the most useful ornamental trees. The yellow cypress is the only species native to Canada.

Yellow cypress, *Chamæcyparis nootkatensis,* is a west coast species which is too tender in eastern Canada, although it and some of its varieties have grown for a time, but once above the snow-line they are killed back. Varieties with bluish foliage are attractive and when hardy are well worth growing.

There are many varieties of Lawson cypress, *Chamæcyparis Lawsoniana*, and most of them succeed well near the west coast of British Columbia where the winters are mild. In eastern Canada they are not hardy. Some of the best varieties are *Allumii*, *argentea*, *erecta glauca*, *erecta*, *glauca*, *gracilis*, and *pyramidalis*.

White-cedar, *Chamæcyparis thyoides*, is hardy in eastern Canada and is interesting as being a native of the eastern states. It is rather loose in habit with dull-colored foliage, and, on the whole, is not very ornamental, though interesting.

Hinoki cypress, *Chamæcyparis obtusa*, is a Japanese species which is fairly hardy at Ottawa if grown in a rather sheltered place, but needs a milder climate for best development. There are several good varieties which show to advantage in the coast region of British Columbia, among the best being var. *aurea*.

Sawara cypress, *Chamæcyparis pisifera*, proves fairly satisfactory in eastern Canada, being practically hardy. It is not as ornamental, however, as its varieties. Among the best of these is var. *filifera*, which may be considered perfectly hardy at Ottawa, and, after a forty-year test is still in excellent condition, the best specimens being about twenty-three feet in height. The graceful pendulous form of this tree and its linear leaves and branchlets make it a most attractive lawn specimen, and it cannot be recommended too highly. Some specimens are now developing more tree-like characters with a strong central leader. Var. *plumosa* is a fine form, more compact in its habit of growth than the type. The leaves are bluish-green above and silvery on the under side. The tips of the branches often winter-kill at Ottawa and turn brown, rendering the specimen rather unsightly until the new growth is made. The golden-leaved form is not so hardy or satisfactory. This variety reverts to the type after fifteen or twenty years, branches appearing and taking the lead with foliage of *C. pisifera*. Where var. *squarrosa* is hardy, as on the west coast, it is perhaps the most beautiful of the retinisporas because of its soft light bluish-green foliage. However, in eastern Canada it is the least satisfactory as it kills in patches in the winter, becoming very unsightly, although when somewhat protected by other trees it comes through fairly well.

The arbor-vitæ.

The American arbor-vitæ is one of the most useful trees in eastern Canada, and in British Columbia the western arbor-vitæ, *Thuja plicata*, is also very valuable. Not only is the American arbor-vitæ one of the most durable so far as the wood is concerned—and it is particularly valuable for fence, telegraph, and telephone poles—but it makes the best evergreen hedge plant for eastern Canada and is one of the most ornamental lawn trees when given room for full development.

While the ordinary wild type of American arbor-vitæ, *Thuja occidentalis*, makes a well-shaped and attractive specimen tree, there are many horticultural forms which give great variety to the landscape. Many of these have been tested at Ottawa during the past forty years, and some have been found much more satisfactory than others in their ability to withstand climatic conditions. Among the best of these are: *Douglasii pyramidalis*, an attractive pyramidal variety, not so narrow or columnar as *fastigiata*. It has very distinct foliage and is one of the hardiest forms. Because of its general soft appearance, caused by its small foliage, and on account of its having withstood severe tests well, *Ellwangeriana* is one of the most satisfactory as a lawn specimen. It is really a semi-dwarf with broad outline, and after thirty years is only about fifteen feet high at Ottawa. *Globosa* is another reliable variety, well named, as its outline is almost globose. This also is a semi-dwarf, being only nine feet high after forty-three years at Ottawa. It has never been injured by winter. Var. *fastigiata* or *pyramidalis* is usually known as the pyramidal arbor-vitæ and is one of the most striking hardy evergreens. It is columnar in habit—specimens at Ottawa thirty feet in height are only six feet across at the base. Occasionally limbs of this variety are injured in winter, but, as a rule, it is hardy. Var. *Vervæneana* has proved reliable. It is more graceful in habit than the species and a slower grower. It has yellowish foliage which is not definite enough to make it specially attractive on this account. Var. *robusta* or *Wareana*, often called the Siberian arbor-vitæ, would seem to be even hardier than the type as it has succeeded on the prairies where the type or species did not. It is more compact than the latter, with characteristic bright green foliage. Many other varieties might be mentioned, none of which is as satisfactory as those just described. The golden-leaved sorts are more attractive when young than later.

Retinispora ericoides is sometimes *Thuja occidentalis* var. *ericoides*, and sometimes a chamæcyparis, but it is usually sold under the name of retinispora. It is of dwarf habit, with soft fine leaves and weak branches, and in winter is badly injured by snow at Ottawa, and usually there is more or less scalding of foliage. After the new growth is made, however, it is a pleasing object.

Western arbor-vitæ or giant-cedar, *Thuja plicata*, is a very beautiful tree when growing wild in the mountains of western Canada and at the Pacific Coast. While it is not often found there under cultivation, it makes a fine lawn tree, though requiring much room to develop to its full extent. When this species is obtained from the colder parts of its range, it does well at Ottawa, although a comparatively slow grower there. It is such an attractive tree that it should be tested more than it is.

The junipers.

The junipers are not planted widely for ornament in Canada. Although some may not be particularly attractive, others make good lawn specimens and the low-growing sorts are very useful for covering banks or for rocky places. They are of comparatively little value for their wood in Canada, as none of them becomes more than a small tree and, except *Juniperus scopulorum*, are little more than shrubs at the best.

The savin, *Juniperus Sabina*, and its varieties, is the most generally useful juniper for ornamental planting in Canada. The vars. *cupressifolia* and *tamariscifolia* should be much more extensively employed where low-growing evergreens are desired. They are particularly effective when covering steep slopes or planted among rocks or in sandy places, where they look much at home. These varieties sometimes reach a height of three to four feet, but often grow close to the ground. They are dense in habit, very effective in a mass, and are hardy, doing well in the prairie provinces. The type has reached six feet in height at Ottawa.

The common juniper, *Juniperus communis*, has many varieties. The commonest one in Canada in most of, if not all, the provinces is var. *depressa*, also sometimes called var. *nana*. It forms broad masses usually on stony or dry soil, and reaches a height of three to four feet. It is seldom planted for ornament, but it does much to improve the appearance of otherwise barren places. Var. *aurea* is a golden-leaved form of var. *depressa*, and is also hardy and rather attractive. The var. *montana*, sometimes called *alpina*, is found in the northern and mountainous parts of Canada. The most ornamental forms of the common juniper are var. *suecica* and var. *hibernica*. Neither of these is, however, quite satisfactory at Ottawa, as the tips of the previous year's growth are usually killed in winter and the branches are rather unsightly until new growth has been made. Both are very compact and upright growers, in fact, quite columnar. The Irish juniper has greener leaves than the Swedish. They do well in the coast region of British Columbia. The Swedish is, perhaps, a little hardier than the Irish.

Prostrate juniper, *Juniperus horizontalis*, has been confounded with *J. Sabina*. It grows wild in most of the provinces of Canada and usually lies close to the ground and trails over it, where it forms a virtual carpet. The foliage is bluish and when large masses are seen it has a very pleasing effect. It does well as a ground-cover in the prairie provinces.

The red-cedar, *Juniperus virginiana*, does well in eastern Canada as it is native there, but, owing to the dullness of the foliage, the type is not particularly valuable for ornamental planting. One of the best varieties is *elegantissima*, which is yellow-tipped, making a pleasing contrast in color. The habit is also more graceful than some. The var. *Schottii* has brighter green foliage than the type and is more attractive. Var. *glauca* has bluish foliage, which is quite distinct, but does not seem so hardy as the others. The pyramidal form is striking in outline, but the foliage is not very attractive.

Western red-cedar, *Juniperus scopulorum*, is native in the Rocky Mountains and through to the Pacific Coast. It is much like *J. virginiana*, but is a larger tree. It is not known in cultivation in eastern Canada.

The upright-growing forms of the Chinese juniper, *Juniperus chinensis*, have not proved sufficiently hardy in eastern Canada to be entirely satisfactory, except var. *mas*, which has done well. The low-growing varieties, such as *pendula* and *Pfitzeriana*, make very ornamental shrubs of compact habit, about four feet in height.

The specific name of the Japanese juniper, *Juniperus rigida*, would suggest a stiff habit. On the contrary, this is one of the most graceful junipers. At Ottawa, a specimen planted in 1896 is about sixteen feet in height. The young branches are pendulous and the general habit of the tree pleasing. The foliage is of a yellowish-green, being distinct in color from most other species. This juniper is well worth planting as a lawn specimen.

Experiences with certain conifers in southern Connecticut.—George P. Brett

The site on which the following coniferous evergreens are grown is an exposed hilltop, three hundred feet above Long

Island Sound and about five miles from the water. The soil is thin, never more than a foot deep, with a subsoil of bowlder clay of extreme hardness called locally "hardpan," almost impervious to water and breakable only by the pick or dynamite.

The yew deserves to be much more widely grown for ornament than is now the case. Free from enemies, a fairly rapid grower, it can be used for many purposes. It makes excellent hedges, stands pruning well, and the bright red berries contrasted with the deep green foliage make these shrubs in the autumn a most beautiful picture.

With the white pine practically eliminated from planting by the many insect enemies to which it is now subject, except in plantations in which it can be nursed and sprayed with care, the Scots pine becomes the most rapid grower and the best species to use for covering waste spaces, for windbreaks, or for blocking out inequalities of the landscape. Very variable in habit, some of these trees have a tendency to spread in a most ungainly manner, horizontal branches being thrown out equal in length to the height of young trees, while others assume a pyramidal form or develop a round-topped head and retain a satisfactory appearance for many years. Apparently free from insect enemies, the Scots pine will grow under any conditions, not minding extreme dryness or even water conditions at the roots such as would be fatal to most other pines that can be planted safely in the North.

The white pine, the Bhotan, and some other of the soft-needle pines suffer severely from the pine weevil, and unless constant care is taken and the trees are given frequent spraying, these trees lose their leading shoots and become mere bushes, presenting a ragged and unsightly appearance and are, of course, then useless for timber purposes. These trees, together with *P. Banksiana* and *P. Cembra*, also often suffer from a comparatively new insect enemy, the imported sawfly, the larvæ of which, almost as numerous on these trees as the so-called tent-worm is on the wild cherries, denude the trees of their needles, and, as there are several broods a year, the new growth in its turn is destroyed, so that the tree eventually dies unless it is saved by spraying or other methods. On young trees, the best plan is to crush the caterpillars with the hands, gloved or otherwise, as they appear, but this requires constant watching throughout the summer because of the several broods. Another recently discovered enemy, but attacking only the white pine, is the pine-tube builder, which also feeds on the foliage, but is not, so far, a very serious menace.

Swiss stone pine, *Pinus Cembra*, is a very slow grower, only about two inches of upward growth being the average of several specimens, the tree being otherwise perfectly healthy.

Pitch pine and *P. ponderosa* are among the very slow growers in this locality, some trees, ten to twelve years of age, having attained a height of only six to seven feet in this period.

Red pine, *Pinus resinosa*, is one of the most satisfactory pines, being apparently without enemies and having a vigorous growth, not usually averaging more than a foot a year, however, against the two feet or thereabouts of the Scots pine. This species will not grow when planted in a swamp, as is stated by some authorities.

Austrian pine is another very satisfactory species, growing about equally as fast as *P. resinosa*. The Scots, *resinosa*, and Austrian pines are all excellent trees for field planting and for covering waste spaces and rocky worthless land.

The firs are difficult to establish under these conditions and the losses have been large, fully fifty per cent in the case of *Abies concolor*, and with smaller losses in some of the other varieties. *A. concolor* does well when once established, specimens after barely holding their own for two or three years afterward making an annual growth of eight to nine inches and forming perfect-shaped trees. *A. Veitchii* is the least satisfactory of the firs in this location, the upward growth being very small and the lower foliage becoming unsightly. *A. Nord-*

manniana and *A. homolepis* are more satisfactory than *A. Veitchii*, the annual growth being six inches or more and the trees making otherwise a satisfactory appearance, except that *A. homolepis* tends to lose the lowest branches as time goes on.

The most satisfactory spruce for exposed situations is, without doubt, the native white spruce, *Picea glauca*. It is not quite so rapid a grower as the Norway spruce, but makes an annual growth of usually not less than one foot, and its handsome blue-green foliage is much denser than that of the Norway. It is one of the best trees for a windbreak or for dense hedges. This spruce, however, should not be grown in sheltered positions or anywhere where the summers are extremely dry and hot.

The Norway spruce is the quickest grower of all the spruces, some trees going upward at the rate of two feet or even more a year. Like the native black spruce, however, the foliage, especially of the lower branches, tends to become ragged and unsightly, and the side of the tree exposed to the severe winds of winter is nearly always less dense than its southern aspect. This is also true of the black spruce which suffers as an ornamental tree also by reason of its persistent cones, which give the tree a moth-eaten ragged appearance.

Picea pungens, both in the *glauca* and green varieties, and *P. Engelmanni*, are slow growers, seldom making more than six inches of upward growth a year. They appear to have no insect enemies, but *P. Engelmanni*, the Douglas fir (Pseudotsuga), and some of the firs frequently lose their leading shoots, apparently from the perverse habit of the birds which perch on the young and tender leaders and sway back and forth in the winds of early spring. However, in the spring of 1923, Douglas fir was attacked by immense numbers of aphis feeding on the new growth. Subsequent experience has shown that nicotine sulfate mixed with fish-oil soap makes a good remedy, one spraying being sufficient.

The Black Hills spruce, form of *Picea glauca*, is a very satisfactory tree, with an annual growth of nearly a foot. Its perfect deep green foliage, interspersed with the white inner surface which shows on the new growth, makes a most pleasing picture. It seems to be hardy under all conditions and to have no insect enemies.

The hemlocks are somewhat unsatisfactory in the location described. All kinds purchased from nurseries have perished and only *Tsuga canadensis*, transplanted from the wild, has succeeded. Even here the losses have been large, fully fifty per cent, as the tree is intolerant of wind and needs shade through the first few years. The situation is exposed to very severe winds from the north and northwest throughout the autumn, winter, and well into the spring months, and the hemlock seems to resent these conditions. Even when planted with specially prepared windbreaks, the losses have been rather large.

The common juniper is wild throughout western Connecticut. The type, however, is very rare, and most specimens are *Juniperus communis* var. *depressa*, a dwarf bush usually not exceeding three feet in height and very often six to eight feet across in perfect specimens. It is very easily transplanted, preferring dry situations, will not prosper except in well-drained soils, and can be planted to great advantage on rocky hillsides. As winter comes on, the tips of the new foliage present a pinkish appearance and make a very beautiful picture.

The red-cedar, *Juniperus virginiana*, is not planted as an ornamental tree nearly as much as its merits deserve. Easily transplanted at almost any season of the year from the hillsides and abandoned fields in which it grows abundantly, it becomes, under cultivation and care, a handsome tree with a bright full foliage, and is useful for planting along roadsides and for hedges and for blocking out unsightly objects in the landscape. It is not a fast grower as compared with some of the pines and spruces, but makes, under favorable conditions, an annual growth of about eight inches. There are numerous forms in young trees, some being May-pole shafts twenty· feet in height, not more than two feet broad anywhere, and covered with dark green foliage from the ground to the top of the tree. A group of these trees with their, in many cases, spire-like heads, makes a beautiful picture against the winter sky. In later years the branches have a tendency to spread and in picturesque old age become horizontal and even drooping, the tree then requiring much more room, but young specimens retain their shape for many years and can be used in formal planting and for numerous other purposes. In young trees the foliage of native specimens often rivals *J. virginiana* var. *glauca* in color and retains this bluish tinge for many years, the foliage of such trees being usually finer than that of the type. The red-cedar is easily grown from seed but requires shade for the first two or three years, as is the case with most seedling conifers.

Certain conifers that succeed in other places in similar latitude have not been satisfactory on this Connecticut plantation, and with others the writer's experience may not be the same as that generally recorded. Various of these disconnected observations may be assembled in a few paragraphs. These experiences illustrate how local may be the success with given kinds of conifers. *Taxus baccata* var. *aurea* does well but the type has never succeeded. *T. baccata* var. *repandens* is probably the best of the low prostrate subjects about doorways and foundations. *Cephalotaxus drupacea* var. *fastigiata* and *C. Fortuni* are perfectly hardy in sheltered positions. *Torreya nucifera* is also hardy under the same conditions. *Pinus nepalensis* has nearly all the troubles of the white pine, but it is so beautiful when properly grown that the amateur is warranted in making every effort to keep it in good health. A good method of combatting the pine weevil on this species is to paint the upper branches with a strong solution of lime-sulfur about the end of April or early in May according to the season. *Pinus Bungeana* in ten or twelve years remains only a bush, in several trees on the plantation, with no signs of assuming arboreal form. *Pinus Coulteri* does well, but *P. Sabiniana* has been tender. *Pinus koraiensis* does not like harsh winds, and its growth in a sheltered location is double or more than in an exposed windy place. Four specimens of *Pinus Pinaster* in sheltered positions are healthy; the tree has a straggling habit. Of *Pinus serotina* several trees are alive but grow hardly at all. The great advantage of *Pinus Banksiana* is the fact that it grows well anywhere except in water, even where hardly any soil exists.

Of the firs, *Abies firma*, while only ten or twelve feet high, is quick-growing and very handsome, without apparent disease or trouble. *Abies lasiocarpa* is sometimes winter-killed whereas the var. *arizonica* is perfectly hardy. *Abies nobilis* has not been successful but the var. *glauca* is hardy and grows quickly. *Abies numidica* and *A. Pinsapo*, while not very fast growers, do well in sheltered positions. *Abies sachalinensis* and var. *nemorensis* grow readily but give little promise of becoming handsome trees, whereas *A. koreana* is one of the handsomest of the conifers and worthy of being grown much more widely. *Abies sibirica* has been killed several times. *Abies cilicica* has not been tender. *A. cephalonica* and its var. *Apollonis* are among the hardiest and most beautiful firs in the collection. A pendulous form of *A. alba* is a curious and interesting plant.

Little can be said for the Norway spruce; it is a short-lived tree at this place, likely to get thin and scraggy as the years go by; the top usually dies at twenty-five or thirty years of age. *Picea Smithiana* is not an early or fast grower, but the trees have never suffered from frost. Probably the three best spruces from the point of view of the amateur have been *Picea Koyomai*, which is perfectly hardy, and *P. Omorika* and *P. orientalis*, these latter needing some protection from winter winds. The Japanese *Picea bicolor* is tender and a very slow grower.

In junipers, *Juniperus chinensis* var. *Sargentii* is one of the most satisfactory of the ground types. *J. conferta* has been perfectly hardy; but *J. horizontalis* and var. *Douglasii* (Waukegan juniper) as well as *J. Sabina* var. *tamariscifolia* have suffered severely, due perhaps to the fact that they are growing in clay whereas their natural habitat appears to be in sandy, rocky or open soils. Meyer juniper, *J. squamata* var. *Meyeri*, is a very handsome tree when well grown; it is sometimes tender in winter, particularly if the autumn has been dry.

The kinds of Chamæcyparis are tender in winter winds but thrive in sheltered positions. *C. thyoides* is very handsome when young; this and *C. nootkatensis* sometimes kill to the roots but they always come up again. The type form of *Chamæcyparis Lawsoniana* sometimes has the branches killed in winter; however, the varieties *Allumii*, Silver Queen, Triomphe de Boskoop are perfectly hardy. *Cupressus arizonica* and *C. Goveniana* have both failed although one of the former is just alive after five years. *Cupressus Macnabiana* sometimes browns in winter, even in a sheltered position, but forms a very handsome tree. *Thuja orientalis* is mostly tender and requires a sheltered position; there are many beautiful varieties but care has to be exercised in choice of location. The Rosedale arbor-vitæ, which grows in the South, is a very handsome little tree of which several specimens are in the plantation; parts of the foliage sometimes brown in winter but always come back. *Thuja occidentalis* var. *Ohlendorffi* has proved to be very tender.

Both Sequoias several times obtained from California grow two or three years and then are killed in winter. *Cryptomeria japonica* and var. *Lobbii* do well even exposed to winter winds, but var. *sinensis* in a sheltered position loses branches nearly every year. *Taxodium distichum* does well in wet land, contrary to others' experience; while specimens on well-drained land lose their branches, those in the swamps are apparently hardy. Seedlings of Sciadopitys have been very tender and difficult to raise, but the adult trees are hardy. *Cedrus atlantica* and var. *glauca* have done well, and considerable success has been attained with Lebanon and Deodar cedars, in sheltered positions.

Experience has shown it to be good practice to spray conifers once or twice in the season, say in late April or early May (as stated above under Picea) with nicotine sulfate mixed with fish-oil soap for aphis and the like, to which may be added a very little arsenate of lead if insects are present.

In propagating conifers by cuttings, it is well to caution the amateur that pines are extremely difficult to raise that way and firs and spruces not too easy, whereas yews, retinisporas and arbor-vitæ can be grown from cuttings by anyone who will give care and attention to them. With seeds, the writer has usually added a little sulfur to sharp sand, using the mixture in seed-beds of pine where damping-off was prevalent, with good results in most cases.

CHAPTER X

INSECTS, DISEASES AND INJURIES OF CONIFERS IN NORTH AMERICA

ALTHOUGH conifers may not be ravaged and eaten up like many other ornamental plants, there are, nevertheless, insects and diseases against which the grower must be on guard. The present chapter is newly prepared from the latest experiences by competent experts in these subjects: the insects by C. R. Crosby, Extension Professor of Entomology in the New York State College of Agriculture at Cornell University, assisted by Dr. M. D. Leonard; the diseases and injuries by D. S. Welch, Assistant Professor of Plant Pathology in the same institution.

I. INSECTS OF CONIFEROUS EVERGREENS

C. R. Crosby and M. D. Leonard

The number of insects doing serious damage to conifers under conditions of cultivation is relatively few, and the discussion of the depredations need not be extensive. This account begins with insects more or less common to all conifers—the borers and bark-beetles. Then follow the insects preying specially on pine, spruce, larch, juniper and arbor-vitæ.

Borers and bark-beetles.

Conifers that are in a weakened or unhealthy condition from insect depredations or other causes are subject to attack by a host of borers and bark-beetles of many kinds. The borers may burrow just under the bark or in the solid wood, often causing decay to ensue. Bark-beetles bore through the bark and construct brood chambers between the bark and the wood in which they deposit their eggs. The larvæ or grubs form burrows which gradually increase in size as they become larger. These burrows are half in the wood and half in the inner bark. When abundant they girdle the tree or branch, causing its death. When the bark is removed, their burrows are evident in impressed grooves in the surface of the sapwood. These engraved patterns are characteristic of the species and have given the insects the popular name of "engraver beetles."

The depredations of borers and bark-beetles can be prevented only by keeping the trees in a healthy and vigorous condition, since most of these pests are unable to gain entrance or breed in thrifty trees. After the tree has been weakened so that the infestation has begun, little can be done to prevent its death. Drought-injured trees are especially subject to attack by bark-beetles. Proper watering during dry periods will often avoid infestation. To prevent the multiplication and spread of the insects it is well to cut out all injured branches or badly infested trees and burn them immediately so that the beetles cannot emerge.

The gipsy-moth (Porthetria dispar). Figs. 101, 102.

The gipsy-moth is a serious forest and shade-tree pest throughout the greater part of New England. It is a European insect and was introduced into eastern Massachusetts in 1869 where it has become a much more serious pest than in its native home. The winter is spent in the egg stage. The egg-masses are oval in outline, light brown in color, covered with hairs from the moth's body, and are placed on trunks of trees or in any sheltered place. The eggs hatch in the spring just as the buds are bursting, and the caterpillars feed on the tender foliage. The young caterpillars are not able to feed on the leaves of pine, but the older ones thrive on this food plant. If other trees are growing with them, the partly grown caterpillars may migrate to the pines, causing a stripping of the leaves. The larvæ

101. Gipsy-moth.

become full grown about the first week of July. The full-grown caterpillar is about two inches long; the ground color is dark gray and there are eleven pairs of prominent tubercles on the back. The first five pairs are blue and the last six dark red. There is only one generation a year, the moths appearing the latter part of July.

The gipsy-moth may be controlled in ornamental plantings by spraying the trees with arsenate of lead, five pounds of powder in one hundred gallons of water. The application should be made as soon as the eggs have hatched, as the older caterpillars are more resistant to the poison. Pines are less subject to injury when grown by themselves because the young larvæ do not have jaws strong enough to devour the leaves. The

102. Gipsy larva (*Porthetria dispar*).

removal of deciduous trees from pine groves will make it easier to protect the latter from the ravages of the gipsy-moth. In the winter, trees should be examined carefully for egg-masses and the eggs killed by saturating them with crude coal-tar creosote to which a little lampblack has been added as a marker. It is also good practice to band the trunks with "tree tanglefoot" to prevent the ascent of migrating caterpillars.

The white pine weevil (*Pissodes strobi*). Figs. 103, 104.

White pine is subject to the attacks of a weevil which kills the central leader and other shoots, thus ruining the symmetry of the tree and causing the trunk to be crooked and misshapen. Norway spruce is also sometimes attacked. The parent insect is a small brown snout-beetle with a whitish spot near the hind end of each wing-cover. The beetles emerge from hibernation in May and, after feeding for a time on the terminal shoot, they deposit their eggs in punctures in the twig. The eggs hatch in a few days and the larvæ burrow in all directions through the shoot, riddling the tissue and causing the death of the branch. The grubs become full grown in August and the beetles emerge in early fall and go into hibernation under trash and in similar sheltered places. There is only one generation a year.

103. White pine weevil (*Pissodes strobi*).

Spraying thoroughly with lime-sulfur solution, one gallon in eight gallons of water, or with lead arsenate, three pounds in one hundred gallons of water, about May 1, will afford protection.

The injury may also be lessened to a considerable extent by systematically jarring the beetles from the leaders into a large-sized insect net. The jarring should begin in April or May when the beetles first appear and should be repeated at intervals of a week as long as the beetles are to be found. A close watch should be kept of young trees and all infested leaders should be cut out and burned. The first

104. Work of the white pine weevil.

examination should be made in June and the trees gone over again in August to remove any leaders that were overlooked or have become infested since the previous cutting. If all but one of the top laterals is removed, it tends to stimulate recovery.

Pine leaf-scale (Chionaspis pinifoliæ). Figs. 105, 106.

Austrian and other hard pines, when grown for ornamental purposes, are especially subject to attack by the pine leaf-scale. The mature female scale is about one-tenth inch in length, elongate, rounded behind and pointed in front. The color is pure white with a yellowish shield at the pointed end. The male scales are smaller, narrower, and have a ridge along the back. The winter is usually passed in the egg stage. The eggs are reddish and are closely packed under the old scale of the mother. The eggs begin to hatch in May and the young scale insects crawl out on the new leaves where they settle down, insert their bristle-like mouth-parts and begin feeding. A scale-like covering is soon formed. Hatching continues over a considerable period. In the cooler parts of its range only one brood is produced annually but farther south there are two broods and possibly a partial third.

105. Pine leaf-scale (*Chionaspis pinifoliæ*).

106. *Chionaspis pinifoliæ* as shown on the leaves.

When this scale is abundant, the growth of the leaves is retarded, they turn reddish, die, and fall off. Infestations as serious as this are rather uncommon, but it is not unusual to find trees which have a distinctly grayish color due to the presence of myriads of the scales.

In cases in which the pine leaf-scale is present in threatening numbers, it may be held in check by spraying with nicotine sulfate, one pint in one hundred gallons of water in which four to five pounds of soap have been dissolved. To be most effective, the application should be made soon after the eggs have hatched and before the young insects have formed a protective scale. This will be in June or early July. It has been reported that good results can be obtained by spraying with a miscible oil, one part in sixteen parts of water,—in the spring before the buds have started. Care should be taken, however, to do the spraying on a bright sunny day when there is no danger of freezing and thus avoid possible injury to the foliage. Summer applications of oil sprays have been reported by some as safe and effective but other experimenters have found them likely to injure the foliage under certain conditions. Oil sprays should be used with great caution on choice conifers.

The pine sawfly (Neodiprion pinetum).

The larvæ of several species of sawflies attack the foliage of the pine. The most common species in the East is known as Abbott's sawfly. The larvæ, when full grown, are three-fourths inch in length, yellowish-white in color, marked with rows of rectangular black spots. The eggs seem to be laid over an extended period so that larvæ of different sizes may be found at almost any time throughout the summer. Whole trees may be defoliated, but it is more common to find the injury restricted to individual branches. The insect passes the winter in cocoons under trash on the ground. There is only one generation a year.

On small trees, jarring the larvæ on to a screen or some similar device is a good method of control. On larger trees the larvæ may be killed by spraying with arsenate of lead at the rate of three pounds of powder to one hundred gallons of water.

Pine bark-aphid (Chermes pinicorticis).

White pines growing under more or less adverse conditions are especially subject to attack by a small reddish aphid which is rendered very conspicuous by a covering of white waxy material. Scotch and Austrian pines are sometimes slightly infested, but the injury is negligible. The insects confine their attack to the smooth bark of the trunk and branches and congregate at the base of the needles. Badly infested trees become sickly, the leaves turn yellowish and in severe cases the tree may die.

The aphid passes the winter in the egg stage under the protection of the mass of wax. The eggs hatch in April and May, the young scatter over the bark, settle down, and become covered with a mass of waxy white threads. On badly infested trees the bark has the appearance of being white-washed. There are several generations during the season. It is probable that this plant-louse has an alternate food plant, but this phase of its life history has not been studied.

The pine bark-aphid may be controlled satisfactorily by thorough spraying with a miscible oil and nicotine in the spring while the insect is in the egg stage. When good water pressure is available, the pest can be held in check by washing the trees with a stiff spray of clear water.

The pitch-mass borer (Parharmonia pini).

The trunks of healthy pine trees are often disfigured by large unsightly masses of gum, caused by the larvæ of a beautiful, blue-black and orange, narrow-winged moth which burrows in the inner bark and sapwood. The insect sometimes requires three years to complete its development. It may be held in check by carefully removing the mass of pitch and killing the borer in its burrow.

European pine-shoot moth (Rhyacionia buoliana).

First discovered in this country in 1914, the pine-shoot moth is now widely distributed throughout the eastern United States and Canada. It attacks by preference Austrian, Mugo, Resinosa and Scotch pines. The eggs are deposited by the moths on the twigs near the buds in July or August. The young bore into the buds but become only partly grown by fall. They resume feeding in the spring. Each larva then may destroy several buds in the terminal cluster. They also bore into the new shoots, killing them. The presence of the insect is indicated in June or July by the lopping over of infested shoots. The growth is often stunted and the tree deformed.

In infested plantings the trees should be watched carefully

and all infested shoots cut out and burned as soon as noticed. E. P. Felt recommends that this practice should be supplemented by spraying the latter part of June with a two per cent summer oil combined with nicotine and lead arsenate and repeating the application a week later.

Spruce gall-aphid (Chermes abietis). Figs. 107, 108.

Norway and white spruces are subject to attack by a plant-louse which causes the formation of cone-shaped galls at the base of the smaller twigs. These galls are about one inch long and bear a striking resemblance to a small pineapple. The infested twigs may die, and when the galls are numerous the tree may assume a ragged and unsightly appearance. Young trees are most liable to serious injury.

107. Spruce gall-aphid on larch.

The plant-louse which produces the galls lives over winter in a partly grown condition, hidden away in cracks of the bark around the buds. In the spring these aphids complete their growth and about the middle of May deposit a cluster of approximately three hundred yellowish eggs. These eggs hatch in about a week and the young lice crawl to the tender growth where they station themselves on the leaves which have already begun to show indications of the developing gall. The formation of the gall is apparently initiated by the feeding of the parent plant-louse. As the gall increases in size, the leaf tissue grows over the young aphid which thus comes to occupy a closed cell. Within this retreat the aphid passes through four stages; the cell then opens and it escapes. This usually takes place in August. At the last molt the plant-louse acquires wings and then takes her position on a spruce leaf where she deposits a cluster of eggs, leaving her dead body over them as a protection. On hatching, the young lice scatter over the near-by branches and attach themselves to the leaves and in crevices around the buds. It is in this condition that the insect passes the winter.

It is thought by some that the life history of the insect is not as simple as is indicated above but that there is a regular migration from spruce to larch and from larch to spruce. It is probable that a migration takes place when both kinds of trees are growing near each other. In cases in which larches are not present, the insect seems to be capable of breeding indefinitely on spruce.

108. Work of spruce gall-aphid (*Chermes abietis*).

The spruce gall-aphid can be controlled effectively on ornamental plants by thoroughly spraying with nicotine sulfate, one-half pint in fifty gallons of water in which three pounds of soap have been dissolved. The application should be made in early spring before new growth starts. Miscible oils have also been used with good results but as they occasionally injure the trees it is better to rely on the nicotine and soap. In case the spraying has been neglected till too late in the season, much can be done to reduce the numbers of the lice by cutting off and burning the galls before they open. This method is not to be recommended when spraying is possible. When the trees have become infested in the nursery, it is well to fumigate them before planting out.

The Colorado blue spruce and also the Sitka spruce are subject to attack by a closely related gall-forming plant-louse (*Chermes cooleyi*). The galls are similar in structure to those caused by the spruce gall-aphid, but are more elongate and are at the end of the twig instead of at the base. The same species also attacks Engelmann spruce. Its life history is similar to that of the form previously treated. It may be controlled by the same measures. The fact that this species regularly migrates to Douglas fir and breeds there during part of its life cycle would indicate the undesirability of planting these two conifers on the same or adjoining estates.

Red and black spruces in the East are likely to have the tips killed by the formation of a tight cone-shaped gall which superficially resembles the true cone of the tree. This gall is produced by a plant-louse (*Chermes pinifoliæ*) which spends part of its life cycle on the leaves of the white pine, where it is known as the white pine leaf-aphid. Winged forms appear on the pine in May and June and the next generation settle on the young leaves. The lice are covered with a white waxy secretion which renders them conspicuous. They cause the leaves to turn yellowish and may materially stunt the new growth.

On spruce this insect may be controlled by removing and destroying the galls before the lice emerge. On pine, spraying with nicotine sulfate and fish-oil soap will give effective control. The lice are destroyed in great numbers by insect enemies, and artificial control measures are rarely necessary.

Norway, white, red, and black spruces are also attacked by another closely related plant-louse (*Chermes similis*) that forms loose terminal galls on the twigs. This species may be controlled by an early spring application of nicotine sulfate and fish-oil soap.

The spruce bud-worm (Harmologa fumiferana).

The most serious pest of the great spruce forests of the northern United States and Canada is a bud-worm, the larva of a small light brown gray-mottled moth. Outbreaks occur at intervals of several years and large areas of forests are defoliated and in many cases killed. At such times ornamental trees do not escape attack, but may be seriously injured by the small caterpillars.

The caterpillars hibernate in an early stage of their development and resume feeding in the spring as soon as the new growth appears. They cut off the needles at the base and then web them together with silk, forming a loose shelter in which they live and continue feeding. The caterpillars become full grown about the middle of June in Maine and pupate within the web. The moths emerge a week or ten days later and lay their eggs in small oval clusters on the spruce needles. The eggs hatch in about a week and the young caterpillars feed sparingly for a time before going into hibernation. There is only one brood a year.

On ornamental trees the spruce bud-worm may be controlled by spraying in the spring, just after the new growth starts, with lead arsenate, three pounds of powder in one hundred gallons of water. The application should be repeated a week or ten days later.

The spruce mite (Paratetranychus ununguis).

Spruces and juniper are subject to attack by a minute mite or red-spider that injures the foliage, often causing the needles to turn brown and drop off. The mites spin delicate silken threads which often web the leaflets together. The winter is passed in the egg stage. The eggs are placed on the twigs usually at the base of the needles. They hatch in April or May and the young mites immediately begin feeding on the leaves. Somewhat less than three weeks are required for the completion of the life cycle and there are several generations produced each season. The injury is most apparent in periods of hot dry weather.

The eggs of the spruce mite can be killed in the early spring before any new growth starts by lubricating oil emulsions containing about two per cent of oil. When the mites become serious during the growing season they can be held in check by thorough spraying with nicotine sulfate, one-half pint in twenty-five gallons of water in which one pound of soap has been dissolved. The treatment should be repeated a week or ten days later to kill the newly hatched young. Since the mites thrive best under dry conditions, frequent watering of the trees will tend to keep them in check. Syringing the foliage with a stiff stream of water will wash off many of the mites.

The spruce sawfly (Neodiprion abietis).

This pest occasionally attacks fir, spruce, and pitch pine. It may be controlled by the same methods as the pine sawfly.

The spruce leaf-miner (Olethreutes abietana).

This pest occasionally causes serious injury to ornamental plantings of spruce, especially blue spruce. The adult is a small grayish-brown moth marked with inconspicuous silvery-white bands. The larva is a semi-transparent brownish or greenish caterpillar with a shiny yellowish-brown head and is about one-third inch in length when full grown. The larva at first tunnels inside the needles themselves and later webs together a number of needles to form a nest. The needles of the nest die and turn brown, giving a very unsightly appearance to the infested tree. The nest is so compactly built that contact sprays will not penetrate to the larvæ and since the young larvæ are mostly leaf-miners, stomach poisons are not effective against them.

The only control measure which has given any satisfactory results is to cut off and burn the nests before the adults emerge. This should be done in October or November or very early in the spring.

The larch case-bearer (Coleophora laricella). Fig. 109.

Young vigorous larch trees are frequently attacked by a small case-bearer that mines in the leaves, causing a yellowish unhealthy appearance of the foliage. Badly infested trees may turn brown early in the season and after repeated attacks may die. European larch and tamarack, or American larch, are subject to attack by this insect both in woodlands and in ornamental plantings.

The larva of the larch case-bearer crawls into a leaf which

has been burrowed out and carries this case as a protection for its tender body. The insect passes the winter in a partly grown condition within its dark gray cylindrical case. At this time the cases are about one-seventh inch in length and are relatively slender.

The hibernating cases may be observed readily on infested twigs, lying flat on the bark or projecting at various angles from the twigs. In the spring the case-bearer migrates with its case to the buds where it burrows as far as possible into the leaf, but retains a hold on the case. One larva will attack and mine a large number of leaves while it is completing its growth.

109. The larch case-bearer (*Coleophora laricella*).

When full grown the larvæ attach themselves and their cases to the bark at the base of short side branches where they pupate. The tiny moths emerge two to three weeks later and mate in a short time. Early in June the females begin laying their brown ridged eggs on the leaves of the larch. On hatching the larvæ bore directly through the egg-shell into the leaf and burrow in the tissues. Early in September the case-bearing habit is assumed, using for a case either a portion of a leaf already mined or perhaps a new leaf. In either event, the larva lines part of the hollow leaf with silk, cuts off both ends, and migrates to new leaves, carrying the case about in typical fashion. In the latter part of October they migrate from the leaves to the twigs, where they fasten one end of the case to the bark and hibernate in this condition.

No practical method of control is known for this pest in forest areas. In ornamental plantings, however, a dormant spray of lime-sulfur solution, diluted at the rate of one part in eight parts of water, has given good results. It is advisable to make this application just as late as possible in the spring before the buds start growing. The hibernating case-bearers may also be killed by spraying with miscible oils. An application of lead arsenate in the spring when the larvæ resume feeding will destroy them.

The larch sawfly (Nematus erichsonii).

The larch, both under cultivation and in the forest, is subject to severe defoliation by the larva of a sawfly. The insect hibernates as a larva in tough brownish cocoons on the ground under the litter beneath the trees. The sawflies appear in late May or early June. The female inserts her eggs in the young green terminal twigs, causing them either to die or to become bent and distorted. The eggs hatch in about a week and the larvæ become full grown in three to four weeks. When abundant, the tree is completely defoliated and the growth seriously checked. The young larvæ are pea-green in color, with dusky heads. When full grown the head is black and the body glaucous-green. There is only one generation a year. On reaching maturity the larvæ descend and spin their cocoons under trash or in the ground.

The larch sawfly can be controlled effectively on ornamental trees by spraying with lead arsenate, three pounds of powder in one hundred gallons of water. The application should be made late in May just as the eggs are hatching. When only a few trees are to be protected and when spraying is objectionable, the insect may be eliminated almost entirely by collecting and destroying the cocoons in the autumn. The soil and litter around the tree should be removed to a depth of an inch or two and carted away. It should be buried or disposed of in such a way as to kill all the cocoons. Isolated trees may be rendered free from attack for several years by this treatment.

Woolly larch aphid (Chermes strobilobius). Fig. 110.

The leaves of the larch are often badly infested by a small nearly black plant-louse which covers itself with a conspicuous mass of wax-wool. Infested trees often have the appearance of being dusted with flour.

The life history of this plant-louse is extremely complicated. The insect hibernates both on larch and on spruce and can breed for at least two years on larch, but there is a regular migration between these two trees. On the spruce the lice form galls which are similar to those of the spruce gall-aphid. On the larch the

over-wintered females and their eggs may be found in abundance in early May at the base of the leaf-clusters. On hatching, the young crawl to the leaves where they settle down and secrete a white waxy covering. The aphids are most abundant in late June although they are present in smaller numbers until fall.

This plant-louse rarely causes enough injury to spruce to make remedial measures necessary. The methods suggested for the control of the spruce gall-aphid would be equally applicable to the present species. On larches the insect may be killed by spraying with nicotine sulfate and soap or with a miscible oil in May when the young are hatching.

110. *Chermes strobilobius.*

The juniper scale (Diaspis carueli).

Junipers occasionally become badly infested by a small white scale that sometimes is abundant enough to give the trees a whitish appearance. Arbor-vitæ and yellow-cedar (and perhaps other related kinds of conifers) are also attacked but to a less extent.

Badly infested trees may require treatment. Miscible oils or lubricating oil emulsions may be used for dormant applications. For summer applications the white oil emulsions with nicotine are indicated.

The juniper webworm (Ypsolophus marginellus).

Ornamental junipers often become badly infested by colonies of reddish-brown white-striped caterpillars that web the leaves together forming nests within which the larvæ feed. The parent moth is about one-half inch across the wings; the front wings are yellowish-brown, with a white stripe on each margin. The moths are on the wing in June.

This pest can be controlled safely by spraying in the spring before the moths emerge with lead arsenate, three pounds in one hundred gallons of water. An early spring treatment with summer strength oil sprays may be employed to destroy the over-wintered caterpillars before the moths emerge and thus prevent the spread of the insect to other trees.

The bagworm (Thyridopteryx ephemeræformis).

Arbor-vitæ and red-cedar in southeastern New York, central Ohio and southward are subject to attack by the larva of a moth which protects itself by a silken bag into which are incorporated bits of leaves and small twigs. White pines and spruce are sometimes attacked. The larva remains in this bag throughout its entire feeding period and carries the bag with it wherever it goes. It protrudes the head and front part of the body when moving about or feeding. The young larvæ appear in May or June and maturity is reached in the fall. The female moth is wingless and does not leave the bag till after she has deposited her eggs. The bag containing the eggs remains on the tree throughout the winter firmly attached to the twig by a band of silk. In this way the twigs are often girdled and killed. When abundant, defoliation may be severe and the trees stunted and killed.

The bagworm may be controlled effectively by spraying with lead arsenate, three pounds of powder in one hundred gallons of water, as soon as the larvæ have all hatched, that is, some time early in June. In case only a few trees are affected, hand-picking the bags in the fall or early spring is an effective measure.

Arbor-vitæ is subject to attack by a small leaf-mining caterpillar (*Argyresthia thuiella*) that kills the tips of the leaves. Badly infested trees take on a brownish appearance. The moths appear in May and June and deposit their eggs in the angles of the leaves. On hatching the larvæ bore directly into the leaves.

A considerable degree of control may be obtained by spraying with one pint of nicotine sulfate and three pounds of lead arsenate in one hundred gallons of water applied in late June or early July.

II. DISEASES AND INJURIES OF ORNAMENTAL CONIFERS

D. S. Welch

The many diseases and injuries to which plants are subject present a serious problem to the nurseryman and grower of coniferous trees. From the time a seed germinates until the plant reaches old age it is subject to the attacks of various agents tending to set up injurious processes which interfere with its normal activity. All such processes are called disease in the broad sense of the term, regardless of the nature of the causal agent. Diseases may be brought about by many agencies both living and non-living, such as bacteria, fungi, insects, heat, poisonous gases, chemicals and the like.

Some causes of disease are very obscure or exceedingly minute so that special instruments are required for their recognition and for this reason it is often necessary to depend on the evidence furnished by the affected plant in identifying a given trouble. Such evidence is supplied by the various reactions of the plant such as wilting, blighting, dwarfing, gall formation, color changes, or other abnormalities. By watching for these changes the grower may know when his plants are diseased and if he has sufficient knowledge of the significance of the symptoms he may definitely recognize the disease and apply the proper control measures.

Everyone is familiar with the more common signs of disease in plants; it is the interpretation of these symptoms which is sometimes difficult. Some are often obscure and these may be just the ones which are important in indicating the early presence of disease at a stage when control measures may be expected to give some promise of success.

Not all diseases are fatal to the plant affected, nor is it necessary for a disease to be fatal in order for it to be considered important. Many of the most destructive diseases merely injure the appearance of the plant without actually causing much damage. Such diseases are of particular importance to the grower of ornamental materials.

Among the many known causes of disease, fungi are by far the most important and a brief description of these peculiar plants will be given here. Fungi differ from ordinary green plants particularly in their form and their lack of green coloring. They do not possess the ability to make their own food such as starch and sugar, materials which are manufactured in the green plants, and therefore, they are dependent on the living or dead parts of other plants for these compounds which are essential to their life. In form the fungi are very varied, ranging from the immense toadstools, puff-balls and bracket forms, several feet in diameter to the minute filaments visible only with the aid of the microscope. Not all fungi cause disease in plants, in fact the greater number of them are merely scavengers in the vegetable kingdom, living on dead material and performing a very useful function by aiding in the formation of humus.

The reproduction of fungi is generally accomplished by spores, very minute bodies no larger than dust particles, which are often produced in enormous numbers. These spores are carried about by air currents or washed by splashing rain or running water into wounds or other places where they are able to enter the plant and cause infection.

In addition to the diseases caused by living agents such as fungi and bacteria, many plants, and particularly the woody trees and shrubs, suffer from troubles which originate in unfavorable environmental conditions. Inadequate food supply or a lack of certain essential food elements, reduced or excessive water supply, dry air conditions, shade or exposure may have the effect of producing disease. It is obvious that some of these adverse conditions result from unwise selection of trees or shrubs for planting in certain places but many times they are the result of changed conditions brought about by carelessness or ignorance on the part of the grower. When plants have not been too severely damaged by such abuse, they may be restored to reasonable health by suitable treatment.

Trees by their very nature and habit of growth are slow to adapt themselves to new conditions and any attempt to make radical changes in their location or surroundings should be undertaken only after a thorough study of the situation. The moving and replanting of large trees is successful only in the hands of skilled and experienced persons.

This account deals only with the more important diseases and injuries of conifers. For the convenience of those consulting this chapter the subject matter has been arranged after the following outline:

1. Diseases and injuries peculiar to conifer seedlings and nursery stock.
2. Diseases and injuries common to trees of all ages.
3. Diseases and injuries of older trees.
4. Fungicides.
5. Tree surgery.

1. Diseases and injuries peculiar to conifer seedlings and nursery stock

Damping-off (caused by various fungi).

This disease is one of the most serious with which the grower of young nursery stock has to contend. Young plants are subject to attack as soon as the seed germinates and they are never out of danger until a considerable quantity of woody tissue has developed in the stem, usually at the end of two or three months.

Evidence of the disease appears in various forms. The first symptom may be the failure of the seedling to emerge from the ground or somewhat later the seedling may show a rotted area at the base of the stalk, near the surface of the soil. This causes the plantlet to fall over sideways and quickly wither and die. The latter symptom is most commonly observed and it indicates that the disease has become thoroughly established. Later some seedlings may shrivel and die while erect, indicating the death of the roots.

Damping-off may be caused by the activity of one or more of several fungi inhabiting the soil. Damp soil and humid atmosphere with relatively high temperatures are factors which contribute to the severity of the attack by furnishing conditions suitable for the development of the fungi. The organisms usually active in causing damping-off are: *Corticium vagum* var. *solani*, *Pythium debaryanum* and various species of Fusarium and Botrytis. It is practically out of the question to find good fertile soil which does not harbor one or more of these fungi. The presence of moisture and organic matter favors their development and in general the conditions which are advantageous to the growth of seedlings also stimulate the fungi.

Control of damping-off is accomplished by the eradication of the pathogenic organisms in the soil and by the manipulation of the environment so as to produce conditions unfavorable for fungous growth. A certain amount of protection may be given by proper care of soil and control of soil-moisture, together with a carefully regulated system of shading. These are the ordinary precautions taken in any well-regulated nursery, and if weather conditions are favorable the disease may never become serious. On the other hand, it is good insurance to take further precautions, particularly in areas where the disease has been known to be serious in the past.

For the eradication of the disease-producing organisms in the soil, heat and chemical substances are the agents ordinarily employed, the latter being in general more satisfactory for beds in the open. The use of live steam introduced into the soil through pipes or into an inverted pan is a common method of soil treatment by heat. Chemicals which may be used are sulfuric acid, formalin, corrosive sublimate, calomel, and aluminum sulfate.

For soil treatment for growing conifer seedlings, sulfuric acid has proved one of the simplest and most effective agents. The amount required for effective control varies with different soils and it is not possible to give any standard formula which will serve in all cases. An average strength is three-sixteenths of a fluid ounce of clear commercial sulfuric acid to one quart of water for each square foot of soil. The application is made immediately after the seeds are sown. If the soil is rather dry and porous it will be necessary to water the beds once or twice a day to prevent acid injury to the plants. The grower should make preliminary tests with this method in order to discover the exact strength of acid most suitable for his soil. Amounts given for different soils vary mostly between one-eighth and one-quarter of a fluid ounce to a square foot. Sulfuric acid has the additional advantage of being an efficient weed killer and the cost of weeding treated beds is greatly reduced.

In fertilizing for the growing of conifer seedlings the use of lime or wood-ashes should be avoided since an alkaline soil reaction favors damping-off. Stable manure or other organic materials when used in quantity are likely to increase the amount of the disease. In planting, care should be taken not to plant the seeds too deeply, and broadcast sowing is recommended in order to avoid unnecessary crowding of the seedlings during the period when they are most susceptible.

Whitespot.

This injury may be mistaken for damping-off. It occurs in seed-beds during very hot weather when the clear rays of the sun strike directly on the soil at the base of the seedling. It appears more frequently on the darker porous soils. At first glance the symptoms are very similar to damping-off but a closer observation will reveal that there is a small sunken grayish-white lesion, usually on the side of the stem exposed to the sun, but sometimes encircling the whole stem. Seedlings thus affected may remain turgid and upright for several days but sooner or later they fall over and die.

A useful distinguishing point between whitespot and damping-off is the fact that in the latter disease the affected plants occur in groups and the disease spreads in the beds from certain centers while in whitespot the affected seedlings are scattered here and there throughout the bed. Whitespot is apparently due to the excessive heating of the soil surface and satisfactory control has been obtained by shading and frequent light watering.

Juniper blight.

Growers of *Juniperus virginiana* stock frequently have trouble with blight. It attacks a number of plants belonging to the Taxaceæ and Pinaceæ but the genus Juniperus is most susceptible. The species vary somewhat in their ability to withstand the disease, the *J. virginiana* stock and horticultural varieties, especially var. *tripartita,* being very susceptible. *J. chinensis* and its varieties may show considerable resistance while *J. excelsa* is practically immune.

The disease is caused by a fungus, *Phomopsis juniperovora,* which attacks the cortical tissues causing cankers which girdle the stem and result in the death of a part or the whole of the plant. The typical symptoms are a browning of the foliage and drying out of the tissues of the stem. On examining the plant just below the dead parts, the canker may be seen on the stem by cutting a long slice so as to expose the inner bark.

The disease is much more serious during rainy seasons. Control is difficult because of the widespread occurrence of the disease, the great number of coniferous plants which may harbor the fungus and the various ways by which the fungus may hibernate. Sprays have not proved entirely satisfactory, due to the difficulty of getting a suitable adhesive which will stick the spray to the foliage. Strict sanitation measures will aid considerably in control. These involve cleaning up all diseased and dead plants and plant debris, and destroying these materials, preferably by burning. Various races of *Juniperus virginiana* seem to differ in susceptibility and the source of seed is apparently an important factor. It has been shown that plants grown from seed from the Platte River region are particularly susceptible. In the selection of seed from whatever source, freedom from debris is important in the control of juniper blight.

2. Diseases and injuries common to trees of all ages
Sun-scorch.

The moisture relations of woody plants are very important and many of the troubles encountered in the growing of coniferous trees may be traced to some deficiency in water supply or some failure in the water-holding capacity of the plant.

Most conifers require an abundance of moisture in the soil, but this is not alone able to sustain them under trying conditions of drought. A very common disease is caused by the rapid drying of leaves which takes place in hot dry weather during the growing season. This may happen even when the roots are adequately supplied with moisture, the actual injury being due to the inability of the tree to transport water to the leaves fast enough to replace that lost by evaporation.

The symptoms are yellowing followed by a browning and death of the foliage. The injury is frequently confined to the more exposed parts of the tree and is usually observed after hot days and exposure to hot dry winds. Seedlings are often killed outright. When the conditions of heat are not extreme, control may be accomplished by shading and frequent watering. In the case of large trees little can be done except to maintain vigor by mulching, watering, and judicious fertilizing.

Winter-drying.

This injury, sometimes called winter-killing, is similar in nature to sun-scorch but it takes place during the dormant or winter season, when the ground is frozen. Under these conditions the leaves continue to lose water and the roots, being embedded in frozen soil, are unable to supply water to replace that lost. Thus the plant suffers in much the same way as from summer drought and if the weather becomes warm and the plants are exposed to a drying wind the damage may be severe. This injury may be expected particularly in mild winters when there is a light snow cover. The symptoms become apparent in late winter or early spring, and usually the whole tree presents a uniform appearance. The needles gradually die from the tips downward, finally becoming reddish-brown in color, the terminal buds are often killed and in extreme cases all the leaves may fall from the tree.

Control of this trouble frequently depends on an understanding of local conditions. Damage is most likely to trees with shallow root systems when grown in exposed situations. In trees with uninjured vigorous roots the injury may be avoided or checked by adequate mulching and proper drainage. The junipers are more resistant to this type of injury than are other conifers.

Freezing-to-death is caused by the direct action of severe cold. As a result, the tissues are killed in a part or whole of the tree. The young and more delicate tissues are most susceptible to this injury, hence the cambium region is the place usually damaged. Leaders and branch tips also suffer, especially after growth starts in the spring.

Wilting and discoloration followed by a water-soaked appearance and death are the most common symptoms. Frost-injury to roots occurs in open winters when the normal snow cover is lacking. The results of such root freezing are often not visible until the next growing season. This damage is very likely to occur in trees like the pines, hemlock, and European larch, which possess a shallow root system. It is frequent in white pines. Where the exposure is not too great, it may be prevented by the use of a mulch.

Frost-cankers result when the repeated freezing and thawing on the exposed side of the trunk kills the tender cambium. This is very common on pine and spruce. The dead bark peels off leaving the exposed sapwood, or becomes sunken and remains attached. Subsequent growth of the tree produces a raised callus around the margin of the area. To prevent the entrance of wood-rotting fungi, the dead area of the bark should be cut away smoothly down to the wood and protected by a suitable dressing. A coat of shellac, followed by any heavy water-proof paint as soon as the surface is dry, will give protection (see under tree surgery).

Frost-cracks occur when sudden changes of temperature cause unequal expansion and contraction of the wood in the trunk. The split often takes place with a loud report. A longitudinal crack is formed running up and down the tree and the tissues are prevented from healing together again by the repeated opening and closing caused by changes in temperature. A raised callus usually forms on either edge. Frost-cracks are of importance chiefly on account of their disfiguring effect and because they serve as avenues of entrance to insects and fungi.

Cracks of this type may heal over naturally if not repeatedly exposed to low temperatures. The healing may be hastened by using strong staples to close the wound. The exposed surface of wood and bark should be sterilized and water-proofed (see under tree surgery) when the crack is wide open in the winter, and the stapling should be done the following spring. Staples may be made of iron and should be very strong, about three-eighth inches in diameter and four to five inches wide. Bark and wood should be removed to allow the staples to be driven flush with the wood and, after the treatment, the exposed tissue should be painted with a good wound dressing.

Phacidium blight.

This disease is found only in northern latitudes where there is considerable snow cover for several months during the year. It is of most importance in the nursery, on spruce and fir, but young trees of pine and arbor-vitæ may also be attacked. In plantations the parts of trees covered by snow may suffer serious injury. The symptoms are a light browning of the foliage, occurring in closely planted nursery beds in sub-circular patches up to two feet or more in diameter or in continuous strips when plants are in separated lines. In older trees masses of branches on one side may be browned and if the trees have previously suffered from the disease the newly infected areas are seen to be contiguous to the old. Leaves of all ages are equally liable to attack. The leaves sometimes drop during the first season but commonly adhere throughout the winter.

The disease is caused by a fungus closely related to, if not identical with *Phacidium infestans* of Europe. Unlike most fungi the organism produces its spores in the autumn and infection takes place just before winter sets in.

A strong spray of home-made lime-sulfur applied in the late fall furnishes effective control of the disease on white and Norway spruce in plantations (see under fungicides). In the nursery, a similar application of reduced strength is satisfactory. The spraying should be thorough, making sure that the liquid covers the under parts of the plants and the surface of the ground. The spraying should be done as late as possible in the fall.

Leaf-cast.

This name is applied to a group of similar diseases which occur on pine, fir, spruce, larch, and juniper. The characteristic symptoms are browning and dropping of the foliage in an irregular fashion, accompanied by the black erumpent fruiting-bodies which appear as lines or roundish dots along the middle of the lower side of the dead leaves. Spores from these fruiting-bodies are carried by air currents to other trees. Leaf-cast is sometimes serious on small trees on account of the resulting defoliation.

Infection in nurseries may be reduced by destroying all diseased needles, both from the tree and from the ground, and spraying with a 4–4–50 bordeaux mixture to which has been added a suitable adhesive such as casein or Kayso (see under fungicides).

Cytospora canker.

This disease, which affects several species of spruce and fir, is manifested by the dying of the lower branches, accompanied by dropping of the needles. A close examination reveals dead cankered areas in the bark of twigs or larger branches which may be slightly swollen but are usually not distorted. There is a pronounced resin flow from the injured region and the exuded pitch may be the most conspicuous sign of the disease after the needles have fallen from the branch. The cause of this disease is a fungus, a species of Cytospora. If portions of the cankered branches are cut off and wrapped in moistened cloth or paper, the fungus will appear in a short time as long worm-like yellowish-white tendrils oozing out from inconspicuous fruit-bodies embedded in the bark. These tendrils consist of countless small spores held together by a gelatinous material which is dissolved by water. The disease is very destructive on the blue spruce (*Picea pungens*) and has been reported on the variety Kosteriana as well as on Norway spruce (*Picea Abies*) and Douglas fir (*Pseudotsuga Douglasii*). This malady is particularly distressing when it attacks specimen trees located in conspicuous places. Recovery of the parts attacked is out of the question and the removal of the diseased branch or limb is imperative. The cause of this disease has but recently been demonstrated and control measures remain to be perfected. A very obvious step is to remove and destroy by burning all diseased or suspected parts. This is best done in the winter and should never be attempted when the tree is wet. The fungus probably enters through abrasions in the delicate bark of the susceptible parts. Injuries caused by careless workmen, birds, rodents or other animals may be the occasion for new infections. Thorough spraying of the branches with a strong solution of bordeaux mixture beginning in the spring and repeating once or twice during the growing season should aid in the control of the disease.

Rust diseases.

These diseases are particularly important in the growing of nursery stock and young trees. They occur especially on the pines and junipers, less frequently on the firs and spruces. Any part of the plant except the root may be attacked, and the result is usually severe injury or death.

Owing to their conspicuous symptoms and destructive effects, these rust diseases are readily recognized, but since their effective control usually depends on the application of definite measures before the symptoms become evident, a knowledge of the life habits of the causal fungi is of decided value to the grower.

At this point it may be well to mention that the term "rust" as used by plant pathologists applies to diseases caused by a group of fungi belonging to the order Uredinales and commonly known as the rust-fungi. The name is derived from the rusty orange-red spore masses typical of the group. The term rust is not intended to indicate all conditions where there is a rusty brown discoloration of the foliage although in common usage it is often applied in this sense. The latter symptoms may be the result of any one of many types of disease in the plant.

Many of the rust-fungi have the peculiar habit of living on two very different host plants during their complete life cycle. The rust parasite grows on the one host plant for a time, then passes to the other, returning eventually to the first and continuing this alternation as long as the two plants are living in proximity. In most cases, if either host species is removed from the vicinity the fungus dies. The safe distance varies considerably in different diseases. Effective control of many rust diseases depends on an understanding of this principle of double life, or heteroecism, in the fungi concerned.

White pine blister-rust is without doubt the most destructive disease of white pines (*i. e.* those pines having their needles in fascicles of five). The disease is believed to have been introduced from Europe on white pine planting stock about the year 1900. It appears to have begun its spread simultaneously from several

points in New England and New York and it has advanced across the country in all directions in spite of every effort which has been made to check its progress. At the present time it is found throughout the important pine-growing regions in eastern United States and it is rapidly becoming established in the Northwest, where it threatens the very valuable stands of western white pine (*Pinus monticola*) and sugar pine (*P. Lambertiana*).

The fungus causing white pine blister-rust (Fig. 111) lives for part of its life on some species of currant or gooseberry (the genus Ribes). Practically all Ribes species are susceptible but the cultivated black currant or European black currant (*R. nigrum*) is most important. This is because of the great number and high vitality of the spores produced on this plant which serve to infect the pine. White pines of all ages are susceptible, but trees up to twenty years of age suffer most. Infection takes place through the needles and occasionally by way of the smaller branches and the

111. White pine with blister-rust.

fungus spreads into the larger limbs or main trunk. At any point girdling may take place and then the parts above the infection soon die.

The early symptoms, which include those appearing during the first twelve or fifteen months, are very difficult to diagnose. At first a small yellowish spot appears on the needle, some months later a slight swelling appears in the cortical tissues somewhere below the infected needle. A slight exudation of a yellowish pitchy substance in small droplets on the surface of the diseased area is a further indication of infection. However, the large bright orange blisters with their powdery contents do not appear until three or four years after the infection has started. In the meantime a dead area (canker) has been forming in the bark and the death of the parts above or beyond the canker may be observed.

The needles usually persist in plants killed by the white pine blister-rust and the reddish-brown "flags" exhibited by the dead branches are the first symptoms to catch the eye of the casual observer. Usually in the third or fourth spring after infection, the blisters are ripe. They then burst open, liberating countless masses of orange-yellow spores which are easily carried by wind and air currents. They are able to travel by this means for many miles, probably a hundred or more, although most of them are carried only a short distance. These spores are not able to re-infect the pines but they readily infect the currant or gooseberry leaf, initiating the so-called "alternate stage."

On the Ribes the symptoms are not very striking and here the disease may entirely escape notice. During the summer, spread may occur from one currant or gooseberry plant to another by means of spores produced in small yellow pustules on the under side of the leaves. Late in the season on these same pustules appear hair-like projections, brown in color, and often sufficient in number to give a felt-like appearance to the under side of the leaf. Upon these projections are produced numerous small spores which are discharged into the air and are borne away to reinfect the pines. These spores are relatively short-lived and lose their effectiveness after having been blown a few hundred yards.

Absolute control of white pine blister-rust may be accomplished by a complete eradication of all species of currant and gooseberry both wild and cultivated within a given radius. For the European or cultivated black currant (*Ribes nigrum*) the safe distance is one mile, for other species of Ribes it is three hundred yards. Experience has shown that after an area has been eradicated as completely as possible, it should be gone over again every year or two. Seedlings readily become established from seeds present at the time of the first eradication or brought in by birds, and large plants are sometimes overlooked.

Eradication of the infected cankers on the pine is rarely feasible. In the case of valuable ornamental trees it may be worth while but it should not be attempted except by an experienced person familiar with the disease. Treatment can be given any time during the year but the cankers are found most easily while the orange spores are being produced, from April to June. Successful treatment depends primarily on the ability to find the cankers and determine accurately the margin of the diseased area. Affected twigs and branches should be cut off seven or more inches back of the orange-yellow blisters. If no blisters are present, they should be cut off five or more inches back of the extreme edge of the canker and flush with the next whorl of healthy branches.

Infections on larger limbs and trunks can be treated successfully by removing all diseased bark and a strip at least two inches wide at the side and four inches at the ends of apparently healthy bark from around the edge of the canker. Large wounds should be protected from the attacks of other fungi and insects by a coating of shellac, followed by a covering of some bark-colored paint. Frequent inspections subsequent to the above treatment are desirable. If the tree will be nearly girdled by the necessary cutting or if nearly all of the branches must be removed it is useless to attempt to save it.

Eastern gall-rust, caused by the fungus *Cronartium cerebrum*, forms globose galls on the stems of twenty-seven species of two- and three-needled pines, most of which are native to the eastern and southern United States. The alternate stages of this rust are found on many species of oak (Quercus). A similar disease is present on the two- and three-needled pines and oaks in the

West. There is some evidence that the western form may re-infect from pine to pine.

Some two- and three-needled pines, especially the lodgepole and western yellow, are injured by the Castilleja rust, *Cronartium filamentosum*. The symptoms strongly resemble white pine blister-rust. The alternate stage occurs on various species of a common weed (Castilleja).

The sweet-fern rust (*Cronartium comptoniæ*) frequently causes severe damage to two- and three-needled pines in nurseries and young plantations. Losses have been particularly severe in forest trees planted outside of their natural range as, for example, *Pinus sylvestris* in the northeastern United States. The alternate hosts are sweet-fern (*Comptonia asplenifolia*) and sweet gale (*Myrica Gale*).

A conspicuous but not very destructive leaf blister-rust is caused on pitch pines by *Coleosporium solidaginis*. This is of frequent occurrence on the Norway or red pine (*Pinus resinosa*). It alternates to species of Aster or Solidago.

Rust witches-broom diseases of spruce are caused by species of Melampsorella, the alternate stages of which are found on Alsine (sandwort), Cerastium (mouse-ear chickweed), and Stellaria (chickweed).

A similar disease on firs (Abies spp.) is caused by a Melampsorella having Cerastium or Stellaria as alternate hosts.

Rust diseases occur on many of the junipers. These are called Gymnosporangium rusts although they have individually been given more common names such as apple rust, hawthorn rust, and quince rust. The alternate hosts are found mostly in the following genera: Pyrus (including the cultivated apple and pear), Cratægus (hawthorn), Amelanchier (juneberry or service-berry), Aronia (chokeberry), Sorbus (mountain-ash), Cydonia (quince), Spiræa, Philadelphus, Cotoneaster, and others, all in the family Rosaceæ.

On the junipers these rusts form globose galls, commonly known as cedar-apples, which may attain two inches in diameter, or swellings of the twigs or branches in which the affected part may increase several times its normal size (Fig. 112). Occasionally witches-broom or twiggy effects are produced. During moist weather in spring these galls or swellings are covered with gelatinous masses of bright orange color. On these are produced spores which infect the alternate hosts. Small yellow spots appear on the foliage of the broad-leaved host. These spots swell to form cushion-like areas, from the under surface of which are extended several tube-like processes within which spores are produced which will reinfect the juniper. Severe defoliation often occurs when leaves are badly affected. An important disease of apple is caused in this way.

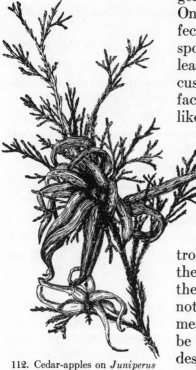

112. Cedar-apples on *Juniperus virginiana*.

As in the case of the blister-rusts, the best method of control is to remove one or the other of the hosts for at least one mile from the vicinity. If the damage does not appear to warrant such drastic measures, some degree of control may be attained by carefully removing and destroying all diseased parts as fast as they appear on either host.

Gas and smoke injury.

Certain gases escaping from manufacturing plants are very destructive to evergreen foliage. The junipers are the only conifers which show any considerable resistance to this type of injury. Fumes from smelters, pulp mills, coke ovens, blast furnaces and chemical manufacturing plants are likely to contain sulfur, chlorine and other chemicals extremely toxic to plant tissue. Smoke from the burning of coal, when present in considerable quantity, has a harmful effect on trees in cities. The injured trees show a dying and browning of the needles from the tips downward. Certain gases like chlorine produce a bleaching effect which is useful in recognition. Continued exposure may result in repeated defoliation and death of the tree. The degree of injury is governed by the distance from the source of the fumes, by the direction of the prevailing winds, and by the topography of the country.

The control of this trouble depends on the removal or suppression of the poisonous gases in the air. This is usually beyond the power of the individual grower and rests with the producers of the fumes. In many cases a serious effort is being made to abate this nuisance by use of special devices or high smokestacks. When trees are grown in a gas-infested territory, only the more resistant species and varieties should be considered.

Injury from illuminating gas.

Another serious injury results when illuminating gas is allowed to escape into the soil in the vicinity of tree roots. The death of many trees in cities may be ascribed to this damage. Fortunately for the grower of conifers, these trees appear resistant to this type of injury. The symptoms of illuminating gas injury are obscure and not particularly characteristic so that it is often necessary to demonstrate the presence of gas in the soil before being certain of a diagnosis. A general sickly appearance, with dwarfing and yellowing of the foliage followed by partial defoliation may be the first visible indication of trouble. Dead branches occur in the tops and the wood has a tendency to become brittle. The bark is shed easily, particularly from the lower part of the trunk. The detection of the odor of gas in holes driven in the soil with a crowbar or in an excavation is the most conclusive evidence of gas injury of this type.

If the exposure is of long duration and the visible damage is already severe, recovery is questionable. First attention should be given to stopping the leak. Following this, all affected roots should be removed, since the poisoning effect is caused by the absorption of certain toxic materials directly into the tree through the roots. The soil should be dug up and well aërated, or replaced by fresh soil, and in case the tree is entirely removed, it is better to wait for a year at least before replanting on the same spot.

Public service companies operating gas lines may be held liable for damages to trees resulting from negligence in the care of their pipes. They are usually willing to investigate any suspected cases of gas injury due to leakage.

3. Diseases and injuries of older trees

Electrical injuries.

Electrical injuries may be divided into those due to the natural phenomenon of lightning and those caused by high-tension wires.

The common effects of lightning are familiar to all; but trees may be injured in a number of freakish ways, some of which are more difficult of diagnosis. Sometimes trees are cleft longitudinally, or are completely shattered by very powerful discharges. When these are less powerful, strips of bark may be torn from the trunk either in continuous lines or at various isolated points. The whole or a portion of a tree may be killed, often without any external sign of injury. In such cases it is probable that the root system has been killed or a portion of the living tissue has been girdled. Many trees are struck without causing any injury evident to the casual observer. Sometimes a small channel is killed in the cambium and the growth in that region is stimulated so that in the following years the tree develops a slight ridge over the injured place.

The ordinary alternating current of low voltage (usually 110 volts) used for household purposes has little effect even when the bare wire is in direct contact with the tree. The damage in this case is local and the injury consists of a slight burning at the point of contact, resulting in death of a small area near the wire. Alternating currents, even of high potency, cause relatively little damage to trees and large individuals are rarely killed.

The effect of direct currents on trees is likely to be much more severe. Direct currents are used especially for electric railroads and, for such purposes, trolley feeders may carry 500 to 550 volts. Here also a local burning may take place but there is also the possibility that the tree may be severely damaged by acting as a conductor between a wire and the ground. This is particularly to be feared when the wire is negatively charged. This condition does not usually exist, but it may happen either through accident or intent that the polarity of the system is reversed. The direct damage to the tree appears to be due to the heating of the moist tissues nearest the source of

113. Sporophores on trunk of tree.

the positive charge. When a near-by track or soil pipe is positive, this heating occurs in the larger roots and at the base of the trunk and quickly leads to the death of the tree.

In seeking to avoid electrical injuries from wires it is obvious that the primary effort should be to avoid contact between the wires and the tree. If their proximity is unavoidable, proper insulation is essential. Companies operating high tension wires may be held liable for damages due to carelessness or neglect. Suspected cases of improper wiring should be brought promptly to their attention.

Wood-rots. Fig. 113.

The wood of older coniferous trees is particularly subject to decay by fungi. These parasitic organisms gain entrance through broken branches or other wounds which expose the wood. The spores or seeds of the fungi are present in the air and easily come to rest on any unprotected wood surface where they germinate and grow into the tissue, using the wood itself as food. Their progress is slow, some may penetrate only a few inches a year but when once established they may work for many years in the interior of the tree before producing any external evidence of their presence. After decay has been going on for some time it is difficult, if not impossible, to eradicate.

After the fungous growth has continued some time, resulting in extensive decay, the fruiting-bodies are produced. These are usually hoof-shaped or bracket-shaped structures protruding from the side of the tree, located frequently at old wounds or knot-holes. From the under side of these fruiting-bodies the seeds or spores are produced in enormous numbers. They are so small that they are invisible and are carried about by wind and air currents. Some of them reach new wounds and start growth as before.

Wood-rot may affect any part of the tree, but the heartwood of the trunks and larger roots suffers most. The sapwood of living coniferous trees is less subject to rot, partly on account of the resinous exudation which quickly follows wounding. Many species of fungi cause wood-rot in coniferous trees and a description of them would be out of place in this volume.

The best control of wood-rots is through protection of the tree and avoidance of infection. Where large branches or tops are broken off or pruned, the surface should be quickly and carefully treated as described under tree surgery. The fruiting-bodies, sometimes called punks, are a constant menace to near-by trees and they should be removed and destroyed, preferably by burning. This will have no effect on the decay in the tree, but will reduce the possibilities of more infections.

Root-rot.

A serious and rather common disease of the cortex and sap-wood of the larger roots is caused by the fungus *Armillaria mellea* (Fig. 114). This organism lives in the soil on decaying roots and other woody material. It produces long flat root-like strands which penetrate into healthy roots, causing decay of the root and death of the tree. The fruiting-bodies are formed on the ground near exposed roots or at the base of the tree. They are umbrella-shaped plants, sometimes called mushrooms or toadstools. The stalk and cap are honey-yellow in color, a fact which has given the name honey-mushroom to this fungus. Spores are formed in large numbers on the sides of the leaf-like gills on the under side of the yellow cap. The spores are wind-blown or carried by rain down into the soil.

114. Fruiting-body of *Armillaria mellea.*

Once the fungus has become established in the soil, the production of fruiting-bodies becomes unnecessary, since the long black shoestring strands may grow for long distances in the soil and thus reach other trees. For this reason also the disease is particularly difficult to control and when found on young trees planted in recently cleared land or near old stumps, it presents a serious problem.

Control of the root-rot caused by *A. mellea* involves the selection of a planting site, if possible, free from the fungus and the avoidance of injuries to the root at or near the soil level. If the disease is discovered in the early stages there is a chance that the tree may be saved. All the soil should be removed from the butt and main roots. The diseased portions should be located by careful cutting with a sharp knife, and all the diseased roots should be traced out as far as possible, cut off and burnt. The exposed surface wherever cuts are made should be painted with shellac around the margin adjacent to and including the bark and when the whole surface is dry it should be painted with a good water-proof paint such as coal-tar, asphalt or house paint. When the surface has become dry the soil may be replaced, leaving exposed a space about eighteen inches around the butt.

In plantations, or where a number of trees are growing nearby, diseased individuals may be isolated by digging a trench about two feet deep all around just outside the roots. No roots or fungous strands should be allowed to cross this trench. Badly affected individuals should be removed and burnt on the spot together with all litter and leaf-mold in the vicinity. The soil should then be turned over and treated with a generous application of five per cent zinc chloride solution. This area should remain unplanted for at least three years during which period the soil should be turned over repeatedly and allowed to dry in the sun.

4. Fungicides

Materials applied to plants for the purpose of killing fungi are called fungicides. These substances may protect the plant by interfering with the attacking fungus or they may actually disinfect the plant by destroying the fungus after it has become established. Fungicides usually act as protectants rather than as disinfectants. Within recent years the number of fungicides has increased enormously. They fall into three general groups, however, and the prospective purchaser needs to know the sort of material that he must have to serve his particular purpose.

Copper-containing fungicides.

The most commonly used copper fungicide is bordeaux mixture which consists of a mixture of copper sulfate (blue vitriol, or bluestone), lime, and water. For mixing the fungicide at home the following directions may be followed:

A stock solution of the copper sulfate is made by dissolving the blue vitriol in water at the rate of one pound of the crystals to one gallon of water. This must be done in a wooden, glass, or earthenware container. If the crystals are suspended in a sack at the top of the solution, they will dissolve more quickly. A stock solution of lime is made by slowly adding water to stone lime at the rate of one gallon of water to a pound of lime. When fully slaked, the mixture is a thick creamy paste. Hydrated lime may be used in place of stone lime, but air-slaked lime should never be employed.

The final mixture is made by adding the stock solution to water in the desired proportions. The formula 4–4–50 indicates four pounds of copper sulfate, four pounds of lime, and fifty gallons of water; or using stock solution as prepared, four gallons copper sulfate stock solution, four gallons lime solution, and forty-eight gallons of water. The copper sulfate solution is added to the water first, then after thorough mixing the lime solution is added with constant stirring. The mixture must be used as soon as made. Bordeaux mixture is available on the market in dry form, ready to be added to water, but the resultant spray material is slightly inferior to the home-made product.

Certain practical considerations have led to the development of dry materials in the form of dusts. These are applied in powdered form, no water being required. Copper-lime dust is commonly used where the application can be made on wet foliage and in quiet air.

Copper sulfate solution made by dissolving one ounce of the crystals in one gallon of water makes a good disinfectant for exposed wood surfaces. The solution cannot be kept in a metal container.

Sulfur-containing fungicides.

The commonest spray in this group is lime-sulfur. It may be purchased as a heavy amber-colored liquid which mixes readily with water. The standard commercial product should test 32 degrees with the Baumé hydrometer.

A home-made lime-sulfur has certain advantages in the control of some diseases on conifers. The following formula and method of preparation has been kindly supplied by J. H. Faull of the Arnold Arboretum from his unpublished notes. This spray has been used by Faull with very satisfactory results in the control of Phacidium blight: put thirty-four pounds of lime into a wooden barrel and slake; then add seventeen pounds of sulfur and ten gallons of water; stir and boil (with live steam if available) for one hour (the preparation should actually boil for one hour); add forty gallons of water and allow to stand for twenty-four hours or more to permit the residue to settle; then siphon off the clear liquid into pails and strain with cheese-cloth from the pails into the sprayer. When used late in the fall, this may be applied without further dilution to trees in plantations. For seed-beds a two-thirds strength of the foregoing formula is recommended.

In recent years, sulfur dusts have found considerable favor. These dusts are now obtainable in a very finely divided form, either as ground sulfur or colloidal sulfur. They are sold in combination with other fungicides and insecticides under many trade names. The purchaser should know what he wants before attempting to buy these materials. The formulæ are required by law to be printed on the container.

The common insecticides, nicotine sulfate or arsenate of lead, may be added in suitable form and proportion to any of the above fungicides without impairing the effective properties of either ingredient. These insecticides have practically no fungicidal value.

Mercury-containing fungicides.

Inorganic compounds of mercury such as bichloride of mercury (corrosive sublimate), calomel or mercuric cyanide are sometimes used as fungicides. The extremely toxic effects shown by these substances make them very useful as disinfectants but their great solubility and poisonous action on living tissue restrict their use as protectants. Bichloride of mercury and mercuric cyanide are very poisonous to animals. Bichloride of mercury is frequently used in a solution of one part of the substance to 1,000 parts of water as a wound disinfectant, but extreme care is necessary in order to prevent injury to the cambium at the margin of the wound by contact with the poison.

Organic mercury compounds are being offered for sale as fungicides in the form of various patented preparations. Some of these have been thoroughly tested by reliable agencies and have been found suitable for certain purposes. As a rule, the organic mercury compounds should be used only on the recommendation of a plant pathologist familiar with the particular problem.

Difficulty is often encountered in getting fungicides to adhere to conifer foliage. A spreader or sticker, such as casein, flour, powdered skim-milk, or Kayso, at the rate of five pounds for every fifty gallons of spray, is often added for this purpose.

5. Tree surgery

Much can be done to protect and prolong the life of valuable trees by the application of a few simple principles in pruning and treatment of wounds.

Pruning or the removal of entire parts, such as twigs, branches, or large limbs, is an operation which the tree owner must often perform. The future well-being of the tree frequently depends on the treatment which it receives at such a time. Wherever twigs or smaller branches are broken or diseased, the simplest and safest procedure is to remove them entirely. Perfectly sound healthy branches also may have to be removed for some reason, the principles involved in any case being the same. Each twig or branch should be cut back in such a way that no stub is left, and the resulting wound should be trimmed flush with the limb or trunk and slightly pointed above and below to facilitate healing. The trimming should be done with a clean sharp knife, cutting straight in as far as the wood but not into the wood, and the entire outline should be smooth and continuous.

The bark is the natural protective coating of the tree and any injury to this affords an opportunity for the entrance of destructive organisms. Fortunately the bark has the power of renewing itself if it is clean and free from infection. Early and prompt attention to wounds or openings in the bark is essential to the proper recovery of the injured area. The new growth will take place along the margin and it is, therefore, necessary immediately to protect the freshly cut tissues from drying out. This may be done by applying a good coat of orange shellac to the exposed sapwood and bark. The shellac not only prevents the drying out of the living tissues but also protects the delicate living cells of the growing region from the disinfectant which should next be applied. Commercial creosote has been used for a disinfectant but it is now being replaced by substances like copper sulfate or mercuric chloride which permit the use of oil paints as a final covering.

After the application of the disinfectant the surface should be allowed to become thoroughly dry before the final covering is added. This is very important because the permanence and effectiveness of the final coat depends on the preparation of the surface for its reception. Many materials may be used for the last or outer coat. For small wounds, liquid grafting wax is very suitable. Coal-tar, the natural product, is recommended, as is also an asphalt paint with a mineral oil base. There are many so-called tree paints on the market, most of them containing some form of coal-tar or asphalt. Those paint preparations claimed to possess disinfecting properties should be avoided. Ordinary house paint of the darker colors makes a satisfactory covering and has the advantage of being easily obtainable.

In the case of large wounds, regardless of the covering protectant used, it is absolutely essential that the surface be inspected every two to three years and the paint renewed. The paint on a tree cannot be expected to be more permanent than that on a wooden house.

Where the wound is of long standing so that decay has set

in, as evidenced by a discoloration or softening of the tissues, the removal of the affected wood is sometimes desired. It is now generally accepted as a fact that it is practically impossible to remove decay fungi which have become established in the heartwood of living trees. The chief object of excavating and cavity treatment should, therefore, be to facilitate growth around and over the wound and to improve the appearance of the tree. In the case of small openings the same principles as described above for wound treatments are adequate.

When the cavity is large, the question of treatment by filling with asphalt mixtures or concrete or by the "open treatment" should be left to the judgment of owners in consultation with some reputable tree expert. The filling of large cavities should not be attempted by inexperienced persons except for the purpose of experiment.

INDEX

Synonyms are printed in Italic type